ATTENTION!

Please take a few moments to fill out this card and return it so that we can notify you of any revisions and errata to the 2005 Codes, as well as release notices of future National Code documents, such as the upcoming User's Guide – NBC 2005, Structural Commentaries (Part 4 of Division B) on CD-ROM. Unless you specify otherwise in the space provided below, we will also send you, free of charge, IRC's *Construction Innovation*. This quarterly newsletter contains explanatory articles and comments on the contents of the National Codes and the code development process, along with announcements of public reviews, of proposed changes to the Codes, Code-writing committee recruitment and training seminars on the Codes. The newsletter will also keep you abreast of IRC's research activities and product evaluations.

Please return this card without delay to receive this information. In order to meet federal privacy requirements, we must inform you that your name and address are being collected so we can notify you of revisions and errata to the National Codes. Our mailing list is protected and confidential; your personal information will **not** be released to any organization. **If you have purchased this publication directly from NRC, you need not return this card because we already have your name in our database.**

You can mail this postage paid card or photocopy this sheet and fax it to us at 1-613-952-7673.

Name_____

Company Name_____

Street _____

City _____ Province_____

Postal Code _____

Tel. _____ Fax_____

E-mail _____

IRC-05NBCPT4-V2

Please check (✓) one:

- ❏ Architect/Specification Writer
- ❏ Home Builder/Renovator
- ❏ Contractor
- ❏ Building Official/Inspector
- ❏ Fire Service
- ❏ Bookstore
- ❏ Educator/Student

- ❏ Engineer/Consultant
- ❏ Technologist
- ❏ Owner/Manager
- ❏ Federal/Prov. Government
- ❏ Municipal Government
- ❏ Manufacturer/Supplier

Other specialization_____

- ❏ Check here if you do NOT wish to receive *Construction Innovation*.

MAIL ➤ POSTE

Canada Post Corporation
Société canadienne des postes

Postage paid   Port payé
if mailed in Canada   si posté au Canada

Business Reply   **Réponse d'affaires**

0033357380   01

0033357380-K1A0R6-BR01

NATIONAL RESEARCH COUNCIL CANADA
INSTITUTE FOR RESEARCH IN CONSTRUCTION
CLIENT SERVICES
1200 MONTREAL RD
OTTAWA ON   K1A 9Z9

User's Guide – NBC 2005 Structural Commentaries (Part 4 of Division B)

Issued by the

Canadian Commission on Building and Fire Codes

National Research Council of Canada

First Edition 1996
Second Edition 2006

ISBN 0-660-19506-2

NR24-8/2005E

NRCC 48192

© National Research Council of Canada 2006
Ottawa
World Rights Reserved

Printed in Canada

Second Printing
Includes errata released on December 1, 2007

2   4   6   8   10   9   7   5   3   1

Aussi disponible en français :

Guide de l'utilisateur – CNB 2005 Commentaires sur le calcul des structures (Partie 4 de la division B)
CNRC 48192F
ISBN 0-660-97063-5
NR24-8/2005F

Table of Contents

Introduction

The purpose of these Commentaries is to make available to the designer detailed design information that will assist in the use of Part 4 of Division B of the National Building Code of Canada 2005 (NBC). The Commentaries are provided as background information and, in some cases, as suggested approaches to certain design questions, but not as mandatory requirements.

Because the information provided in these Commentaries cannot cover all conditions or types of structures that occur in practice, and also because new information may become available in the future, the designer should try to obtain the latest and most appropriate design information available. For unusual types of structures, specialized information such as theoretical studies, model tests or wind tunnel experiments may be required to provide adequate design values.

The Commentaries were prepared with the assistance of the following:

D.E. Allen	J.G. MacGregor
W.A. Dalgliesh	W.G. Plewes
A.G. Davenport	J.H. Rainer
D.J.L. Kennedy	W.R. Schriever
D.A. Lutes	D.A. Taylor

Commentary J, Design for Seismic Effects, was prepared with the assistance of the Canadian National Committee on Earthquake Engineering, which advises the Canadian Commission on Building and Fire Codes on provisions for earthquake engineering in the NBC, with a special contribution from A. Heidebrecht.

Commentary K, Foundations, was prepared with the assistance of a task group appointed by the Standing Committee on Structural Design and consisting of the following members: V. Milligan (Chair), L. Brzezinski, D. Klajnerman, W.E. Lardner and E.Y. Uzumeri.

Commentary L, Application of NBC Part 4 of Division B for the Structural Evaluation and Upgrading of Existing Buildings, was prepared with the assistance of a task group appointed by the Standing Committee on Structural Design and consisting of the following members: R. Halsall (Chair), R.H. DeVall, V.C. Fenton, J. Khan, D. Mitchell and E.Y. Uzumeri.

Revisions to Commentaries A, D, G, I, K and L to reflect the technical changes to NBC Part 4 of Division B were made by:

D.E. Allen (Task Group Chair)	J.G. MacGregor
D. Becker	A. Metten
P.K.S. Chan	R. Morris
P.A. Irwin	R.G. Sexsmith
P.L. Jarrett	A.F. Wong
D.J.L. Kennedy	

The following staff members of the Institute for Research in Construction supported the task group: M. McBride, A.H. Rahman and C.R. Taraschuk.

Commentary A

Limit States Design

1. Limit states design, introduced into the National Building Code of Canada in 1975, was initially developed for steel structures, and then for concrete structures, which had been designed based on ultimate strength design prior to 1975. It was later developed for wood, cold-formed steel and masonry structures, then in 1983 for aluminum structures, and finally in 1995 for foundations. Allowable stress design has been gradually phased out as an alternative to limit states design for steel, concrete, wood, masonry and foundations, but is still used as the basis for some standards and specifications not directly referenced by NBC Section 4.3. Since limit states design is now well understood by civil-structural engineers, this Commentary, which was written in 1975 to introduce the new method, has been shortened and combined with the Commentary on load combinations. The content of the latter has been revised to take into account major changes to the load combinations in NBC Subsection 4.1.3. and to the importance factors previously contained in various Subsections of NBC Section 4.1. Commentary A also serves as an introduction to this User's Guide and ties various parts of NBC Part 4 together.

2. The main changes to the limit states requirements of NBC Section 4.1. are as follows:
   - the adoption of the companion action format of limit states design for load combinations, which is now used worldwide,
   - the separation of load due to snow and rain, S, from live load due to use and occupancy, L,
   - the consistent use of importance factors applied to snow, rain, wind and earthquake loads, including an importance factor for serviceability depending on the use and occupancy of the building, and
   - the modification of the return period for snow, rain and wind loads from 1/30 years to 1/50 years, which is now used worldwide.

The methods for determining loads are therefore harmonized. Snow, rain and wind loads are now calculated using a single return period and varying importance factor, which brings them in line with the approach used for earthquake loads. All loads and effects are combined using the companion action format, which provides a clear set of load combinations with direct physical meaning. The separation of load due to snow and rain from load due to use and occupancy allows for a more logical determination of load factors and load combinations based on the variability of loads and the probability of them acting together. The base return period for snow and wind loads has been increased from 30 years to 50 years to more closely match the expected service life of a building while maintaining the same target probability against failure as in the 1995 NBC. The 50-year return period is consistent with the approach taken by most other countries. Finally, NBC Section 4.1. was reorganized; for example, the content of Subsection 4.1.10., Other Effects, was moved into Subsection 4.1.5., Live Load Due to Use and Occupancy, where it belongs.

Limit States

3. All building structures have the same basic functional requirements, namely that they should be safe from collapse during construction and that they should be safe from collapse and be serviceable during the useful life of the building. The onset of various types of collapse and unserviceability are called limit states:
   - the limit states concerning safety are called ultimate limit states (ULS) and include the exceeding of load-carrying capacity, fracture, overturning, sliding and large deformation;
   - the limit state concerning failure resulting from many load repetitions is called the fatigue limit state (FLS) and applies mostly to crane-supporting structures; and
   - the limit states concerning serviceability are called serviceability limit states (SLS) and include deflection of the structure causing building damage, deflection or local damage of the structure

causing malfunction of the building, and vibration of the structure causing annoyance to the occupants or malfunction of sensitive equipment.

Previous design methods—working stress design, plastic design, ultimate strength design—emphasized only one limit state, usually associated with a limiting stress or member strength. Limit states design recognizes all categories of failure and, more importantly, provides a unified methodology for design calculations. It takes into account, by means of separate factors, the variability of both the loads and the resistances to provide consistent probability against failure, including the consequences of failure as related to the use of the component or the structure as a whole. As well, due to the advent of lighter composite-acting construction with less stiffening and less damping from curtain walls and partitions, serviceability requirements such as deflection and vibration of the structure have become more critical in structural design, and deserve the same consideration as strength requirements. The unified methodology for design calculations is the main reason why the limit states method has been adopted internationally.[1]

Methods of Analysis

4. Previous design methods put the main emphasis on a particular structural theory such as elastic or plastic theory. No particular theory, however, applies universally to all limit states and all types of construction. Elastic theory is generally applicable for serviceability limit states, the fatigue limit state, and ultimate limit states of linearly elastic systems; plastic theory is generally applicable for ultimate limit states of ductile systems; and stability analysis is generally applicable for overturning. Traditional static analysis of the structure is used mostly for the design of structures, however dynamic analysis of structures is becoming more widely used for calculating the effects of dynamic loads such as earthquake, wind and those due to human activities (see Commentary D). The appropriate theory is either implicit or indicated in the structural material standard referenced in NBC Section 4.3., or chosen by the engineer. Many standards explicitly recognize inelastic behaviour of the material, when appropriate, and also require second-order geometric effects to be taken into consideration. To calculate earthquake effects, dynamic analysis is now required by NBC Subsection 4.1.8. for all buildings except those in areas of low seismicity and those meeting certain configuration and design restrictions in areas of higher seismicity. NBC Sentences 4.1.3.2.(9) and (10) and Subsection 4.1.8. all require that, for the structural analysis, consideration be given to overall stability and the displaced configuration of the structure (P-$\triangle$ effects).

5. The aim of design calculations using the limit states method is to prevent failure, that is to say, the attainment of a limit state. However, unpredictable factors such as loads and workmanship enter into the calculations, so the aim is in fact that the probability of failure be sufficiently small. The more serious the consequences of failure, the smaller its probability of occurrence should be. Satisfactory failure probabilities are achieved through the use of reliable materials, competent structural engineering, manufacture and erection, and by the use of safety and serviceability criteria in the design calculations. The safety and serviceability criteria should provide adequate human safety and serviceability on the one hand, and economy on the other hand, i.e. optimum cost-effectiveness or smaller failure probabilities.[2] This is achieved in limit states design through the statistical definition of specified loads and material properties and the use of load factors, resistance factors and importance factors.

Safety and Serviceability Criteria

6. The general form of safety criteria for the ultimate limit states used or referenced by NBC Part 4 can be expressed as follows:

$$\text{factored resistance} \geq \text{effect of factored loads, or}$$
$$\phi R \geq \Sigma \alpha_i S_i \tag{1}$$

Information on the factored loads, load combinations, and the effect of factored loads can be found in Paragraphs 10 to 25. The factored loads are selected to achieve a small probability of exceedance. The factored resistance is the calculated resistance of a member, connection or structure multiplied by a resistance factor, which takes into account the variability of material properties and dimensions, workmanship, type of failure (e.g. gradual versus sudden) and modelling uncertainty in the prediction of resistance. The factored resistances, including the resistance factor, are specified in the material design standards referenced in NBC Section 4.3.

7. The general format of criteria for the serviceability limit states can be expressed as follows:

$$\text{serviceability limit} \geq \text{effect of service loads}$$

Information on the service loads and serviceability load combinations can be found in Paragraphs 27 and 28. The serviceability limits are specified or recommended in NBC Sentences 4.1.3.5.(3) and 4.1.8.13.(3), in Commentaries D, E, I, J and K of this User's Guide, and in the material design standards referenced in NBC Section 4.3.

Specified Loads and Resistances

8. In the limit states method, specified loads and specified material properties used to calculate resistance are defined on the basis of probability of occurrence. Values so defined are called characteristic values. Material properties are controlled by statistical sampling and the characteristic value corresponds to a limiting probability of unfavourable test values called the lower exclusion limit. Climatic loads are based on measurements taken at weather stations and the characteristic value corresponds to the probability of exceedance per year (or its reciprocal, the return period). Characteristic values for material properties and loads used in the NBC are given in Table A-1. Where statistical information is lacking, for example for live load due to use and occupancy, the specified values correspond to the existing nominal values. For specified snow and wind loads, the annual probability of exceedance for the basic climatic data was reduced from 3.3% (30-year return period) to 2.0% (50-year return period) in the 2005 NBC to be consistent with most other countries, including the United States. The material resistance of new materials or new control methods should be defined on the basis of a 5% exclusion limit and their material stiffness should be defined on the basis of a 50% exclusion limit; where statistical sampling is used, a 75% confidence level is recommended for the estimate of the exclusion limit.

Table A-1
Characteristic Values for Loads and Material Properties in the NBC

Materials	Lower Exclusion Limit[1]
Concrete (cylinder test)	≈9%
Wood (full-size and small clear wood tests)	5%
Steel (yield in tension)	1%
Masonry (for prism tests)	≈9%
Load	Return Period
Dead	Not defined
Use and Occupancy	Not defined
Snow	50 years
Wind	50 years
Earthquake	2500 years[2]

[1] Probability of test values being less than the nominal value.
[2] See Commentary J.

Importance Factor

9. In previous editions of the NBC, the importance of the structure in relation to the use and occupancy of the building was treated differently for different loads. There was a general importance factor designated γ in NBC Subsection 4.1.3. and another one designated I in the Subsection on earthquake loads, while the Subsection on wind loads handled importance by specifying a smaller annual

Commentary A

probability of exceedance (1/100 for post-disaster buildings vs. 1/30 for other buildings vs. 1/10 for cladding). In order to standardize the calculation of the different environmental loads, importance factors were established for each load specified in NBC Subsections 4.1.6. (snow and rain), 4.1.7. (wind), and 4.1.8. (earthquake). The importance factor is not applied to dead load nor is it applied to live load due to use and occupancy because the loads specified in NBC Table 4.1.5.3. already take into account the more serious consequences of failure depending on occupancy (e.g. assembly occupancies). For buildings in the Low Importance category, however, a factor of 0.8 may be applied to the specified live load due to use and occupancy as stated in NBC Sentences 4.1.5.1.(2) and 4.1.5.2.(2). The importance factors are summarized in Table A-2.

10. The importance factor for the serviceability limit states is taken equal to or less than 1.0 because of the less serious consequences of failure and because design criteria for serviceability are more subjective than for strength and stability.

Table A-2
Importance Factors

Importance Category	Earthquake, I_E		Wind, I_W		Snow, I_S	
	ULS	SLS	ULS	SLS	ULS	SLS
Low[1]	0.8		0.8	0.75	0.8	0.9
Normal	1.0	(2)	1.0	0.75	1.0	0.9
High	1.3		1.15	0.75	1.15	0.9
Post-disaster	1.5		1.25	0.75	1.25	0.9

[1] A factor of 0.8 may be applied to live load due to use and occupancy for buildings in the Low Importance category.
[2] See Commentary J.

Load Combinations in NBC Part 4

11. Limit states criteria specified in NBC Article 4.1.3.2. and recommended in this Commentary are intended to provide an acceptable and relatively uniform degree of reliability in the design of structural members under different load combinations. The criteria take into consideration the probability of failure due to the simultaneous occurrence of the loads specified in NBC Subsections 4.1.4. to 4.1.8. Paragraphs 12 to 18 explain and provide guidance on the load combinations given in NBC Table 4.1.3.2. Paragraphs 19 to 25 provide guidance for situations where the load combinations given in Table 4.1.3.2. do not apply. For the structural evaluation of building structures not within the scope of the standards listed in NBC Section 4.3., including building envelopes, the generalized load combinations stated in Paragraph 12 are recommended. Paragraphs 12, and 26 to 28 provide a guide for the determination of loads and load combinations for the fatigue and serviceability limit states.

Generalized Load Combinations

12. Structural loads can be divided into three categories: permanent loads (such as dead load and earth pressure), variable loads (such as use and occupancy, snow and wind loads), and rare loads or situations (such as earthquake or fire). In general, load combinations can be determined by splitting the loads specified in NBC Part 4 into two components:[3][4] a sustained or frequently occurring component (e.g. dead load, earth pressure, sustained live load) and a transient component, which acts rarely and for a short time only (e.g. impact, wind, earthquake, short-term accumulation of people and/or objects). Because the transient components of different loads are unlikely to occur simultaneously, the critical load combination for a given structural effect is estimated by combining the factored permanent loads with the factored variable or rare load having the largest transient component, plus the sustained or frequent components of all other variable loads. This principle, called the companion action principle[4] and recommended by ISO,[1] has been applied to determine the following generalized factored load combinations for both the ultimate and serviceability limit states.

Load Combinations for Variable Loads

The load combinations where all loads are permanent or variable are:

$$\Sigma \alpha_{G_i} \cdot G_i + \alpha_{Q_1} \cdot Q_1 + \Sigma \alpha_{CQ_i} \cdot Q_i \tag{2}$$

where
G_i = permanent load such as D or H or T or P,
Q_1 = principal variable load such as L or S or W or other load, taken in turn,
Q_i = any variable load such as L or S or W,
α_{G_i} = principal load factor for the permanent load, G_i,
α_{Q_1} = principal load factor for the principal variable load, Q_1,
α_{CQ_i} = companion load factor for other variable loads, and
where the second term in Equation (2) is the principal variable load and the last term comprises the companion (expected) variable load or loads.

Load Combinations for Rare Loads or Situations

The load combination when there is a rare load or situation is:

$$\Sigma G_i + E + \Sigma \alpha_{CQ_i} \cdot Q_i \tag{3}$$

where E is the specified load due to earthquake or other accidental load (e.g. a vehicle impact). Paragraph 25 provides guidance for resistance to fire—a rare event affecting the building structure.

Table A-3 gives, for the ultimate limit states, the recommended principal load factors and companion load factors related to each of the loads listed for the calculation of the generalized factored load combinations using Equation (2) for variable loads and Equation (3) for a rare load or event.

Table A-3
Load Factors (Ultimate Limit States)

Load		Principal-Load Factor, α_{G_i} or α_{Q_1}	Companion-Load Factor, α_{CQ_i}
Permanent Loads	D (alone)	1.4	—
	D (with variable loads)	1.25[1] or 0.9[2] or 1.0[3]	—
	H	1.5 or 0.0 or 1.0[3]	—
	T	1.25	—
	P	1.0	—
Variable Loads	L	1.5[4]	0.5[5]
	S	1.5	0.5 or 0.25[3]
	W	1.4	0.4 or 0.0[3]
	T_S[6]	1.25	—
Rare Load	E	1.0	0.0

[1] For dead load due to earth, plants and trees, see NBC Sentence 4.1.3.2.(7).
[2] For counteracting dead load resisting failure (counteracting companion loads not included).
[3] For rare load combinations.
[4] 1.25 for controlled fluids; see NBC Sentence 4.1.3.2.(5).
[5] 1.0 for storage areas, equipment areas and service rooms; see NBC Sentence 4.1.3.2.(6).
[6] T_S is the short-term variable effect caused by imposed deformations due to variations in temperature or moisture content, or a combination thereof.

Commentary A

Load Combinations for Strength and Stability in NBC Table 4.1.3.2.

13. The load combinations given in NBC Table 4.1.3.2. are a simplified version of Equations (2) and (3) and are applicable to most buildings and to structural systems within the scope of the standards currently listed in NBC Section 4.3. The load combinations given in NBC Table 4.1.3.2. are based on reliability analyses,[5] which determined that, when conservative companion-load factors are used in load combinations 2 to 4, the more critical companion action acting alone results in a probability of failure that is the same or less than for cases such as D + L where there are no companion loads. In other words, the load combination D + L + S + W need not be considered. The load T listed in NBC Article 4.1.2.1. and in Equation (2) is not included in NBC Table 4.1.3.2. because research and experience show that, except for secondary moments due to prestressing, this load is not likely to affect the strength and stability of structural systems that have ductility and redundancy. If a structural system lacking these properties is used, then load combinations should be determined from Equation (2) or (3) with the appropriate fractile of T included. Due to the very short duration of some specified loads, the probability of their simultaneous occurrence is extremely small. Thus, according to load combination 5 of NBC Table 4.1.3.2., earthquake load is not considered simultaneously with wind load.

Load Factors in NBC Table 4.1.3.2.

14. Applying the principal load factor to one of the specified loads accounts for variability of the load and load patterns, bias in the relationship between the nominal load and the expected value of the load for the event being considered, and normally accepted modelling approximations in the structural analysis. The principal load factors are determined based on these considerations as well as on experience gained from buildings built in accordance with previous editions of the NBC. The principal load factors for rare loads such as earthquake are taken equal to 1.0 because of their low annual probability of occurrence. The level of performance for rare loads allows building damage while maintaining life safety. The principal load factors are taken equal to 1.5 for live load due to use and occupancy and for earth pressure, 1.5 for snow load, 1.4 for wind load, and 1.25 for liquids whose depth is controlled.

15. The dead load factor of 1.25 accounts for the systematic and random variation of the dead load but is insufficient to accommodate dead load changes due to construction substitutions or subsequent alterations. Designs should anticipate and account for reasonable increases in the dead load of architectural or mechanical superimposed dead loads, of cast-in-place toppings and cover slabs that may be sensitive to the camber and deflection of the supporting members, and due to the addition of roofing or other materials during the life of the structure. For soil, superimposed earth, plants and trees, the dead load factor is increased to 1.5 but may be reduced in accordance with NBC Sentence 4.1.3.2.(7). Load combination 1 given in NBC Table 4.1.3.2. has been added to ensure the reliability of structural components that are dominated by dead load.[5]

16. The load factors for the serviceability limit states are taken equal to 1.0 or, for companion loads, less than 1.0 because of the less serious consequences of failure and because design criteria for serviceability are more subjective than for strength and stability.

17. The principal and companion load factors specified in the factored load combinations in NBC Table 4.1.3.2. are based on reliability analyses[5] calibrated according to past experience using previous editions of the NBC. The determination of load factors was carried out in two phases: the first phase involved determining values that provide uniform values of the reliability indices for a range of ratios and load types; in the second phase, the factors were reviewed and adjusted where necessary to reduce major inconsistencies with former practices.

18. The resistance factors given in the referenced material design standards, which take into account the variability of material properties, dimensions and workmanship, the type of failure (e.g. gradual versus sudden) and uncertainty in modelling resistance, have been developed for use with the load factors in the NBC to arrive at the desired target reliability index.

Overturning, Uplift, Sliding and Stress Reversal

19. Counteracting loads such as dead load prevent overturning, uplift, the sliding of structures as a whole, and stress reversal or force reduction in structural members, which results in a reduced resistance, for example due to the buckling of truss diagonals or due to the reduced flexural

resistance of concrete columns. In such cases, counteracting loads that act to resist failure and deviations, which decrease rather than increase the dead load, are critical.[6][7] For load combinations 2 to 5 given in NBC Table 4.1.3.2., counteracting variable loads are therefore taken equal to zero, and the load factor for counteracting dead load (actually, a resistance factor) is taken equal to 0.9 in load combinations 2 to 4, and equal to 1.0 in load combination 5. The dead load factor 0.9 has been increased from 0.85 because some gravity live load is expected to occur in most buildings. The dead load factor of 1.0 in the load combination that accounts for earthquake allows for the greater uncertainty in the magnitude of earthquake load and the reduced level of performance permitted with respect to building damage.

20. When assessing overturning, designers should consider the following:
    (1) the reaction of the foundation material is at such a distance from the toe of the building structure so as to generate the necessary reaction, and
    (2) the dead load acts through the centre of gravity of the deflected structure.

Cantilever Retaining Walls

21. When assessing overturning of cantilever retaining walls, designers should consider the following:
    (1) the reaction of the foundation material is at such a distance from the toe of the retaining wall so as to generate the necessary reaction, and
    (2) the dead load acts through the centre of gravity of the deflected retaining wall.

22. CAN/CSA-S6, "Canadian Highway Bridge Design Code,"[14] and the Canadian Foundation Engineering Manual[8] provide additional guidance on the design of cantilever retaining walls.

Full and Partial Loading

23. Full and partial loading considerations are required as per NBC Article 4.1.5.3. for live load due to use and occupancy, NBC Article 4.1.6.3. for snow load, and NBC Article 4.1.7.3. for wind load. To achieve an acceptable reliability, pattern loading requirements for live or snow load should be considered in conjunction with the dead load multiplied either by 1.25 on all spans or 0.9 on all spans, whichever produces the most critical effect.

Load Combinations for Industrial Buildings

24. For building structures subjected to unusual loads not specified in NBC Part 4, for example those where liquids are stored, the load combinations given in NBC Table 4.1.3.2. may not apply. For guidance on industrial buildings with crane operations, see CAN/CSA-S16, "Limit States Design of Steel Structures."[10]

Load Combination for Determination of Fire Resistance

25. A rare event such as a fire results in the temporary change of material properties causing large structural deformation as well as the potential for collapse. Structural fire resistance is defined as the time to structural failure when the structure is subjected to a standard fire. Structural fire resistance is determined based on fire tests or calculations that take into account the forces in the structure due to the applied loads, including those produced by high temperatures, and the properties of materials at high temperatures. The following load combination based on Equation (3) is recommended for an accidental event for design:[9]

$$D + T_S + (\alpha L \text{ or } 0.25S) \tag{4}$$

where $\alpha = 1.0$ for storage areas, equipment areas and service rooms, and 0.5 for other occupancies, and T_S can be taken equal to zero for statically determinate structures or for structures that have sufficient ductility to allow the redistribution of temperature forces before collapse.

Loads and Load Combinations for Fatigue Limit State

26. The variable of overriding importance in structural fatigue that dominates the propagation of cracks in metal components is the range of stress. The stress range to be used in the design is dictated by the

variable loads. Because many cycles of load are required to cause fatigue, specified live loads that occur with reasonable frequency are used in design and not the extreme factored loads that have a very small probability of occurrence in the life of the structure. CAN/CSA-S16, "Limit States Design of Steel Structures,"[10] and CSA S157, "Strength Design in Aluminum,"[15] only require detailed design against fatigue for more than 20,000 repetitions of load, except for the unusual case of fatigue-sensitive details with high stress ranges. Moreover, because cracks propagate in tensile stress fields only, the presence of a compressive stress field due to dead load, if sufficiently large, may obviate the development of cracks. In these circumstances, the accompanying dead load stresses should be assessed as discussed in CAN/CSA-S16.[10] Environmental loads, such as snow or wind loads, do not generally have a nearly sufficient number of cycles to be considered for the fatigue limit state. A possible exception is wind-excited vibrations such as vortex shedding and aerobics (see Commentary D). CAN/CSA-S16[10] also addresses the concept of distortion-induced fatigue.

Loads and Load Combinations for the Serviceability Limit States

27. Loads and load combinations for serviceability calculations depend very much on the serviceability limit state and on the properties of structural materials (e.g. creep and cracking). Table A-4 provides guidance on the loads that need to be considered for serviceability criteria contained in NBC Part 4, in material design standards referenced in NBC Section 4.3., and in Commentaries D, E, I, J and K of this User's Guide. Table A-4 also provides guidance on the load combinations of factored service loads (based on Equations (2) and (3)) that need to be considered depending on the limit state. Loads acting in combination do not need to be considered for vibration calculations. On the other hand, damage to the building structure or envelope may require the consideration of many loads in combination, particularly if the components are brittle.

Table A-4
Loads and Load Combinations for Serviceability[1]

Limit State	Structural Parameter	Loads	Load Combinations	References
Vibration serviceability	Acceleration	L_C,[2] W_C[2]	L_C[2] or W_C[2]	Commentary D Commentary I CAN/CSA-S16[10] CAN/CSA-O86[11]
Operation of moving equipment	Deflection: Long-term	D, H, T_P,[3] P	$D + H + T_P$[3] + P	CAN/CSA-S16[10]
	Short-term	L	L	
Damage to non-structural components	Displacement: Long-term	T_P,[3] P	T_P[3] + P	Commentary D Commentary E CSA A23.3[12] CAN/CSA-O86[11] CSA S304.1[13] CAN/CSA-S16[10]
	Short-term	L, S, W, E	$L + \alpha$[4]S or S + α[4]L or W or E	
Damage to structural components	Stress, strain, crack width	D, H, L, S, W, E, T_P,[3] T_S[5]	D + H + L + T_P[3] + [L or S or W or E or T_S[5]] + companion loads	CSA A23.3[12] CSA S304.1[13] Commentary E

[1] S and W include an importance factor for serviceability.

[2] Subscript C refers to the cyclic components of load effects (e.g. acceleration).

[3] T_P, includes creep (or soil settlement) under $D + H + L_P + P$, where L_P is the sustained component of live load due to use and occupancy.

[4] The companion load factor, α, is usually assumed to be 0.5 for live load due to use and occupancy, except for storage occupancies, where it is assumed to be 1.0, and 0.5 for snow load in cold climates.

[5] T_S is the short-term variable effect caused by imposed deformations due to variations in temperature or moisture content, or a combination thereof.

Load Combinations for Settlement and Deflection of the Building Structure

28. Table A-5 presents recommended simplified combinations of service loads to determine the settlement of foundations causing building damage, and the deflection of the building structure causing building damage or impeding the operation of equipment such as cranes or elevators. For cases 2 and 3 in Table A-5, deflection of the building structure causing building damage is the sum of the short-term deflection occurring after the attachment of non-structural building elements, plus the long-term component of deflection due to D, H, T_P and P resulting from shrinkage or moisture change and creep of materials occurring after the attachment of non-structural building elements. Because of the approximations required, the long-term deflection resulting from shrinkage or moisture change and creep is usually taken into account by specific empirical deflection limits stated in the design standards listed in NBC Section 4.3.

Table A-5
Recommended Load Combinations for Serviceability Limit States Governed by Deflection

Case	Serviceability Parameter	Load Combinations
1	Differential settlement of foundations	$D + H + \alpha^{(1)}L + \alpha^{(1)}S^{(2)}$
2	Long-term deflection of building structure[3]	$D + H + T_P{}^{(4)} + P + \alpha^{(1)}L + \alpha^{(1)}S^{(2)}$
3	Short-term deflection of building structure[3]	$(L + \alpha^{(1)}S^{(2)})$ or $(S^{(2)} + \alpha^{(1)}L)$ or $W^{(2)}$ or E

(1) The companion load factor, α, is usually assumed to be 0.2 to 0.5 for snow load and for live load due to use and occupancy, except for storage occupancies, where it is assumed to be 1.0.

(2) Importance factors 0.9 and 0.75 are applied in NBC Subsections 4.1.6. and 4.1.7. to determine service loads S and W.

(3) For deflection of the building structure causing building damage, see Paragraph 27.

(4) T_P includes deflection caused by long-term moisture changes in materials (e.g. shrinkage), while creep deflection is calculated using the applied loading $D + H + P + \alpha L + \alpha S$.

References

[1] General Principles on Reliability for Structures. International Standard ISO 2394. Geneva, 1986, 18 pp.

[2] M.K. Ravindra and N.C. Lind. Theory of Structural Code Optimization. Journal of Structural Division, Proc. Am. Soc. Civ. Eng., Vol. 99, ST7, July 1973, p. 1541.

[3] Guidelines for the Development of Limit States Design. CSA Technical Publication S408-1981. Canadian Standards Association, Mississauga, Ontario.

[4] C.J. Turkstra, Theory of Structural Safety. SM Study No. 2, Solid Mechanics Division, University of Waterloo, Waterloo, Ontario, 1970.

[5] F.M. Bartlett, H.P. Hong, and W. Zhou. Load factor calibration for the proposed 2005 edition of the National Building Code of Canada: Companion-action Load Combinations. Canadian Journal of Civil Engineering, Vol. 30, No. 2, April 2003, pp. 440-448.

[6] D.E. Allen, Safety Factors for Stress Reversal. Publications, International Association for Bridge and Structural Engineering, Vol. 29/II, 1969.

[7] Report of the Committee of Inquiry into Collapse of Cooling Towers at Ferrybridge, Monday, 1 November 1965. Central Electricity Generating Board, London.

[8] Canadian Foundation Engineering Manual, 4th Edition, Canadian Geotechnical Society, 2006. (Available from BiTech Publishers, Suite 173, 11860 Hammersmith Way, Richmond, B.C., V7A 5G1)

[9] B. Ellingwood and R.B. Corotis, Load Combinations for Buildings Exposed to Fires. AISC Engineering Journal, 28(1), 1991, pp. 37-44.

[10] CAN/CSA-S16-01, Limit States Design of Steel Structures. Canadian Standards Association, Mississauga, Ontario, 2001.

[11] CAN/CSA-O86-01, Engineering Design in Wood. Canadian Standards Association, Mississauga, Ontario, 2001.

[12] CSA A23.3-04, Design of Concrete Structures. Canadian Standards Association, Mississauga, Ontario, 2004.

Commentary A

[13] CSA S304.1-04, Design of Masonry Structures. Canadian Standards Association, Mississauga, Ontario, 2004.

[14] CAN/CSA-S6-00, Canadian Highway Bridge Design Code. Canadian Standards Association, Mississauga, Ontario, 2000.

[15] CAN3-S157-M83 (R2002), Strength Design in Aluminum. Canadian Standards Association, Mississauga, Ontario, 1983.

Commentary B

Structural Integrity

1. The strength and stability of building structural systems is addressed in NBC Sentence 4.1.1.3.(1) and in specific requirements in NBC Part 4, and in the CSA material design standards referenced in NBC Section 4.3. This Commentary provides guidance on additional considerations regarding structural integrity as addressed in Sentence 4.1.1.3.(1) and its Appendix Note.

2. Structural integrity is defined as the ability of the structure to absorb local failure without widespread collapse. For example, a cellular or frame arrangement of components that are well tied together in three dimensions has good structural integrity.

3. Building structures designed in accordance with the CSA design standards will usually have an adequate degree of structural integrity, which is generally achieved through detailing requirements for the connections between components. Situations where structural integrity may require special attention include medium-rise and high-rise building systems made of components of different materials, whose interconnection is not covered by existing CSA design standards, buildings outside the scope of existing CSA design standards, and buildings exposed to severe accidental loads such as vehicle impact or explosion. The following paragraphs provide guidance for such situations.

4. A significant number of failures—many of them progressive—occur during construction. The construction sequence should, therefore, be carefully planned and monitored to ensure that partially completed structural systems have sufficient strength, ductility and lateral stability to resist progressive collapse if a construction accident causes significant damage to a structural element or if local failure of a permanent or temporary structural element occurs.

Identification of Hazard[1]

5. The hazard is the risk of widespread collapse with serious consequences that arises from local failure caused by accidental events not addressed by the loads specified in NBC Part 4. Key components that can be severely damaged by an accident with a significant probability of occurrence (i.e. approximately 10^{-4} per year or more) should therefore be identified, and measures should be taken to ensure adequate structural safety.

Safety Measures

6. The occurrence of widespread collapse resulting from accidental events can be prevented through safety measures such as the following:
   (a) Control of accidental events: Such measures include the erection of protective devices (e.g. curbs, guards) against vehicle impact, the inspection of key elements or ground conditions for deterioration during use, and blow-out panels to reduce explosion pressures.
   (b) Local resistance: This consists of designing key members to resist accidental events.[2] Some major structural members, for example, are so strong that most accidental events are unlikely to cause serious structural damage. Ductility of the key members and of their connections to the structure can also provide substantial additional resistance to accidents not normally considered during design.
   (c) Design of tie forces: Structural integrity can often be achieved indirectly by providing certain minimum criteria for vertical, horizontal and peripheral ties in buildings.[3][4][5]
   (d) Alternate paths of support: Here it is assumed that the key member has failed, and the damaged building is checked to ensure that it can support the dead load plus a portion of the live load and wind load.

(e) Control of widespread collapse: This measure consists of dividing the structure into areas separated by planes of weakness, which will prevent a collapse in one area from propagating into adjacent areas. This method is described in Commentary C.

7. Any building system should be considered as a whole and effectively tied together in such a way as to not be sensitive to local accidental failure.

8. Additional information for specific building structural systems is contained in References [3] to [9]. Reference [6] contains additional references regarding concrete building systems.

References

[1]   H. Griffiths, A. Pugsley and O. Saunders, Report of the Enquiry into the Collapse of Flats at Ronan Point, Canning Town. Her Majesty's Stationary Office, London, 1968.

[2]   Dansk Standard DS 410 - English Translation. Loads for the Design of Structures: Chapter 17 - Accidental Action. Dansk Ingeniorforening, Copenhagen, 1983.

[3]   J.E. Breen, Developing Structural Integrity in Bearing Wall Buildings. Journal of the Prestressed Concrete Institute. Vol. 25, No. 1, January-February 1980, pp. 42-73.

[4]   M. Fintel and G. Annamalai, Philosophy of Structural Integrity of Multistorey Load-bearing Concrete Masonry Structures. Concrete International, Vol. 1, No. 5, May 1979.

[5]   I.J. Speyer, Considerations for the Design of Precast Concrete Bearing Wall Buildings to Withstand Abnormal Loads. Journal of the Prestressed Concrete Institute, Vol. 21, No. 2, March-April 1976.

[6]   Cement Association of Canada. Structural Integrity. Concrete Design Handbook, Ottawa, 2006.

[7]   British Standards Institute. BS 5628: Code of Practice for the Structural Use of Masonry: Part 1 – Unreinforced Masonry: Section 5 – Design: Accidental Damage, London, 1978.

[8]   B.R. Ellingwood and E.V. Leyendecker, Approaches for Design Against Progressive Collapse. Journal of Structural Division, Proc. Am. Soc. Civ. Eng., March 1978, pp. 413-423.

[9]   D.A. Taylor, Progressive Collapse. Can. J. Civ. Eng., Vol. 2, No. 4, December 1975.

Commentary C

Structural Integrity of Firewalls

1. NBC Sentence 3.1.10.1.(1) requires that, where structural framing members are connected to or supported on a firewall and their fire-resistance rating is less than that required for the firewall, the connections and supports for such members must be designed so that the collapse of the framing members during a fire will not cause the collapse of the firewall. NBC Sentence 4.1.5.18.(1) requires that the firewall be designed to resist a factored lateral load of 0.5 kPa under fire conditions.

2. These requirements, along with others in NBC Subsection 3.1.10., form part of the general requirement that a fire not spread between compartments separated by a firewall within the required fire-resistance rating for that wall (4 h for high fire hazard occupancies and 2 h for other occupancies). To achieve this, the firewall must not be damaged to such an extent that it allows a fire to spread within these periods.

3. In order to meet the requirement for structural integrity of firewalls, the following loading conditions must be applied.

Lateral Loads on Firewalls

4. NBC Sentence 4.1.5.18.(1) requires that firewalls be designed for a factored lateral load of 0.5 kPa so that, during a fire, the firewall will not collapse due to the explosion of unburned gases, glancing blows from falling debris, the force and thermal shock of a firehose stream and wind pressure. If the structure exposed to the fire has less fire resistance than that required for the firewall, it is assumed to have failed and therefore to provide no lateral support to the firewall.

5. NBC Sentence 4.1.5.18.(1) also requires that the firewall be designed in accordance with the typical structural requirements applicable to interior walls with regard to wind and earthquake, as well as pounding damage.

6. The building structure, including the firewall, should also be designed to provide structural integrity in accordance with the recommendations of Commentary B.

Thermal Effects

7. The thermal expansion of a structure exposed to a fire must not damage the firewall as this would allow the premature spread of fire through the wall.

8. To assess the potential for such damage, the thermal expansion of the structure should be estimated based on a 500°C temperature increase in combination with the thermal coefficients given in Table E-1 of Commentary E. The expansion of the structure toward the firewall can be assumed to begin at a vertical plane in the fire compartment at 20 m from the firewall or half the width of the fire compartment, whichever is less.

9. In assessing thermal effects, attention should be given to the effect that distortion of the firewall due to temperature differential through the wall has on the stability of the firewall.

10. If thermal movements are sufficient to damage the firewall, either adequate clearances should be provided or the firewall and structure on both sides should be detailed to prevent wall damage.

Commentary C

Design Approaches

11. Some design approaches that satisfy the general requirements for the structural integrity of firewalls are described in Paragraphs 12 to 15.

Double Firewall (NBC 3.1.10.1.(2))

12. The structure on each side is tied to a separate firewall in such a way that, when the structure exposed to fire fails, only one firewall will collapse without damaging the remaining firewall. A schematic example is shown in Figure C-1. Each wall should have at least half the total required fire-resistance rating. The separation between the walls must satisfy the requirements regarding thermal expansion stated in Paragraphs 7 to 10 and those regarding earthquakes stated in Commentary J.

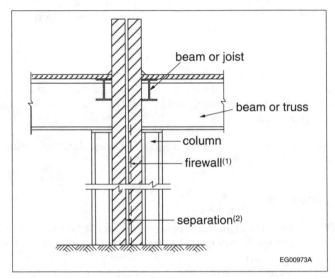

Figure C-1
Schematic example of a double firewall

Notes to Figure C-1:
(1) Each firewall must be tied to the adjacent structure in accordance with Paragraph 12 and reinforced in accordance with Paragraphs 4 and 5.
(2) Firewalls must be separated in accordance with Paragraph 10.

Cantilever Firewall

13. In this design approach, the structure on either side is not connected to the firewall, so that the collapse of the structure exposed to fire does not cause the collapse of the firewall. A schematic example is shown in Figure C-2. Reinforcement of the cantilever wall and foundations against overturning will generally be required to resist the lateral loads specified in NBC Sentence 4.1.5.18.(1). Pilasters will frequently be needed to provide this requisite lateral load capacity.

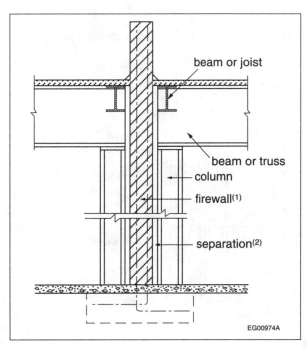

Figure C-2

Schematic example of a cantilever firewall

Notes to Figure C-2:

(1) The firewall is not tied to the structure and is designed as a cantilever from the foundation, with reinforcement and pilasters in accordance with Paragraphs 4, 5, 10 and 13.

(2) Separation may be required in accordance with Paragraph 10.

Commentary C

Tied Firewall

14. In this approach, the structure on each side of the firewall provides lateral support to the firewall and is tied together in such a way that lateral forces resulting from the collapse of the structure exposed to fire are resisted by the structural framework on the other side of the firewall. Lateral forces are recommended in Paragraphs 4 and 5; suitable provisions must be made to transmit these forces to members on opposite sides of the firewall. A schematic example is shown in Figure C-3.

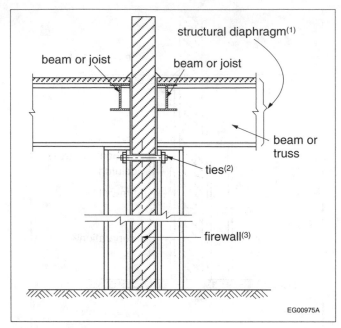

Figure C-3
Schematic example of a tied firewall

Notes to Figure C-3:
(1) Structural diaphragm resistance may be required in accordance with Paragraphs 12, 16 and 17.
(2) Ties must be located and detailed in accordance with Paragraphs 12, 16 and 17.
(3) The firewall must be reinforced and detailed in accordance with Paragraphs 4, 5 and 10.

Weak-link Connections

15. Here, structural components are supported by the firewall in such a way that a failing structure will collapse without causing the firewall to be severely damaged. As with a tied firewall, the structure may also provide lateral support to the firewall. If a weak link is provided on each side of the firewall, the link on the fire side will break away while the link on the non-fire side will not. This approach has traditionally been used in timber construction, where timber beams or joists bear without anchors into pockets of firewalls and can twist free when they collapse.[1][2] Figure C-4 shows a more recent technique for a weak-link connection to a block firewall. If this technique is used, care must be taken to provide adequate anchorage to resist wind uplift and earthquake.

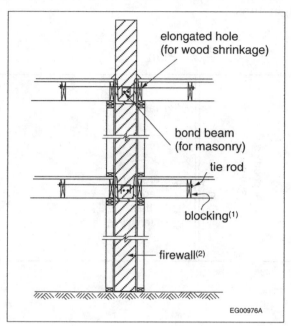

Figure C-4

Example of a weak-link connection used in wood-frame construction

Notes to Figure C-4:

(1) The blocking connection to the wood frame must be detailed to act as a weak link in accordance with Paragraph 15.

(2) The firewall must be reinforced and detailed in accordance with Paragraphs 4, 5 and 10.

Commentary C

Tied Firewalls: Horizontal Forces from Collapsing Structure

16. Where a structure with a lower fire resistance than that required for the firewall is tied through the firewall to the structure on the other side of the firewall, the supporting structure and the ties should be designed for a factored horizontal force equal to $wBL^2/8S$, where w is the dead weight plus 25% of the specified snow load, B is the distance between the ties, L is the span of the collapsing structure between columns perpendicular to the wall, and S is the sag of the collapsing structure which is assumed to be 0.07 L for steel open-web beams and 0.09 L for steel solid-web beams. The supporting structure should be capable of resisting the forces recommended for the ties within a 10 m length of firewall; the other ties are assumed to carry no force (see Figure C-5). The factored resistance of the ties should include a reduction factor of 0.5 to account for a reduced yield strength at high temperature.

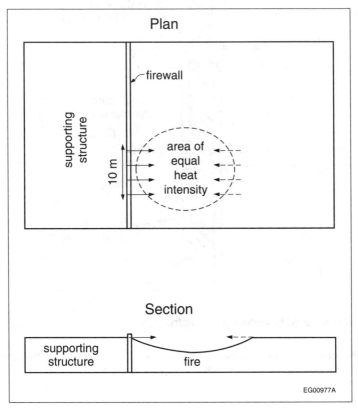

Figure C-5
Horizontal forces on a tied firewall

17. Alternatively, if the firewall is located so that the roof structure has the same resistance to horizontal forces on either side of the firewall (e.g. the firewall is located mid-way between end walls or expansion joints of a structurally symmetric building), only the ties need to be designed for the factored horizontal force $wBL^2/8S$.

References

[1]   Canadian Wood Council. Wood and Fire Safety, Chapter 5, Structural Fire Protection, Ottawa, 1991.

[2]   Canadian Concrete and Masonry Codes Council. Firewalls – A Design Guide, Ottawa, 1992.

Commentary D

Deflection and Vibration Criteria for Serviceability and Fatigue Limit States

1. The following changes have been made to this Commentary, formerly entitled Serviceability Criteria for Deflections and Vibrations:
    *   Tables D-1 to D-4 and the References have been updated to reflect recent experience and testing;
    *   Paragraph 8 on sway vibration of walkways has been added;
    *   the estimation of overloading and fatigue has been simplified and moved to the end of the Commentary in light of its reduced importance; and
    *   a design example for vibration due to rhythmic activity has been added in Paragraphs 16 to 18.

2. The advent of stronger materials, lighter construction, more rigid cladding, smaller damping, longer spans and more accurate strength calculations, which take into account the interaction of building components, means that excessive deflection and vibration now have a greater influence on structural design than before. In the past, building codes controlled excessive deflection and vibration by limiting the member deflection under specified load to some ratio of the span L, for example, L:360 (for cantilevers, L may be taken as twice the length of the cantilever). This widely used criterion dates back to the mid-nineteenth century. To help designers, this Commentary discusses and provides guidance on the problems associated with excessive deflection and excessive vibration.

Deflection

3. Excessive structural deflection can create a variety of problems: cracks in or crushing of non-structural components such as partitions, lack of fit for doors or windows, out-of-plumb walls, end rotation resulting in damage due to eccentric forces, unsightly droopiness, and ponding of water. Cracks, besides being unsightly, may transmit unwanted sound through partitions, or water and cold air through the building envelope, and thus promote material deterioration. Control of cracking in structural concrete is covered separately in CSA A23.3, "Design of Concrete Structures."[23]

4. A number of alternative design solutions can prevent problems caused by excessive deflection. Partition cracking, for example, can be avoided either by making the supporting structure stiff enough or by providing flexible joints in the partitions. Similarly, to avoid cracking, plastered ceilings should be hung from the floor structure, not rigidly attached to it.

5. Table D-1 summarizes the deflection criteria contained in Part 9 and in the design standards referenced in NBC Part 4. These criteria apply to conventional forms of construction under conventional conditions of use. The most severe deflection requirement, 1:720, which applies to members supporting components susceptible to cracking,[1] may not prevent cracking.[3] For new or unusual situations involving concrete structures, more detailed deflection criteria are recommended in Reference [2]; case histories of damage due to excessive deflection—including differential settlement, shrinkage, creep and temperature movements—are presented in References [4] to [7].

Table D-1
Summary of Maximum Deflection/Span Ratios in NBC 2005 and Referenced CSA Standards[1]

Building Component	Referenced Document				
	CAN/CSA-O86[24] Wood	CSA A23.3[23] Concrete	CAN/CSA-S16[25] Structural Steel	CSA S304.1[26] Masonry[2]	NBC Part 9 of Division B
Roof or floor members supporting components susceptible to cracking	[3]	1:480[4] or 1:240[4]	1:360[5]	—	1:360
Floor members not supporting plastered components susceptible to cracking	1:360[6] or 1:180[6]	1:360[7]	1:300[5]	1:480[8]	1:360
Roof members not supporting plastered ceilings, etc.	1:360[6] or 1:180[6]	1:180[7]	1:300[5][9]	—	1:180[10] or 1:240
Wall members	1:180 or 1:360[11]	—	—	1:180 to 1:720[8]	—

(1) Deflection under live, snow or wind load only unless otherwise noted.

(2) Structural support of masonry:
   (a) lateral support of masonry walls – 1:240 to 1:600 depending on type, material and direction of wall flexure;
   (b) vertical support of masonry walls – 1:480 ≤ 20 mm, and
   (c) for glass block walls – 1:600.

(3) For roof or floor members supporting components susceptible to cracking, see Appendix A4.5.2 of CAN/CSA-O86.[24]

(4) Deflection that occurs after the attachment of non-structural components, including creep deflection due to sustained load plus immediate deflection due to live or snow load. 1:240 applies when non-structural components are not likely to be damaged by large deflections.

(5) Special limits are given for steel roof structures (1:180 to 1:240 depending on roofing) and craneways (1:600 to 1:800 depending on crane capacity) on industrial buildings.

(6) 1:180 will control immediate deflection under total load, except for cambered glulam members where live or snow load is applied. 1:360 will control permanent deflection under sustained load. A special deflection criteria is recommended to control ponding on flat roofs.

(7) Immediate deflection due to live, snow or wind load.

(8) Reinforced masonry walls and columns – 1:180 to 1:720 wind deflection; reinforced masonry beams – 1:480.

(9) See Commentary H for a warning on ponding.

(10) 1:180 applies if there is no ceiling.

(11) 1:360 is recommended to control damage to masonry veneer due to wind deflection of wood stud walls. See Appendix A4.5.2 of CAN/CSA-O86.[24]

Floor Vibration

6. Two types of vibration problems arise in building construction: continuous vibrations and transient vibrations. Continuous vibration arises due to the cyclic forces of machinery or certain human activities such as dancing; this vibration can be considerably amplified when the cyclic forces are synchronized with a building frequency—a condition called resonance. Transient vibration is caused by persons jumping or other impact (e.g. dropping of weights in a health club, vehicle impact in a parking garage), and decay at a rate that depends on the available damping.

Floor Vibration Due to Walking

7. The vibration of floor systems due to walking may cause annoyance to occupants. The deflection limits in Table D-1 have, in the past, been used in an attempt to control such vibration but, because of the unsatisfactory vibration performance of buildings designed to these limits, they have been replaced in recent years by new criteria based on the dynamic vibration of building structures.[8][9] Recommended criteria to control vibration due to walking are contained in Reference [10] for steel construction and in Reference [11] for all structural materials, including light-frame construction. A concentrated-load deflection criterion based on experience[12] was used in the NBC Part 9 of Division B span tables to address walking vibration in light-frame floors.

8. An unusual form of vibration present in pedestrian bridges is lateral sway vibration due to resonance caused by heavy pedestrian traffic. Such vibration could occur in a laterally flexible structure used for heavy pedestrian traffic such as a suspended walkway. For guidance on the subject, see the Commentary to CAN/CSA-S6, "Canadian Highway Bridge Design Code."[13]

Floor Vibration Due to Machinery

9. The undesirable effects of continuous vibration caused by machines can be minimized by special design provisions,[8][10] such as locating machinery away from sensitive occupancies, vibration isolation, or alteration of the frequency of the structure.

Floor Vibration Due to Rhythmic Activities

10. NBC Sentence 4.1.3.6.(2) requires that a dynamic analysis be carried out for floor structures (including footbridges) supporting assembly occupancies whose fundamental vibration frequency is less than 6 Hz. This requirement was introduced because of vibration problems with long-span floor structures used for rhythmic activities.[14] to [19] The following paragraphs provide guidance for designers on how to carry out a dynamic analysis for such cases, and recommend criteria to limit floor vibrations during rhythmic activities to levels acceptable for human occupancy of the building.

Dynamic Loading and Response Due to Rhythmic Activities

11. Dancing, foot stamping, jumping exercises and marching are rhythmic activities that create periodic forces with step frequency (e.g. beat of music) in the range of 1 to 4 Hz. For rhythmic activities involving a group of people, the most critical range is 2 to 2.75 Hz. Typical loading cases are shown in Figure D-1. For rhythmic activities, such as dancing, the periodic forces can be approximated by a sinusoidal dynamic load causing vibration at the step frequency, f_s. In the case of jumping exercises, however, the periodic forces shown in Figure D-1 can also create significant sinusoidal load at double the step frequency, $2f_s$, and some sinusoidal load at triple the step frequency, $3f_s$. For any harmonic multiple, i, of the step frequency, the forcing frequency is equal to if_s. The sinusoidal dynamic load applied to the floor for any harmonic can therefore be represented by $\alpha_i w_p \sin 2\pi i f_s t$, where α_i is a dynamic coefficient that varies depending on the activity, w_p is the effective weight of participants per unit area in kPa, if_s is the forcing frequency, and t is time. Table D-2 recommends values of the forcing frequencies, if_s, of the dynamic load based on an estimation of density and weight of participants, w_p, and of the dynamic coefficient, α_i, for typical rhythmic events. These values are based on References [17] and [18] and on recent experience. If the forcing frequency, if_s, is smaller than the fundamental natural frequency of the floor structure (the floor frequency), f_n, the dynamic load has the same effect (e.g. displacement, member force) as a static load of the same magnitude, but if the forcing frequency approaches the floor frequency, the dynamic effect increases with each cycle of vibration to a maximum (see Figure D-2) whose ratio to the static effect is given by

$$\rho = 1 \Big/ \sqrt{\left[1 - \left(\frac{f}{f_n}\right)^2\right]^2 + \left(\frac{2\beta f}{f_n}\right)^2}$$

(1)

where the forcing frequency, f, equals if_s, and β is the damping ratio.[8] If a floor has many people on it, the damping ratio, β, is about 0.06 for a concrete floor and a steel floor with a concrete deck, and 0.12 for a light-frame floor; the damping ratio is about half these values if a floor has few people on it. Damping ratios vary from these suggested values, depending on the influence of non-structural components such as partitions. The dynamic amplification factor, ρ, is shown in Figure D-3 as a function of f/f_n. When multiplied by the cyclic peak dynamic load, $\alpha_i w_p$, the product, $\rho \alpha_i w_p$, is a static load (called the equivalent static load) whose effect is the same as that of the cyclic dynamic load, $\alpha_i w_p \sin 2\pi f t$.

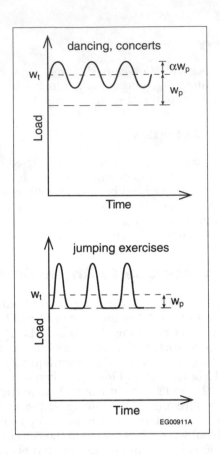

Figure D-1
Load during rhythmic event

Table D-2
Recommended Loading Function for Rhythmic Events

Activity Property	Activity		
	Dancing	Lively Concert[1] or Sports Event	Aerobics
Weight of Participants, [2] w_p, kPa	0.6 (2.5 m²/person)	1.5 (0.5 m²/person)	0.2 (3.5 m²/person)
First harmonic, [3] α_1 (forcing frequency, f_s)	0.5 (1.5 to 2.7 Hz)	0.25 (1.5 to 2.7 Hz)	1.5 (2 to 2.75 Hz)
Second harmonic, [3] α_2 (forcing frequency, $2f_s$)	0.05 (3 to 5 Hz)	0.05 (3 to 5 Hz)	0.6 (4 to 5.5 Hz)
Third harmonic, [3] α_3 (forcing frequency, $3f_s$)	–	–	0.1 (6 to 8.25 Hz)

[1] Values given are for concerts where there is fixed seating. For rock concerts at which seating is not provided, $\alpha_1 = 0.40$ and $\alpha_2 = 0.15$.

[2] Weight of participants is uniformly distributed over activity area. For long-span floors where dancing occurs only on part of the span, the effective uniformly distributed weight over the whole span may be reduced accordingly.

[3] Values of the dynamic coefficient for the i'th harmonic, α_i, are based on commonly encountered events involving a minimum of 20 persons.

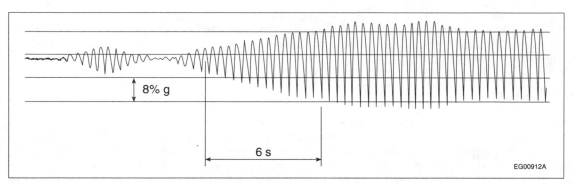

Figure D-2
Resonance during a rock concert (precast stands, f_n = 2.6 Hz)

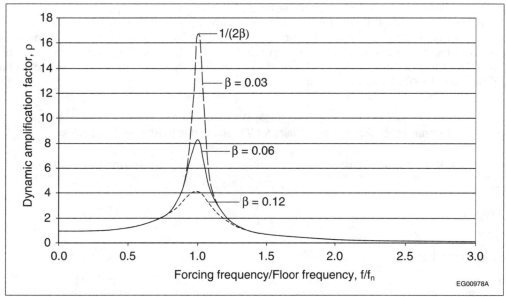

Figure D-3
Dynamic amplification factor, Equation (1)

12. The floor frequency, f_n, should be determined from the dynamic properties of the floor structure, taking into account the flexibility of supports. This can best be carried out using reliable dynamic FEM software. An approximate determination for simply supported joists or beams on girders supported by columns is obtained from

$$f_n = 18/\sqrt{\Delta} \tag{2}$$

where Δ is the dead-weight deflection of the floor structure in mm, which can be conservatively approximated by

$$\Delta = \Delta_j + \Delta_g + \Delta_c \tag{3}$$

where
  Δ_j = the elastic deflection of the joist or beam due to bending and shear, in mm,
  Δ_g = the elastic deflection of the girder due to bending and shear, in mm,
  Δ_c = the elastic shortening of the column due to axial strain, in mm, and

where each deflection, Δ, is due to the total weight supported by the member, including people, and is relative to its supports. Both supports are considered and the most flexible one is used. In the case of joists, beams and girders that are continuous over supports, the elastic deflection, Δ_j

Commentary D

or Δ_g, should be determined by assuming that adjacent spans deflect in opposite directions with no change in slope over the supports and that the weight supported by each span always acts in the direction of deflection.

Human Reaction

13. Floor vibration due to rhythmic activities is much more likely to annoy people than to cause overloading or fatigue. An acceptable level of vertical vibration depends very strongly on the activity of the people who feel the vibration. People in offices or residences become annoyed when accelerations from continuous vibration exceed approximately 0.5% gravity, whereas people participating in rhythmic activities will accept considerably greater than 10% gravity. People such as diners who share a floor structure with dancing will accept approximately 2% gravity. When a floor bay where rhythmic activities are going on is shared with a more sensitive occupancy, then the limit should be based on that occupancy. Other factors besides occupancy affect the acceptability of vibration, in particular the remoteness of the source of vibration from the people affected. For this reason, a range of acceleration limits for different occupancies is recommended in Table D-3. The limit of 4 to 7% gravity given in Table D-3 for a rhythmic activity area in an office or residential building is intended to control floor vibration in other areas of the building containing sensitive occupancies. The limit of 10 to 18% gravity for stadia containing no sensitive occupancies is based on testing[20][21] and feedback from experience.

Table D-3
Recommended Acceleration Limits for Vibrations due to Rhythmic Activities

Occupancies Affected by the Vibration	Acceleration Limit, % gravity
Office and residential	0.4 to 0.7
Dining and weightlifting	1.5 to 2.5
Rhythmic activity area	
in an office or residential building	4 to 7
in a stadium or arena	10 to 18

14. The maximum acceleration, a_{pi}, of a floor structure during a rhythmic event for each harmonic multiple, i, of the step frequency, f_s, can be determined from[17]

$$a_{pi}/g = \frac{1.3\alpha_i w_p/w_t}{\sqrt{\left[\left(\frac{f_n}{if_s}\right)^2 - 1\right]^2 + \left(\frac{2\beta f_n}{if_s}\right)^2}}$$

(4)

where the variables are defined in Paragraphs 11 and 15. The effective maximum acceleration for all harmonics, a_{max}, is obtained from[18]

$$a_{max} = \left[\sum a_{pi}^{1.5}\right]^{2/3}$$

(5)

15. If a floor frequency corresponds to a harmonic forcing frequency, resonance will occur and the accelerations during a rhythmic event will become very large—usually greater than the limit recommended in Table D-3. The floor frequency should generally be greater than the highest significant harmonic forcing frequency, if_s. The following criterion, determined[17] by inverting Equation (4) for sinusoidal loading, is recommended:

$$\frac{f_n}{if_s} \geq \sqrt{1 + \frac{K}{a_o/g}\left(\frac{\alpha_i w_p}{w_t}\right)}$$

(6)

where

a_o/g = acceleration limit as a ratio of the acceleration due to gravity,

K = 1.3 for sinusoidal loading (from Equation (4)),

    = 2.0[18] for jumping exercises (3 harmonics combined), and

    = 1.7[11] for other rhythmic activities noted in Table D-2 (2 harmonics combined),

w_t = total weight supported, kPa, and

where the other variables are defined in Paragraph 11. Table D-4 contains examples of the application of Equation (6) to typical floor structures using the acceleration limits recommended in Table D-3. A simple conservative procedure for the analysis of floor vibration is to compare the floor frequency calculated in accordance with Paragraph 12 with the minimum frequency for acceptable performance given in Table D-4. If the minimum is not met, it is recommended to use a more direct calculation of floor properties and performance, as shown in the example presented in Paragraphs 16 to 18.

Example

16. A 30 m by 50 m ballroom with a floor weight of 5 kPa is to be used for dining and dancing (see Figure D-4). The floor structure consists of a concrete deck on steel trusses of 30 m span supported by steel girders of 5 m span on one-storey columns; the primary flexibility of the floor structure is provided by the trusses. Table D-4 indicates a minimum natural frequency of 6.5 Hz for satisfactory performance of the floor. In accordance with Equation (2), this natural frequency corresponds to a dead-weight deflection of the floor structure, Δ, of only 7.7 mm (span/3900), which is very difficult for a 30-m span to achieve.

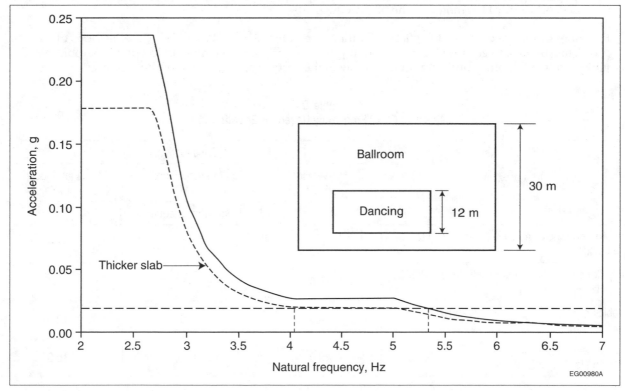

Figure D-4
Ballroom dining and dancing

17. A closer estimation of the minimum required floor frequency is obtained by applying Equations (4) and (5), where the effective weight of people is reduced from 0.6 kPa on the dance floor (from Table D-2) to the equivalent of 0.24 kPa over the whole span (see floor layout in Figure D-4). The calculated maximum acceleration shown in Figure D-4 as a function of floor frequency is based on a damping coefficient of 0.06 and loading assumptions obtained from Table D-2. For a floor frequency of less than 2.7 Hz, vibration of 24% gravity acceleration occurs due to first harmonic

resonance. For a floor frequency between 4 and 5 Hz, vibration of 2.7% gravity acceleration occurs due to second harmonic resonance.

18. To achieve an acceleration limit of 2% gravity, Figure D-4 shows that a floor frequency of 5.3 Hz is needed, which corresponds to a dead-weight deflection of the floor structure, Δ, of 11.5 mm (span/2510): this is still not easy to achieve. However, Figure D-4 shows that an increased mass, w_t, resulting from the addition of 75 mm of concrete means a lower minimum frequency of 4 Hz is acceptable, which corresponds to a dead-weight deflection of the floor structure of 20 mm (span/1500). The increased floor weight results in a moderate decrease of floor frequency. Alternatively, an FEM dynamic analysis to determine floor frequency might indicate that, without the extra concrete, a 5.3 Hz limit is achievable. More examples on the use of Equations (2) to (5) are contained in References [10], [11] and [18].

Measures to Prevent or Correct Unacceptable Vibration

19. Measures to prevent or correct unacceptable vibration due to rhythmic activities include:
    (a) applying administrative controls on rhythmic activities, such as by not allowing high-impact aerobics during office hours,
    (b) relocating the rhythmic activity or the sensitive occupancy,
    (c) providing sufficient stiffness (i.e. increased f_n) or mass (w_t) to satisfy the recommended criterion (see Equation (6)),
    (d) increasing the damping sufficiently to reduce resonant response, for example using tuned mass dampers,[10] or
    (e) providing isolation (floating floor) under jumping exercises to reduce dynamic forces at the second or third harmonic of the step frequency.[10]

For more guidance on correcting floor vibration, see References [10] and [11]. Case histories of problems are described in References [14] to [18], including a case where unacceptable aerobics vibration in a tall office building occurred due to the vertical spring action of the columns.

Table D-4
Minimum Floor Frequency Based on Equation (6)[1]

Activity	Construction		
	Heavy Floor 5 kPa	Medium Floor 2.5 kPa	Light Floor 1 kPa
	Minimum Floor Frequency, Hz		
Dancing and Dining (a_o/g = 0.02, if$_s$ = 2.7 Hz, w_p = 0.6 kPa)	6.5	8.0	11.0
Lively Concerts[2] or Sports Events (a_o/g = 0.05, if$_s$ = 5 Hz, w_p = 1.5 kPa)	6.0	6.5	7.5
Aerobics only (a_o/g = 0.06, if$_s$ = 8.25 Hz,[3] w_p = 0.2 kPa)	9.0	9.5	12.0
Aerobics and Weightlifting (a_o/g = 0.02, if$_s$ = 8.25 Hz,[3] w_p = 0.12 kPa)	9.0	11.0	15.0

[1] Equation (6) is applied to all harmonics (1, 2 or 3) but the governing harmonic is used. In some cases, however, damping × mass is sufficient to reduce high-harmonic resonance to an acceptable level.
[2] Assumes fixed seating (see Note (1) of Table D-2).
[3] Sometimes governed by second harmonic, f = 5.5 Hz.

20. Based on recent documented experience with vibration problems in office and residential buildings, it is strongly recommended that, if an existing floor is intended to be used for aerobics or some other high-impact repetitive activity in the future, activity tests be carried out before making alterations or signing a lease. Such tests evaluate the performance of floors in nearby sensitive occupancies, including that of the floors above or below the activity.

Overloading

21. The total structural effect of a rhythmic activity can be determined from the static effect of the load, $w_t + \Sigma \rho \alpha_i w_p$, where w_t is the total weight supported during the activity, and $\rho \alpha_i w_p$ is the equivalent static load for the dynamic component at each harmonic, i, as defined in Paragraph 11. Overloading occurs if the total load, including static and dynamic components, is greater than the total specified load that the structure can support. A typical example is a floor structure with a floor frequency, f_n, of 5 Hz that supports aerobics. The most critical situation is second-harmonic resonance when high-impact aerobics is carried out at a step frequency of 2.5 Hz on a fully occupied floor. For the second harmonic, f equals f_n, and the dynamic amplification factor, ρ, using Equation (1) equals $1/(2\beta)$. The equivalent static load, $\alpha_2 w_p/(2\beta)$, equals $0.6 \times 0.2/(2 \times 0.06) = 1$ kPa, where α_2 and w_p are obtained from Table D-2 and the damping ratio, β, is assumed to be 0.06. For the first harmonic, $f = 0.5 f_n$ and $\rho = 1.33$ using Equation (1). The equivalent static load, $\rho \alpha_1 w_p$, equals $1.33 \times 1.5 \times 0.2 = 0.4$ kPa, where α_1 is obtained from Table D-2. The third harmonic with $\alpha_3 = 0.1$ and $f = 1.5 f_n$ is very small. The dynamic component of load, $\Sigma \rho \alpha_i w_p$, is therefore approximately equal to $1 + 0.4 = 1.4$ kPa, which is then rounded to 2 kPa to include all vibration frequencies. The total load, $w_t + 2$ kPa, is usually less than the specified dead load plus live load.

Fatigue

22. Potential for fatigue damage can be assessed by estimating the stress range and number of cycles per year for each harmonic. The stress range for each harmonic is equal to twice the stress due to the equivalent static load, $\alpha_i w_p \rho_i$, or the static stress due to the load, $2\rho \alpha_i w_p$. In the example given in Paragraph 21 of a 5-Hz floor used for aerobics, where second-harmonic resonance occurs, the stress range for the second harmonic is equal to the static stress due to $2 \times 1 = 2$ kPa, whereas for the first harmonic, it is equal to the static stress due to $2 \times 0.4 = 0.8$ kPa, while the third harmonic is very small. From field tests of aerobics vibrations, it is estimated that a typical session of high-impact aerobics lasts on average about 10 minutes, during 3 minutes of which second-harmonic resonance occurs. The first harmonic at 2.5 Hz is expected to have a duration of 10 minutes resulting in 1500 cycles, while the second harmonic at 5 Hz is expected to have a duration of 3 minutes resulting in 900 cycles. Other frequency components occur, but they are small and of short duration. Two sessions per day at 300 days per year result in approximately 1 million cycles per year for the first harmonic and 0.6 million per year for the second harmonic. The fatigue life for each harmonic can then be estimated from specified S-N fatigue curves[22] and combined in accordance with the Palmgren-Minor rule.[11] In this example, a close estimate of fatigue life is obtained from the second harmonic only. Design, however, will almost always be governed by human reaction and not fatigue. For an existing building, it is recommended that fatigue life be based on vibration tests during a high-impact aerobics session to estimate acceleration levels versus number of cycles.

References

[1]   W.A. Russell, Deflection Characteristics of Residential Wood-Joist Floor Systems. Housing and Home Finance Agency, Housing Research Paper 30, Washington, D.C., April 1954.

[2]   Allowable Deflections. Subcommittee 1, ACI Committee 435. Journal Am. Concrete Inst., Vol. 65, No. 6, June 1968, p. 433.

[3]   W.G. Plewes and G.K. Garden, Deflections of Horizontal Structural Members. Canadian Building Digest No. 54, Division of Building Research, National Research Council of Canada, Ottawa, June 1964.

[4]   H. Mayer and H. Rüsch, Bauschäden als Folge der Durchbiegung von Stahlbeton-Bauteilen (Building Damage Caused by Deflection of Reinforced Concrete Building Components). Deutscher Ausschuss für Stahlbeton, Heft 193, Berlin 1967. National Research Council of Canada Technical Translation TT1412, 1970.

[5]   O. Pfeffermann, Les Fissures dans les Constructions Conséquences de Phénomènes Physiques Naturels. Annales de l'Institut Technique du Bâtiment et des Travaux Publics, No. 250, October 1968.

[6]   A.W. Skempton and D.H. MacDonald, The Allowable Settlements of Buildings. Proc., Institution of Civil Engineers, Vol. 5, Part III, 1956, p. 727.

Commentary D

[7]   F.R. Khan and M. Fintel, Effects of Column Exposure in Tall Structures – Design Considerations and Field Observations of Buildings. Journal Am. Concrete Inst., Vol. 65, No. 2, February 1968, p. 99.

[8]   W.J. Smith. Vibrations of Structures: Applications in Civil Engineering Design. Chapman and Hall, London, 1988.

[9]   Serviceability of Buildings Against Vibration. International Standard ISO 10137. Geneva, 1992.

[10]   AISC/CISC, 1997, Steel Design Guide Series 11. Floor Vibrations Due to Human Activity. American Institute of Steel Construction, Chicago, Illinois, U.S.A.

[11]   ATC, 1999, ATC Design Guide 1. Minimizing Floor Vibration. Applied Technology Council, Redwood City, California, U.S.A.

[12]   D.M. Onysko, L.J. Hu, E.D. Jones, and B. Di Lenardo: Serviceability Design of Residential Wood-Framed Floors in Canada. Proceedings of the World Conference on Timber Engineering 2000, July 31 to August 3, Whistler, B.C.

[13]   Commentary to CAN/CSA-S6-00, Canadian Highway Bridge Design Code: C3.4.4, Sway Vibration in Pedestrian Bridges.

[14]   Pop Concert Shock for Loading Code. New Civil Engineer International, May 1981, p. 18.

[15]   G. Pernica, Dynamic Live Loads at a Rock Concert. Can. J. Civ. Eng., June 1983, pp. 185–191.

[16]   H. Bachmann and W. Ammann, Vibrations in Structures Induced by Man and Machines. Structural Engineering Document 3e. International Association for Bridge and Structural Engineering, Zurich, 1987.

[17]   D.E. Allen, J.H. Rainer and G. Pernica, Vibration Criteria for Assembly Occupancies. Can. J. Civ. Eng., Vol. 12, No. 3, September 1985.

[18]   D.E. Allen, Floor Vibrations from Aerobics. Can. J. Civ. Eng., October 1990.

[19]   D.E. Allen, Vibrations from Human Activities. Concrete International – Design and Construction, American Concrete Institute, June 1990.

[20]   D. Braun, S.J. Kennedy, D.J.L. Kennedy, and D.E. Allen. Sandwich Plate Systems Risers for Stadia. Structural Stability Research Council, Annual Stability Conference, April 24-27, 2002, Seattle, Washington.

[21]   M. Kasperski, 2001. Menschenerregte Schwingungen in Sportstadien (People-induced vibrations in sports stadia), Bauingenieur, Band 76, December 2001, p. 575–581.

[22]   CAN/CSA-S6-00, Canadian Highway Bridge Design Code: Clause 10.17, Structural Fatigue (see also the Commentary C10.17). Canadian Standards Association, Mississauga, Ontario, 2000.

[23]   CSA A23.3-04, Design of Concrete Structures. Canadian Standards Association, Mississauga, Ontario, 2004.

[24]   CAN/CSA-O86-01, Engineering Design in Wood. Canadian Standards Association, Mississauga, Ontario, 2001.

[25]   CAN/CSA-S16-01, Limit States Design of Steel Structures. Canadian Standards Association, Mississauga, Ontario, 2001.

[26]   CSA S304.1-04, Design of Masonry Structures. Canadian Standards Association, Mississauga, Ontario, 2004.

Commentary E

Effects of Deformations in Building Components

Structural Effects

1. When building materials expand and contract due to temperature changes, considerable forces may be produced in restrained structural elements, i.e., those elements that are not free to expand and contract with the changes in temperature. Often these forces are compounded by those produced by shrinkage, creep and moisture content changes and are therefore difficult to analyze or predict. In many situations, however, the structural designer must consider the probable structural effects of the forces produced by temperature changes along with all other forces; indeed the designer is required to do so according to Sentence 4.1.2.1.(1) of Division B of the National Building Code of Canada 2005 (NBC).

2. In addition to expansion and contraction, temperature changes may produce differential deformation or warping of materials as a result of a gradient in temperature through the thickness of materials or assemblies. Again this may complicate the assessment of deformations or stresses, but a rational judgment must be made in design if building elements are to perform in a satisfactory manner.

3. If these forces are not properly considered, the stresses resulting from such forces can lead to serious failures (usually cracking) in materials and structural members. Failures occur when clearances are insufficient, when fasteners do not allow movement or deformations, or, in the case of restrained elements, when the elements are not strong enough to withstand the stresses induced. An elementary review of thermal and moisture deformations in buildings is given in References [1] and [2]. Table E-1 indicates the order of magnitude of movement to which various materials are liable. Actual values can vary significantly from those in the Table.

Table E-1
Typical Deformation Properties of Some Common Building Materials

Material	Thermal Movement, mm/m per 100 °C	Moisture Movement, mm/m		Modulus of Elasticity, MPa × 10³	Creep Coefficient, [1] φ
		Permanent	Reversible		
Plain concrete[2]					
normal weight	1.0	0.5	±0.1	30	3
Glass	0.9	0	0	70	0
Masonry[3]					
clay	0.7	−0.2 (expansion)	±0.1	20	1
calcium silicate	1.0	0.2	±0.1	15	2
concrete					
normal weight	1.0	0.4	±0.2	15	2
lightweight (autoclaved)	1.0	0.4	±0.2	10	2
aerated (autoclaved cellular)	1.0	0.7	±0.2	6	2
Metal					
aluminum	2.4	0	0	70	0
copper	1.7	0	0	110	0
lead	3.0	0	0	14	0
steel	1.2	0	0	200[4]	0
Natural stone					
limestone	0.4	—	±0.1	60	0
marble	0.5	—	±0.1	35	0
sandstone	1.2	—	±0.3	20	0
Wood (spruce-pine-fir)					
across grain					
radial	4.0	30[5]	±Δmc[5]	1	[6]
tangential	6.0	50[5]	±2Δmc[5]	0.5	[6]
parallel to grain	0.4	1[5]	±Δmc/30[5]	10	1

[1] Deformation under sustained loading = short-term deformation based on modulus of elasticity × (1 + φ).
[2] For reinforced concrete, see CSA A23.3, "Design of Concrete Structures."[24]
[3] For further information, see CSA S304.1, "Design of Masonry Structures."[25]
[4] For cold-formed steel, see CAN/CSA-S136, "North American Specification for the Design of Cold-Formed Steel Structural Members."[26]
[5] Initial drying from green condition to equilibrium is assumed to be 12%; Δmc = per cent change in moisture content from 12%.[21]
[6] Such application is usually avoided.

Design Temperature Ranges

4. In a country like Canada, with its many climatic regions, the extremes of air temperature that have to be considered in the design of exteriors of buildings vary greatly. One way of approaching this problem is to use temperature maps like those given in the Ontario Highway Bridge Design Code[3] giving maximum summer and minimum winter air temperatures. Such a detailed approach may not be necessary for buildings. Instead, the 2.5% July and January air temperatures for the design of

cooling and heating systems given in NBC Table C-2, Design Data for Selected Locations in Canada, in Appendix C of Division B are suggested. This will be illustrated by the three examples below.

5. Because of solar heat gain in summer and radiation heat loss in winter, the range of temperatures that building elements undergo is greater than the ambient air temperature. Tables E-2 and E-3 show typical annual ranges of temperature differences between such elements and ambient air temperatures due to these effects.[2]

Table E-2
Temperature Increase in Excess of Ambient Air Temperature due to Solar Radiation

Surface	Temperature Gain, °C
Dark roofing	20 – 40
Steel and other metal	15 – 25
Concrete and masonry	10 – 15

Table E-3
Temperature Decrease below Ambient Temperature due to Radiation Loss into a Dark Clear Sky

Surface	Temperature Loss, °C
Dark roofing	10
Steel and other metal	5 – 10
Concrete and masonry	5

6. The values in Table E-2 vary according to the colour, slope, orientation and insulation backing of the surface.

Examples: For a horizontal dark-coloured metal surface in three typical climate regions (coastal, central and interior), the range of temperatures for design purposes might be as follows:

Coastal (Victoria):

$(24^{(i)} + 25^{(ii)}) - (-5^{(iii)} - 10^{(iv)}) = 64°C$

Central (Ottawa):

$(30^{(i)} + 25^{(ii)}) - (-25^{(iii)} - 10^{(iv)}) = 90°C$

Interior (Regina):

$(31^{(i)} + 25^{(ii)}) - (-34^{(iii)} - 10^{(iv)}) = 100°C$

7. Except for the very temperate parts of Canada referred to as Coastal, as a simple rule, one may assume a range of exterior surface temperatures of about 100°C for a horizontal relatively dark material. Because of thermal insulation, thermal inertia and other factors, however, the range of extreme temperatures in structural components of a certain thickness will often be somewhat smaller than those in the preceding examples.

8. Temperature variations can be particularly significant in multi-storey apartment and office buildings with exterior columns partially, and in some cases fully, exposed to the weather. Exposed columns, when subjected to seasonal temperature variations, change their length relative to interior columns, which remain unchanged in a controlled environment. Although in low buildings this causes insignificant structural problems, in tall buildings temperature stresses become significant and must be investigated thoroughly.

(i) July 2.5% temperature.
(ii) Dark metal temperature gain.
(iii) January 2.5% temperature.
(iv) Dark metal temperature loss.

Commentary E

9. Dimensional changes occur not only as the result of temperature changes, but also from shrinkage, moisture content changes, chemical processes and creep deformation in the component materials of a building. If the building or component is not free to contract or expand, tensile or compressive stresses result. These stresses can be relieved or reduced to tolerable limits by contraction and expansion joints. Such joints are particularly important to allow contraction to take place along certain pre-selected lines rather than to produce cracks along accidental lines of least resistance.

Effects on Cladding

10. In the design of all buildings, but particularly very long and very high buildings, the effects of movements of the structural members on the cladding elements should be considered. Shortening and lengthening of columns due to temperature and shrinkage effects and creep can crack, buckle or otherwise overstress cladding materials and their fastenings. Deflections and linear movements of beams and spandrels and building sidesway can have similar effects. Failure to consider these differential movements has caused many cases of cladding damage. For example, spalling, cracking and bulging have occurred to brick and stone veneer on a number of tall concrete buildings,[4] necessitating extensive repairs. The phenomenon is not, however, limited to concrete frames, nor are the effects limited to stone and brick cladding. References [5] to [23] discuss these effects in greater detail.

References

[1]   M.C. Baker, Thermal and Moisture Deformations in Building Materials. CBD 56, Division of Building Research, National Research Council Canada, Ottawa, August 1964.

[2]   Estimation of Thermal and Moisture Movements and Stresses. Parts 1-3, British Building Research Establishment Digests No. 227-229. Building Research Station, Garston, Watford, Great Britain, August 1979.

[3]   Ontario Highway Bridge Design Code 1984. Ontario Ministry of Transportation and Communications, Toronto, 1984.

[4]   W.G. Plewes, Failure of Brick Facing on High-Rise Buildings. CBD 185, Division of Building Research, National Research Council Canada, Ottawa, April 1977.

[5]   Principles of Modern Building, Vol. I. Building Research Station of DSIR. Her Majesty's Stationery Office, London, 1959 (in particular see Chapter 2 on Dimensional Stability).

[6]   D.G. Stephenson, Extreme Temperatures at the Outer Surface of Buildings. CBD 47, Division of Building Research, National Research Council Canada, Ottawa, November 1963.

[7]   F.R. Khan and M. Fintel, Effects of Column Exposure in Tall Structures. Paper in three parts. (a) Temperature Variations and Their Effects, (b) Analysis of Length Changes in Exposed Columns, and (c) Design Considerations and Field Observations of Buildings. Journal of American Concrete Inst., Vol. 63, No. 8, August 1966 and Vol. 65, No. 2, February 1968.

[8]   P. Weidlinger, Temperature Stresses in Tall Reinforced Concrete Buildings. Civil Engineering, New York, Vol. 34, No. 8, August 1964.

[9]   K. Jones, Restraint of Structures Attached to Mass Concrete. Journal of Structural Division, Am. Soc. Civ. Eng., Vol. 87, No. ST8, December 1961.

[10] W.T. Marshal, Shrinkage and Temperature Stresses in Reinforced Concrete. Civil Engineering, London, Vol. 56, No. 665, December 1961.

[11] P. Fisher, Differential Temperature Movements in Rigid Frame. Journal of American Concrete Inst., Vol. 59, No. 6, June 1962.

[12] D.W. Allen, The Calculation of Temperature Stresses. Concrete & Constructional Engineering, Vol. LVII, No. 9, September 1962.

[13] G.L. England and A.D. Ross, Reinforced Concrete under Thermal Gradients. Magazine of Concrete Research, Vol. 14, No. 40, March 1962.

[14] J.H. Slack and M.J. Walker, Movement Joints in Concrete. Concrete Society Limited, Grosvenor Gardens, London, Technical Paper, 1967.

[15] Deflections of Reinforced Concrete Flexural Members. Report of ACI Committee 435, ACI Manual of Concrete Practice 1970, Part 2.

[16] H. Mayer and H. Rusch, Building Damage Caused by Deflection of Reinforced Concrete Building Components. Deutsher Ausschuss fur Stahlbeton, Heft 193, Berlin 1967, National Research Council Technical Translation TT1412.

[17] W.G. Plewes, Cladding Problems Due to Frame Movements. CBD 125, Division of Building Research, National Research Council Canada, Ottawa, May 1970.

[18] R.E. Copeland, Flexible Anchorage of Masonry Walls. Concrete Products, Vol. 71, No. 7, 1968, p. 54.

[19] M. Fintel and F.R. Khan, Effects of Column Creep and Shrinkage in Tall Structures – Prediction of Inelastic Column Shortening. Journal of American Concrete Inst., December 1969, Proc. V66, No. 12, p. 957.

[20] D. Foster, Some Observations on the Design of Brickwork Cladding to Multi-storey R/C Framed Structures. BDA Tech. Note, Vol. 1, No. 4, September 1971, The Brick Development Association, 3-5 Bedford Row, London WC1 4BU.

[21] CIRIA, Movement and Cracking in Long Masonry Walls. Practice Note, Special Publication 44, Construction Industry Research and Information Association, London, U.K., 1986.

[22] S.J. Alexander and R.M. Lawson, Design for Movement in Buildings. CIRIA Technical Note 107, Construction Industry Research and Information Association, London, U.K., 1981.

[23] A.T. Hansen, Effects of Wood Shrinkage in Buildings. Canadian Building Digest 244, Institute for Research in Construction, National Research Council Canada, Ottawa, February 1987.

[24] CSA A23.3-04, Design of Concrete Structures. Canadian Standards Association, Mississauga, Ontario, 2004.

[25] CSA S304.1-04, Design of Masonry Structures. Canadian Standards Association, Mississauga, Ontario, 2004.

[26] CAN/CSA-S136-01, North American Specification for the Design of Cold-Formed Steel Structural Members. Canadian Standards Association, Mississauga, Ontario, 2001.

Commentary F

Tributary Area

1. Because live loads are generally given as uniformly distributed loads over a floor area, and because dead loads can usually be considered as uniform loads, either over an area or along the length of a flexural member, design engineers have for years used the concept of tributary area to determine the loads that beams, girders and columns carry. Once the concept is applied to any floor, it is easily extended for multi-storey columns to any number of floors.

2. Earlier design standards recognized that the probability that all the floors of a multi-storey building would be loaded to the full live load simultaneously was very remote. Therefore, to design the columns for the full live load of a number of floors was unduly restrictive, and reductions in the live load were devised as a function of the number of floors supported by the columns.

3. In the 1960 edition of the National Building Code, recognizing that the average live load was a function of the area supported, the rationalization was carried one step further and a reduction of 15% was allowed for beams, girders and trusses supporting areas greater than 20 m^2.

4. In subsequent editions, provisions were included for live load reduction based on tributary areas with two different expressions, one for office and apartment buildings and the other for storage or similar areas.

5. Therefore, for determining the total dead load to be supported by a given member and to determine what live load reduction factor should be applied, a clear definition of tributary area, about which some confusion existed, is needed.

6. In the case of a member that supports the load directly, such as a slab, the tributary area is defined as the area supported by the member bounded by the lines of support. In the case of a member that does not support the load directly but supports other members, the tributary area is defined as the area bounded by the lines of support of the member and the lines of zero shear in the members supported, assuming a uniformly distributed load is acting on the structure. These definitions, which for continuous construction require a structural analysis to determine locations of zero shear, should be followed when determining the forces that members carry. In determining live load reduction, however, the following simplifications are recommended.

Decks and Slabs

7. No live load reduction factors should be applied to wooden or sheet metal decks, precast units or one-way slabs because of the uncertainty of the degree of lateral distribution of loads.

8. The tributary area for a flat slab or the slab portions of two-way slabs with beams is the area bounded by column lines or by a combination of column lines and lines of supporting members such as beams and girders, whichever is the lesser, as shown in Figures F-1, F-2 and F-3.

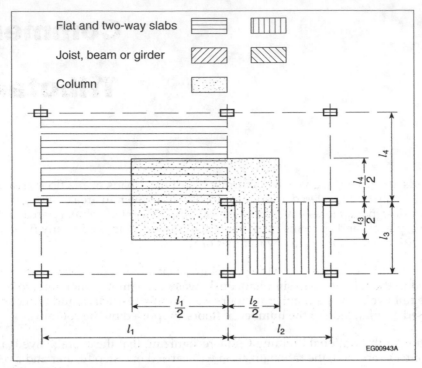

Figure F-1
Tributary areas for flat slabs without beams and girders

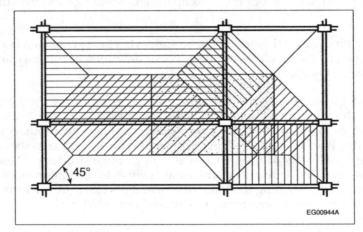

Figure F-2
Tributary areas for a two-way slab with beams

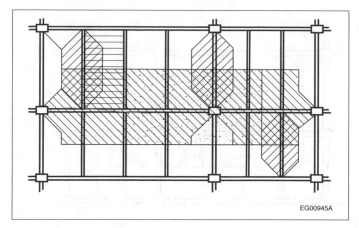

Figure F-3
Tributary areas for a two-way slab with joists, beams and girders

Beams and Girders

9. The tributary area for a member supporting a portion of a floor is the area enclosing the member and bounded by the lines of zero shear in the members supported. For buildings with fairly regular bays, the lines of zero shear in the members supported can be assumed to be halfway between lines of support. Figures F-2 and F-3 illustrate the tributary area of beams supporting two-way slabs. Figures F-4 and F-5 illustrate the tributary areas for joists, beams and girders supporting a one-way slab.

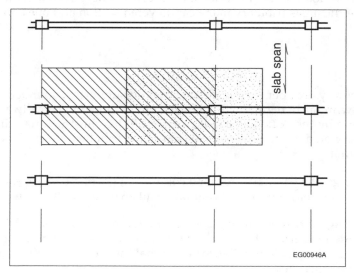

Figure F-4
Tributary areas for a one-way slab with girders

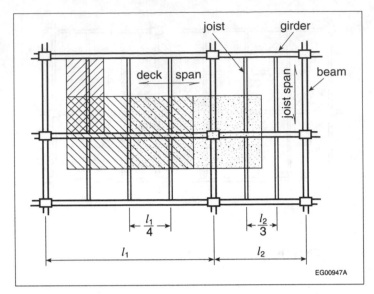

Figure F-5
Tributary areas for a one-way deck or slab with joists, beams and girders

Negative Moments in Continuous Members

10. Tributary area for negative moment over a support may be taken as the sum of the tributary areas of the beams on either side of the support. For cantilever, drop-in beam systems, the tributary area for calculation of the live load reduction factor, as it affects the negative moment at the support, is taken as the sum of the areas tributary to the cantilevered section and one half the length of the drop-in section.

Columns

11. For a column the tributary area per floor is the area of floor supported, bounded by the lines of zero shear. For buildings with fairly regular bays, these can be assumed to be halfway between the column lines, as shown by the dotted area in Figures F-1 to F-5. In structures with beams, joists or girders, the tributary area per floor is half the sum of the tributary areas of each of the floor members framing into it.

12. In multi-storey buildings, the tributary area for a column supporting one use and occupancy is the sum of the tributary areas per floor for that column on all levels above the storey in question.

13. For a column supporting more than one use and occupancy, Article 4.1.5.9. of Division B of the 2005 National Building Code requires that the tributary area for each use and occupancy be considered separately for determining reduction in live load and that the area supporting snow load, which has no reduction, not be included.

Commentary G

Snow Loads

1. The following major changes on how to deal with snow loads were introduced in the 2005 edition of the National Building Code of Canada (NBC):
   - The return period for the ground snow load has been increased from 30 years to 50 years to better correlate with the expected service life of buildings and to be more consistent with the return period used by design codes in other countries; the revised return period results in an increase of about 10% in the ground snow loads.
   - An importance factor, I_s, has been introduced to the expression for calculating the specified snow load, S.
   - Snow loads are now considered separately from the live load due to use and occupancy.
   - The full and partial loading provisions are now applicable to all arched or curved roofs.
   - The use of a wind exposure factor of less than 1.0 is disallowed for High and Post-disaster Importance Category buildings in recognition of the critical role these buildings play in a catastrophic situation, either as post-disaster shelters or as emergency response facilities.
   - In this Commentary, the height-to-width ratio for consideration of unbalanced snow load on arched or curved roofs is reduced to 0.05 and new formulae are introduced.
   - To reduce the confusion between the C_a factor that relates to roof size and the C_a factor that accounts for snow accumulation, the large roof factor has been removed from C_a and is incorporated into the basic roof snow load factor, C_b.

2. Snow loads on roofs vary according to geographical location (climate), site exposure, shape and type of roof, and also from one winter to another. To account for these varying conditions, NBC Subsection 4.1.6. expresses the specified snow load, S, on a roof or other surface as the sum of two components—one being the product of a series of factors—multiplied by the snow load importance factor.

$$S = I_s[S_s(C_bC_wC_sC_a) + S_r] \tag{1}$$

where
   I_s = importance factor for snow load,
   S_s = ground snow load in kPa with a 1-in-50 probability of exceedance per year,
   C_b = basic roof snow load factor,
   C_w = wind exposure factor,
   C_s = roof slope factor,
   C_a = shape factor, and
   S_r = associated rain load in kPa (however, the rain load at any location on a roof need not be taken greater than the load due to snow, i.e. $S_r \leq S_s(C_bC_wC_sC_a)$).

The factors are discussed individually in this Commentary and a series of figures are provided to illustrate their application to various shapes of roofs. The factors are based on measurements obtained during surveys of snow on roofs, on analytical studies of the loads on large flat roofs, and on judgment. Since surveys of sufficient length (about 10 years or more)[1] cover only a limited selection of the most common and simplest roof shapes, the factors are of limited accuracy and may be subject to change as more data become available.

Snow Loads on the Ground

3. In Canada, ground snow loads are used as a basis for the determination of roof snow loads. Therefore, they form part of the basic climatic information needed for building design and are presented in NBC Table C-2, Design Data for Selected Locations in Canada, in Appendix C of

Commentary G

Division B. Each ground snow load given in NBC Table C-2 is composed of two loads: one load, S_s, which is a snow load with a 1-in-50 annual probability of exceedance based on measured depths and densities, and another load, S_r, which is due to the associated rain that may fall into the snow cover (not including any rainfall that exceeds the weight of the snow cover).[2] (See Paragraph 6.)

The snow loads for a given town or city are for the exact latitude and longitude defined in the Canadian Geographical Names Data Base (CGNDB)[3] for that town or city. Snow loads may vary within cities with large changes in elevation. Recommended values of S_s and S_r for significantly different elevations within listed sites and for locations not listed in NBC Table C-2 can be obtained from the Information Services Section, Environment Canada, 4905 Dufferin Street, Downsview, Ontario, M3H 5T4; e-mail: climate.services@ec.gc.ca. Elevations are not given in the CGNDB but can be obtained from commercially available topographic maps prepared by Natural Resources Canada.

Variations with Climate

4. The wide climatic variations across the country produce large variations in snow conditions. The heaviest snow loads occur in the mountainous regions of British Columbia and Alberta; they last the entire winter and vary considerably with elevation. In some coastal locations of British Columbia, little drifting of snow occurs. The Prairie provinces, Yukon, Nunavut and the Northwest Territories have very cold winters, with small annual snowfalls but frequent strong winds, which cause considerable drifting of snow on roofs and on the ground. The region that includes Ontario, Quebec, and interior regions of the Atlantic provinces is marked by moderate winds and snowfalls, and sufficiently low temperatures in most places to allow snow accumulation all winter. In this region, moderate uniform and high drift loads occur. Also, cold northwesterly winds often cause locally heavy snowfalls to the lee of bodies of water such as the Great Lakes and the St. Lawrence River, resulting in increased snow loads.

Local Variations – Mountainous Areas

5. In mountainous areas, ground snow loads increase with elevation. Observations noted by the Institute for Research in Construction of the National Research Council on a number of mountains in British Columbia indicate significant increases in ground snow load with increases in elevation, depending on the local topography and climate.[4] Individual mountains or groups of mountains may cause significant changes in a local or micro climate within short distances. Hence, snow loads listed in NBC Table C-2 apply only at a particular elevation at the specific location as defined by the name and latitude/longitude coordinates given by the CGNDB.[3] Environment Canada should be consulted for specific recommendations regarding other significantly different elevations within a listed location. (See also Paragraph 3.)

Unit Weight of Snow on the Ground

6. Falling snowflakes usually consist of very large complex ice crystals. Because of their large surface area to weight, they fall to the ground relatively slowly. On arrival, this snow accumulates in a loose and fluffy layer with a unit weight of about 0.5 to 1.0 kN/m³. Immediately, however, the snow crystals start to change: the thin, lacy, needlelike projections begin to sublime and the crystals become smaller, irregularly shaped grains. Settlement of the snow results and the unit weight, γ, increases after a short time to about 2.0 kN/m³ or greater, even at temperatures below the freezing point. The unit weight of the snowpack continues to increase with age, ranging from 2.0 to 5.0 kN/m³. As explained in NBC Appendix C of Division B, average values for seasonal snowpacks have been derived for different regions across the country for use in the ground snow load calculations.[2] The snow surveys from which the unit weight is derived are made four times per month (at most). While the survey measurements reflect to some extent the portion of rainfall that is trapped in the snowpack over a period of time, only a small proportion of measurements would have been made directly after a rainfall. Therefore, the measurements probably do not adequately represent the short-term density increase due to the wetting of snow by rain; for this reason, the rain load, S_r, is included in the calculation of roof snow loads.[2]

Snow Loads on Roofs

Unit Weight of Snow on Roofs

7. To calculate loads due to snow on roofs, a measurement or good estimate of the unit weight is necessary. The unit weight of snow on roofs, γ, obtained from measurements at a number of stations across Canada varied from about 1.0 to 4.5 kN/m³. An average value for use in design in lieu of better local data is $\gamma = 3.0$ kN/m³.[5] The unit weight of snow may be considerably greater than 3.0 kN/m³ in some locations such as regions where the maximum roof load is reached only after contributions from many snowstorms, coastal regions, and regions where winter rains are considerable; in such locations, a unit weight as high as 4.0 kN/m³ may be appropriate.

Solar Radiation and Heat Loss

8. Some factors that modify snow loads occur only under special conditions. For example, solar radiation has little effect in reducing loads in cold weather. Similarly, during cold weather, heat loss from roofs is not very effective in melting the snow, particularly on well insulated and well ventilated roofs. These two factors cannot, therefore, be relied upon to significantly reduce the snow load during colder periods. During thaws and toward the end of winter, however, when air temperatures approach the freezing point, solar radiation and heat loss do cause melting.

Roof Snow Load Factors

9. The factors C_b, C_w, C_s and C_a were not obtained by rigorous statistical analyses due to the lack of data, but they have been found to give acceptable and conservative designs.

10. **Basic roof snow load factor, C_b.** The basic roof snow load has been set at 80% of the ground load (i.e. $C_b = 0.8$). This percentage is based on the results of a countrywide survey of snow loads on roofs carried out by the Institute for Research in Construction and a number of volunteers. The wind is less effective in removing snow from large roofs due to the greater quantities involved and because snow may drift from one area to another.[17] Increased values of C_b are therefore specified in NBC Clauses 4.1.6.2.(2)(a) and (b) to account for this effect in the case of large roofs.

11. **Wind exposure factor, C_w.** Observations in many areas of Canada have shown that where a roof or a part of it is fully exposed to wind, some of the snow is blown off or prevented from accumulating, thus reducing the average snow load.

12. Therefore, for roofs fully exposed to the wind, the wind exposure factor, C_w, may be taken as equal to 0.75 rather than 1.0 (or 0.5 rather than 1.0 for exposed sites north of the treeline). This substitution applies under the following conditions:
    (a) the building is on open level terrain containing only scattered buildings, trees or other such obstructions, open water or shorelines thereof, and is expected to remain so during its service life;
    (b) the area of roof under consideration is exposed to the wind on all sides and does not have any significant obstructions, such as parapet walls, within a distance of at least 10 times the difference between the height of the obstruction and $C_bC_wS_s/\gamma$ metres, where the applicable value of C_w is either 0.75 or 0.5, as provided in NBC Sentence 4.1.6.2.(4);
    (c) the loading case under consideration does not involve the accumulation of snow due to drifting from adjacent surfaces such as, for example, the other side of a gable roof; and
    (d) the buildings are not in the High or Post-disaster Importance Categories described in NBC Table 4.1.2.1.

    A value of 1.0 for C_w must be applied to other loadings than the ones marked Case I in Figures G-1 to G-4.

13. The value $C_bC_wS_s/\gamma$ is the height of uniformly distributed snow on a roof without any obstructions, including parapets. Any obstructions lower than this do not generate additional snow loading.

14. In practice it is sometimes difficult to make a clear distinction between roofs that will be fully exposed to winds and those that will not. The designer should, in consultation with the owner, weigh the probability of the roof becoming sheltered by an addition to the building or by adjacent higher buildings or trees. Such changes could cause either drift loads or higher average loads. In considering drift loads—which are the more serious—a minimum distance of at least 5 m should be

maintained from another existing or future building or from the property line to justify disregarding drift loads. This corresponds to the distance used in NBC Clause 4.1.6.2.(8)(c) for multi-level roofs. With regard to higher average loads, it is important to use a wind exposure factor, C_w, equal to 1.0 for any roof area whose exposure may decrease.

15. The designer should also be aware that the snow loads on the roof of an existing building on the same or adjacent property may also be affected by the location of a new higher building or other obstruction.

16. The installation of solar collectors on roofs may result in reduced exposure similar to that around obstructions unless the clear gap under them is sufficiently large to allow scouring and removal by the wind rather than deposition.[6][7]

17. **Regional variation in C_w.** For the exposure factor to have any application there must be wind. Therefore, designers should use $C_w = 1.0$ in the few areas of Canada where winter winds are not strong or frequent enough (such as calm mountain valleys) to produce significant reductions in roof loads.

18. **Roof slope factor, C_s.** Snow loads on a sloping surface act on the horizontal projection of the surface. Under most conditions, less snow accumulates on steep roofs than on flat and moderately sloped roofs, because of sliding, creep, better drainage and saltation.[8][9][10] The coefficient, C_s, as defined in NBC Sentence 4.1.6.2.(5), accounts for these effects by reducing the snow load linearly from full snow load at 30° slope to zero at 70°. A lesser value of C_s is permitted in NBC Sentence 4.1.6.2.(6) for unobstructed, smooth, slippery roofs, such as those made of glass or metal. In this case, the load may be reduced linearly from full load at 15° to zero at 60°. In order for the designer to use the full reductions as described in either of these relationships, the snow should be able to slide completely off the roof surface under consideration.

19. Situations in which public safety may be compromised by snow and ice falling from roofs should be avoided. If snow fences or barriers are required to keep snow and ice on roofs, they should be designed to transmit the substantial forces involved into the building structure.[8][9] Heat-traced gutters, heated drips or some other means to prevent the growth of dangerous icicles due to meltwater from the snow retained on roofs may also be required. Snow and ice falling from the roof of a building may be deflected against the building and cause damage.

20. **Shape factor, C_a.** The shape factor, C_a, for a number of different roof shapes is described in Figures G-1 to G-8. For cases to which Figures G-1 to to G-8 do not apply, shape factors should be determined by the designer based on applicable field observations, special analyses usually accounting for local climate effects,[11][12][13] or on model tests.[6] In an effort to provide guidance, the Institute for Research in Construction has published two collections of interesting non-uniform snow loads as case histories.[14][15]

21. **Drift accumulation on roofs.** When the wind encounters obstructions, regions of accelerated and retarded flow result. The regions of retarded flow are said to be regions of "aerodynamic shade."[16] Because a minimum velocity is required to transport the snow, it settles out where the flow velocity is too low and forms drifts whose shapes are indicated by C_a. In general, the longer the wind duration, the deeper are the drifts on roofs, especially if it is also snowing, and the greater the wind speed, the less uniform are the snowdrifts.

22. Roofs situated below adjacent roofs are particularly susceptible to heavy drift loads because the upper roofs can provide a large volume of snow to form drifts.[5][17] to [20] Canopies, balconies and porches are similarly susceptible. The drifts that accumulate on these roofs and platforms depend mainly on the difference in elevation and on the size of the upper roof.[17]

23. Where the lower level roof area is large, wind blowing for a considerable time at an angle towards the raised portion of the roof may form an elongated "spike" or quartering drift extending leeward of the change in elevation.[21]

24. The provisions in Paragraph 38 cover the typical types of snow load that arise on lower level roofs. For unusual geometries, especially where the roof areas involved are large, model studies can be useful in identifying unusual drift formations.

25. Projections such as penthouses or parapet walls on flat roofs may collect triangular snow drifts that reach the tops of the projections, but the magnitude of the loads is usually less than on roofs situated below adjacent roofs.

26. Wind flow accelerates over gable and arch roofs because it is deflected upwards on the windward sides. On the leeward sides, velocities drop and the snow entrained in the wind and scoured from the other side is deposited. Heavy unbalanced loads often occur as a result of the transfer of snow from one side to the other.[22][23] This unbalance is especially important for domes and for buildings such as arenas, which have long spans and in which a collapse might be catastrophic.[1] Lightweight curved structures, such as cold-formed metal arch buildings, are particularly sensitive to unbalanced snow loads as the self-weight of the structure is relatively small. These structures can generally be analyzed as arches. However, the flexibility of such arches suggests that a second-order analysis is likely to be required to predict their structural behaviour.[18][22] The structures can also be analyzed as shells when special consideration is given to shear transfer and to the axial capacity of longitudinal stiffeners. Load tests may be needed to assess the behaviour and load-carrying capacity of the structural elements, especially when transverse corrugations are present.

27. When the wind flows over peaked or smooth domes, unbalanced snow load will also occur. Data on snow load distributions on domes are not available; wind tunnel or water flume tests are therefore recommended to assist in the selection of appropriate design loads. In the absence of such tests, the following approximate distributions may be considered:
    (a) a uniformly distributed load (adjusted for slope) over the whole dome, and
    (b) the Case II loading shown in Figures G-2 and G-3 applied over a 90° sector, tapering linearly to zero at 22.5° beyond the sector boundaries, and with no snow on the remaining 225° sector.

    Local experience should also be considered. Snow accumulations due to sliding and drifting occur regularly at the bases of domes where they meet the ground; these should not be overlooked.

28. In windless areas, snow covers roofs and the ground in uniform layers. For these locations, the design load can be considered as a uniformly distributed load equal to some suitable fraction of the ground snow load if sliding is not a factor. Truly uniform loads, however, are rare and have been observed only in certain mountain valleys of British Columbia and occasionally in other parts of the country, on roofs that are well sheltered on all sides by high trees. Generally, the winds that usually accompany or follow snowfalls transport new snow from exposed to protected areas. Hence, the probability that high uniform loads will occur on exposed roofs is reduced and the probability that drifts will form is increased. Drifting does not occur in certain local areas on the B.C. coast where heavy snowstorms invariably consist of wet snow. In such locations, the drift requirements of NBC Sentence 4.1.6.2.(8) may be overly conservative. Where the authority having jurisdiction is convinced that drifting will not occur, drift effects need not be considered. However, the influence of creep and sliding snow causing unbalanced loads should be considered on gable roofs with a slope > 15°, arches with a rise to span ratio, h/b, greater than 0.05, and other roofs with a significant slope.

29. In deep snow areas of Canada, in particular the mountains and valleys of British Columbia, the following should be kept in mind:[5][24]
    (a) Snow cornices can become very large and cantilever beyond the edges of flat or sloping roofs a distance equal to the depth of the snow on the roof. This can occur in sheltered or windless areas and on the leeward side of roofs where there is wind. Cornices have been known to overload walls and columns, resulting in failures. In addition, cornices are a hazard if they break off. They can destroy balconies, stairs, porches, attachments of wires, etc., to the building and can be very dangerous to people below.
    (b) When deep snow is deposited on slippery sloping roofs, it has been known to shear off vents, chimneys, aerials, wiring, stacks, skylights and ventilators when it slides. It is a menace to people and things below when it falls. In addition, it may creep off the roof, rotating slowly at the eaves, and may even break windows if it hits the side of the building. Protrusions through the roof should be located at the ridge or be especially protected against the shearing forces of sliding snow.
    (c) Where a roof is L-shaped or has dormers, the snow on each slope will slide in the direction of the ribs or corrugations and accumulate in the valleys. If one slope is longer or steeper, the snow on this slope will predominate and may force the whole mass of snow to slide across the opposing corrugations on the other slope, resulting in a tearing or flattening of these corrugations. If the corrugations hold and the snow does not slide, the restraining load on the lower opposing slope may be very high.

30. **Redistribution of load due to melting.** Loads may get redistributed on roofs as a result of snow or ice melting and flowing or sliding to other areas where it refreezes, or falling to a lower roof where it accumulates as slush or ice. Meltwater from warm—perhaps poorly insulated—parts of sloped roofs may refreeze on colder areas or on the eaves and cause high ice loads and ice damming, water back-up under shingles, and icicles which present a danger if they fall. These situations can be alleviated by taking steps to decrease heat loss from the warm surfaces.

31. Since drainage under the snow cover on flat or nearly flat roofs is not generally as good as on those with slopes, meltwater, slush and ice may be retained longer. Also snow accumulations near projections can melt as a result of heat loss through the roof, solar radiation or exhausted warm air. The resulting meltwater may migrate to the lower areas of the roof causing heavy loads. The centres of bays are particularly vulnerable if the drains are located at points of minimum deflection. This redistribution of load may cause further deflection and lead to an instability similar to that produced by rain ponding (see Commentary H).

Detailed Explanations of Figures

32. Figures G-1, G-2 and G-3 apply to the basic roof shapes: simple flat and shed roofs, simple gable roofs, and simple arch and curved roofs. More complex shapes can often be considered as combinations of these. Where the roofs shown in Figures G-1, G-2 and G-3 are adjacent to higher roofs or have projections or are combined to form valleys, Figures G-4 to G-8 should also be consulted.

33. **Gable, flat and shed roofs (Figure G-1).** On gable roofs, both uniformly distributed and unbalanced loads should be considered for all slopes less than 70° (or 60° for unobstructed slippery roofs), as shown in Figure G-1. Where both slopes are equal to or less than 15°, the load distribution is determined by Case I, but is also subject to the general requirements of NBC Article 4.1.6.3. for "full and partial loading," which now apply to the Case I loading only. On slopes over 15°, Case II, which accounts for unbalanced loading, and Case I both apply. Case II loading is intended to account for snow blown from the windward over to the leeward side as well as snow removed due to sliding from one side. Flat and shed (single-sloped) roofs are subject to Case I and "full and partial" loading only.

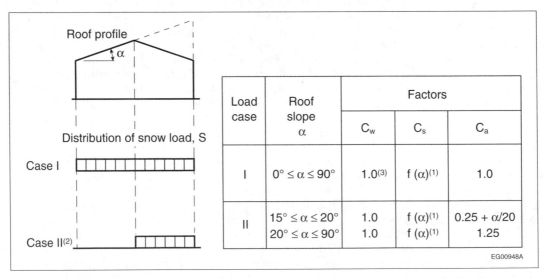

Load case	Roof slope α	Factors		
		C_w	C_s	C_a
I	$0° \leq \alpha \leq 90°$	1.0[3]	f (α)[1]	1.0
II	$15° \leq \alpha \leq 20°$	1.0	f (α)[1]	$0.25 + \alpha/20$
	$20° \leq \alpha \leq 90°$	1.0	f (α)[1]	1.25

EG00948A

Figure G-1

Snow distributions and snow loading factors for gable, flat and shed roofs

Notes to Figure G-1:

(1) Varies as a function of slope α as defined in NBC Sentences 4.1.6.2.(5) and (6).

(2) Case II loading does not apply to gable roofs with slopes of 15° or less, to single-sloped (shed) roofs or to flat roofs.

(3) For Low and Normal Importance Category buildings, as described in NBC Sentence 4.1.6.2.(4), C_w may be reduced to 0.75 or, in exposed areas north of the treeline, to 0.5.

34. **Arch roofs (Figures G-2 and G-3).** Uniform and unbalanced load distributions are particularly important to consider in the design of curved roofs.[19][22][23] In addition, the requirements for "full and partial loading" apply. Case II loading may also be used for the design of domes (see Paragraph 27).

35. Snow accumulations caused by wind and by snow sliding off the surface regularly occur on either or both sides of arches and should not be neglected.[22]

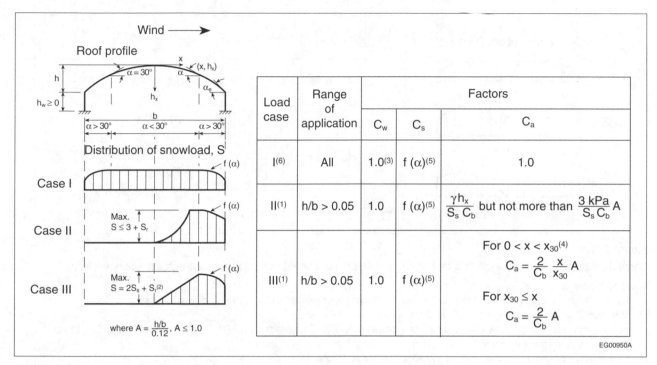

Figure G-2

Snow distributions and snow loading factors for simple arch or curved roofs

Notes to Figure G-2:

(1) Use Case II or Case III, whichever produces the lower total load per unit length of building perpendicular to the span.

(2) Maximum $S = 2S_s + S_r$ occurs at $\alpha = 30°$ or at the edge of the roof if $\alpha_e < 30°$.

(3) For Low and Normal Importance Category buildings, as described in NBC Sentence 4.1.6.2.(4), C_w may be reduced to 0.75 or, in exposed areas north of the treeline, to 0.5.

(4) x_{30} = value of x where $\alpha = 30°$ or value of x at edge of roof if $\alpha_e < 30°$.

(5) Varies as a function of slope α as defined in NBC Sentence 4.1.6.2.(5).

(6) The full and partial loading provisions of NBC Sentence 4.1.6.3.(2) also apply to all curved roofs.

Commentary G

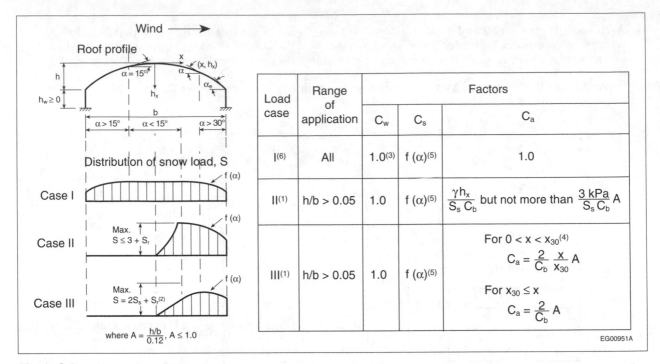

Figure G-3

Snow distributions and snow loading factors for simple arch or curved roofs with unobstructed slippery surfaces

Notes to Figure G-3:

(1) Use Case II or Case III, whichever produces the lower total load per unit length of building perpendicular to the span.

(2) Maximum $S = 2S_s + S_r$ occurs at $\alpha = 15°$ or at the edge of the roof if $\alpha_e < 15°$.

(3) For Low and Normal Importance Category buildings, as described in NBC Sentence 4.1.6.2.(4), C_w may be reduced to 0.75 or, in exposed areas north of the treeline, to 0.5.

(4) x_{30} = value of x where $\alpha = 30°$ or value of x at edge of roof if $\alpha_e < 30°$.

(5) Varies as a function of slope α as defined in NBC Sentence 4.1.6.2.(6).

(6) The full and partial loading provisions of NBC Sentence 4.1.6.3.(2) also apply to all curved roofs.

36. **Valleys in curved or sloped roofs (Figure G-4).** In the design of roofs with valleys, uniform loads and loads accounting for drifting, sliding or creep, and the movement of meltwater are important to consider. A reduction factor due to slope is allowed for Case I loading, because as the snow creeps down the slope and wrinkles and layers at the bottom of the valley, the loads on the upper slopes are reduced. Since Cases II and III describe the worst loads due to drifting and slope effects, the C_s factor is taken as equal to 1.0.

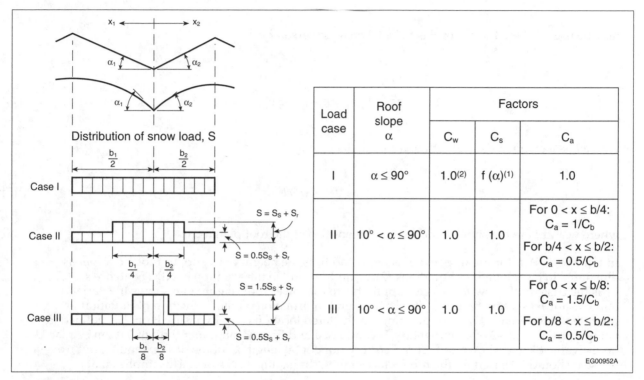

Figure G-4

Snow distributions and snow loading factors for valley areas of roofs

Notes to Figure G-4:

(1) Varies as a function of slope α as defined in NBC Sentence 4.1.6.2.(5).

(2) For Low and Normal Importance Category buildings, as described in NBC Sentence 4.1.6.2.(4), C_w may be reduced to 0.75 or, in exposed areas north of the treeline, to 0.5.

37. **Multi-level roofs, obstructions and parapets.** Multi-level roofs, obstructions and parapets are all "bluff objects" creating turbulent wakes downwind where snow accumulates in drifts. Such objects can be considered as geometrical variations of a rectangular object situated on or adjacent to a lower flat roof. If the object is narrow and lower than the design depth of uniformly distributed snow on the roof, it is, for the purposes of this Commentary, a "non-obstructing" object; if higher, it is considered as an obstruction; if higher than a "non-obstructing" bluff object and wide enough to accumulate a significant amount of snow on its upper surface, it is considered as an "upper level" roof.

38. **Lower roofs (Figures G-5 and G-6).** The load distribution on roofs adjacent to higher ones is taken to be a triangular shape as illustrated in Figure G-5. Thus C_a varies with distance x from the step in roof elevation, being $C_a(0)$ at x = 0 and decreasing linearly to a value $C_a(x_d)$ at the tail of the drift defined by $x = x_d$. The magnitude of the drift on the lower roof depends primarily on the amount of snow that can drift off the upper roof and be trapped in the step. Therefore the loading in the step tends to increase significantly as the size of the upper level roof increases.[17] For roofs with relatively small step heights and, in particular, for large roofs, the step can fill to the top. In this case $C_a(0)$ should be taken as:

$$C_a(0) = \gamma h / C_b S_s \qquad (2)$$

where h is the difference in elevation between the lower roof surface and the top of the parapet on the upper roof, and γ is the specific weight of snow. (Note that in the region of the drift, C_w is 1.0, since the lower roof is sheltered by the roof step.) However, in many cases there may be insufficient snow to fill in the step. Therefore an upper limit on $C_a(0)$ equivalent to

$$C_a(0) = F/C_b \tag{3}$$

may be used, where the factor F is to be taken as the greater of

$$F = 2, \text{or}$$
$$F = 0.35\left(\gamma l_c/S_s - 6\left(\gamma h_p/S_s\right)^2\right)^{0.5} + C_b \tag{4}$$

where l_c is a characteristic length of a roof defined by

$$l_c = 2w - w^2/l \tag{5}$$

where w and l are the shorter and longer dimensions of the roof plan form.

In Equation (4), l_c for the upper roof is used, and h_p is the height of the upper roof's parapet as illustrated in Figure G-5. In Equations (2), (3) and (4), and in the equation in NBC Sentence 4.1.6.2.(1), C_b is the basic roof snow load factor applicable to the lower roof. Figure G-6 shows the variation of the factor F as a function of $\gamma l_c/S_s$. Background information on the derivation of Equation (4) is provided in Reference [17]. For buildings in sheltered locations (i.e. Exposure B or C as defined in Paragraphs 41 and 42 of Commentary I, Wind Load and Effects), an upper limit of 5.0 can be placed on the value of F, as shown in Figure G-6. The horizontal length x_d of the drift extending out from the step should be based on the top surface of the drift having a 1:5 slope. This implies that

$$x_d = 5\left(h - C_b S_s/\gamma\right) \tag{6}$$

in cases where the step fills to the top, or

$$x_d = 5\left(S_s/\gamma\right)\left(F - C_b\right) \tag{7}$$

in cases where the drift is limited by other factors accounted for by Equation (4). The value of C_b in Equations (6) and (7) is that applicable to the lower roof (C_b is normally taken as 0.8 except where the plan dimensions of the lower roof are so large as to produce a value of l_c for the lower roof exceeding 70 m, in which case a higher value of C_b would apply as provided for in NBC Clauses 4.1.6.2.(2)(a) and (b)). Drifts deposited as a result of a change in elevation occur not only when the upper roof is part of the same building but also when it is on an adjacent building not more than 5 m away, as shown in Figure G-5. Where the upper roof is very large, the limiting gap, a, of 5 m should be confirmed by model tests. Where the drift obtained from Figure G-5 is longer than the lower roof, the drift should be truncated at the edge of the lower roof.

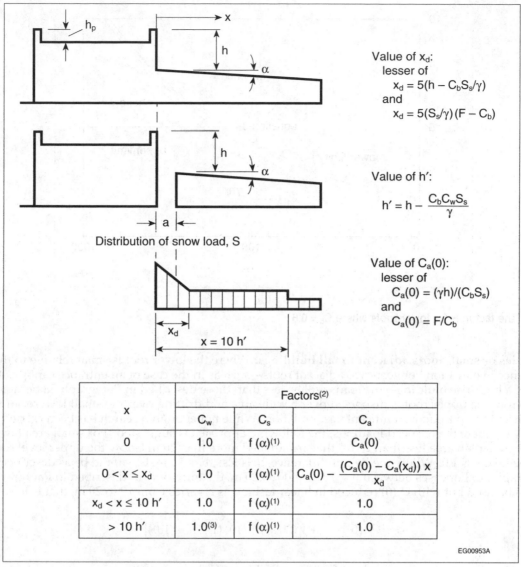

Value of x_d:
lesser of
$$x_d = 5(h - C_b S_s/\gamma)$$
and
$$x_d = 5(S_s/\gamma)(F - C_b)$$

Value of h':
$$h' = h - \frac{C_b C_w S_s}{\gamma}$$

Value of $C_a(0)$:
lesser of
$$C_a(0) = (\gamma h)/(C_b S_s)$$
and
$$C_a(0) = F/C_b$$

Distribution of snow load, S

x	Factors[2]		
	C_w	C_s	C_a
0	1.0	$f(\alpha)$[1]	$C_a(0)$
$0 < x \le x_d$	1.0	$f(\alpha)$[1]	$C_a(0) - \dfrac{(C_a(0) - C_a(x_d))\, x}{x_d}$
$x_d < x \le 10\,h'$	1.0	$f(\alpha)$[1]	1.0
$> 10\,h'$	1.0[3]	$f(\alpha)$[1]	1.0

EG00953A

Figure G-5
Snow distributions and snow loading factors for lower levels of adjacent roofs

Notes to Figure G-5:
(1) Varies as a function of slope α as defined in NBC Sentences 4.1.6.2.(5) and (6).
(2) If a > 5 m or h ≤ 0.8S_s/γ, drifting need not be considered. Where the upper roof is very large, the limiting gap, a, of 5 m should be confirmed by model tests.
(3) For Low and Normal Importance Category buildings, as described in NBC Sentence 4.1.6.2.(4), C_w may be reduced to 0.75 or, in exposed areas north of the treeline, to 0.5.

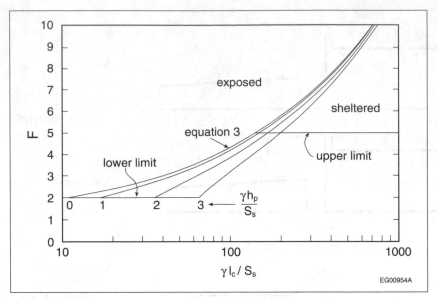

Figure G-6
Variation of the factor, F, for lower roofs where C_b = 0.8

39. **Canopies or small roofs adjacent to tall buildings.** Where the lower roof is small relative to the difference in elevation between two adjacent roofs—such as in the case of an entrance canopy at the base of a high-rise building—the loads will be less than those described in Paragraph 38 because the snow from the upper roof is dispersed over a wide area and drifting over the small lower roof is insufficient to build up a significant accumulation. While not enough research has been carried out to fully evaluate the reduced loadings, the following approach is suggested. For small area lower roofs with a plan area less than 25 m² that are situated more than 20 m below the upper level roof, C_a may be taken as 1.0. Where the height difference, h, is less than 10 m, C_a should be as described in Paragraph 38. For cases between h = 10 m and h = 20 m, the form of drift described in Paragraph 38 should be used but with $C_a(0)$ reduced in linear fashion as h varies from 10 to 20 m, that is to say:

$$C_a (0) = 1 + [((20 - h)/10)(F/C_b - 1.0)] \qquad (8)$$

where C_b is the basic roof snow load factor applicable to the lower roof.

40. For buildings on sheltered sites, the wind exposure factor, C_w, is 1.0 for all areas of the lower roof. For Low and Normal Importance Category buildings on exposed sites, C_w on the lower roof should still be taken as 1.0 within a region sheltered by the step extending outwards from the step a distance equal to 10 h', where h' is the difference in elevation between the top of the upper roof's parapet and the snow surface on the exposed portion of the lower roof. This definition implies that

$$h' = h - C_b C_w S_s / \gamma \qquad (9)$$

where the applicable value of C_w is either 0.75 or 0.5, as provided for in NBC Sentence 4.1.6.2.(4), and C_b is the appropriate value for the exposed portion of the roof, i.e. normally 0.8 but may be higher for large roofs as specified in NBC Clauses 4.1.6.2.(2)(a) and (b).

41. **Multi-level roofs with a sloped upper roof (Figure G-7).** A lower roof should be designed for the loads provided in Figure G-5 plus an additional load produced by the snow that may slide from an upper roof. The following guide is recommended. Because of the low probability that both upper and lower roofs will have the full load over their entire areas simultaneously when sliding occurs, the lower roof should be assumed to carry its full load according to Figure G-5 plus 50% of the total weight of the Case I snow load of Figure G-1 from the portion of the upper roof that slopes toward the lower roof. The distribution should be made based on the relative sizes, slopes and positions of the two roofs. If all the sliding snow cannot be retained on the lower roof because it is too small, appropriate reductions in snow load may be made. A profile of the snow depth on the roof should

be drawn to confirm that the loading is reasonable. Note that some roofs are extremely slippery in nature, and snow can slide from them at a very low angle of roof slope.

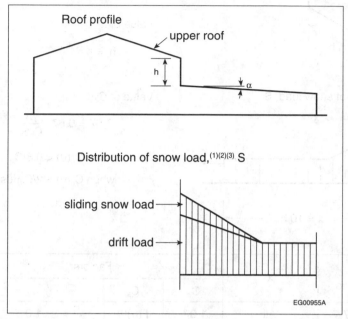

Figure G-7
Snow distributions on lower roofs with a sloped upper roof

Notes to Figure G-7:
(1) Lower roof is designed for drift load (see Figures G-4 and G-5) and sliding snow load (see Paragraph 41).[3]
(2) Upper roof is designed in accordance with NBC Subsection 4.1.6. (see Figures G-1, G-2 and G-3).[3]
(3) In the calculation of C_b and $C_a(0)$ in Notes (1) and (2), l_c and w are taken as the plan dimensions of the lower and upper roofs respectively.

42. **Areas adjacent to obstructions (Figure G-8).** Consideration should also be given to triangular drift loads adjacent to significant vertical obstructions, such as elevator, air-conditioning and fan housings, small penthouses and wide chimneys. The peak load adjacent to the obstruction in Figure G-8 is assumed equal to $0.67\gamma h + S_r$, where h is the height of the obstruction in metres, and γ the unit weight in kN/m^3; it decreases to the design roof load at a distance of 2h from the obstruction. The peak load need not be larger than $2S_s + S_r(C_a(0) \leq 2/C_b)$ nor is it necessary to consider the drift load if the width, b, of the obstruction in Figure G-8 is less than $3.0S_s/\gamma$.

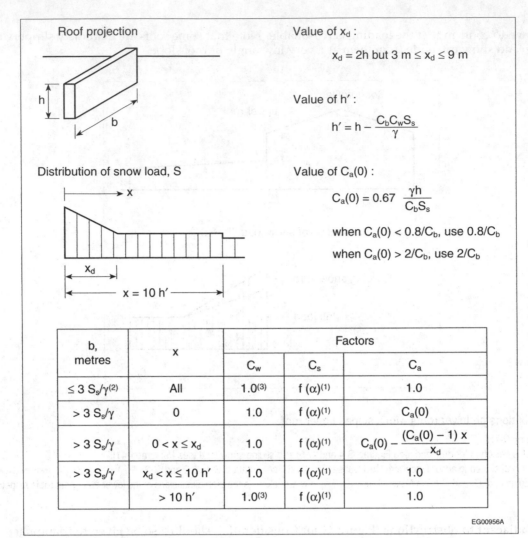

Roof projection

Value of x_d :

$$x_d = 2h \text{ but } 3\text{ m} \leq x_d \leq 9\text{ m}$$

Value of h' :

$$h' = h - \frac{C_b C_w S_s}{\gamma}$$

Distribution of snow load, S

Value of $C_a(0)$:

$$C_a(0) = 0.67 \frac{\gamma h}{C_b S_s}$$

when $C_a(0) < 0.8/C_b$, use $0.8/C_b$

when $C_a(0) > 2/C_b$, use $2/C_b$

$x = 10\ h'$

b, metres	x	Factors		
		C_w	C_s	C_a
$\leq 3\ S_s/\gamma^{(2)}$	All	$1.0^{(3)}$	$f(\alpha)^{(1)}$	1.0
$> 3\ S_s/\gamma$	0	1.0	$f(\alpha)^{(1)}$	$C_a(0)$
$> 3\ S_s/\gamma$	$0 < x \leq x_d$	1.0	$f(\alpha)^{(1)}$	$C_a(0) - \dfrac{(C_a(0) - 1)\ x}{x_d}$
$> 3\ S_s/\gamma$	$x_d < x \leq 10\ h'$	1.0	$f(\alpha)^{(1)}$	1.0
	$> 10\ h'$	$1.0^{(3)}$	$f(\alpha)^{(1)}$	1.0

EG00956A

Figure G-8

Snow distribution and snow loading factors for areas adjacent to roof obstructions

Notes to Figure G-8:

(1) Varies as a function of slope α as defined in NBC Sentences 4.1.6.2.(5) and (6).

(2) If b is less than $3S_s/\gamma$, in m, then the effect of the obstruction on the snow loading can be ignored.

(3) For Low and Normal Importance Category buildings, as described in NBC Sentence 4.1.6.2.(4), C_w may be reduced to 0.75 or, in exposed areas north of the treeline, to 0.5.

Unusual Roofs

43. Snow loads are difficult to predict in some cases, particularly for roofs of unusual shapes, exceptionally large roofs and roofs over which the airflow is significantly affected by other buildings or topographic features. In such cases, the designer should calculate and plot the snow depths to scale applying a unit weight of 3.0 kN/m³ to judge whether the distributions look reasonable. In some circumstances wind tunnel or water flume tests might be used to assist in the evaluation.

Parking Decks

44. Roofs used as parking decks should be designed for the loads noted in NBC Tables 4.1.5.3. and 4.1.5.10., or for the roof snow loads, whichever are greater. Where snow removal may occur, consideration should be given to the loads due to snow removal equipment and to the weight of piled snow.

Sunshades

45. Sunshades consisting of a grillage of metal slats are becoming more common on buildings. They should be designed for snow and ice loads. Where the horizontal projections of the gaps between the slats is 100 mm or less, the snow can bridge the gaps and the sunshade should be considered as solid from the standpoint of snow loading. Where snow and ice can slide from a sloped roof above the sunshade, even gaps that are larger than 100 mm between the slats may make the sunshade behave as a solid surface.

Full and Partial Loading

46. All roof areas, including those to be designed for increased or decreased loads according to Figures G-1 to G-8, must be designed for the full specified load given in NBC Article 4.1.6.2. over the entire area. However, only the flat, shed, low slope gable (< 15°) and curved roofs of Figures G-1, G-2 and G-3 need to be designed for Case I loading distributed on one portion of the area and half of this on the remainder of the area, the location and size of such partial areas being chosen to give the most critical effects in the members and joints concerned. These requirements do not imply checkerboard loading because the probability that checkerboard loading will occur to a degree that will cause the worst conditions for supporting members is generally too remote to be considered in design.[25] On many roofs like the ones shown in Figures G-1, G-2 and G-3, a number of separate cases of full and partial loading will be required to ensure the proper design of all elements.

47. The reason for these requirements is that snow seldom accumulates according to the simple configurations in Figures G-1, G-2 and G-3. Consequently, full and partial loading must be considered for the design of structural members that are sensitive to changes in load distribution (e.g. truss diagonals and cantilevers) and that would not otherwise be designed for unbalanced loads.

Snow Removal

48. Although it is fairly common practice in some areas of Canada to remove snow from roofs after heavy snowfalls, the National Building Code does not allow a reduction of the design load to account for this because:
    (a) snow removal cannot be relied upon (experience in several countries has shown that during and after extreme snowstorms, traffic is immobilized and snow removal crews are either unavailable due to high demand or unable to access certain areas),
    (b) snow cannot be effectively removed from the centre of large roofs, and
    (c) unbalanced loading can occur as a result of certain patterns of snow removal.

49. In special cases, roofs that incorporate melting systems, which periodically clear them of snow, have been designed with reduced design loads. The decision to use such systems should be carefully considered because adequate energy for melting may not be available when required. Furthermore, as the years pass, the importance of keeping the system functioning (perhaps at great cost) may be forgotten.

Ice Loading on Structures

50. Loads due to ice accretion on the exposed surfaces of superstructure members, railings, lattice towers and signs are described in References [26] and [27]. Environment Canada has a model, which is based on climate data at weather stations, to compute ice loading on vertical and horizontal surfaces and cables.

Minimum Roof Live Load

51. NBC Articles 4.1.5.3. and 4.1.5.10. provide for a minimum uniform roof live load of 1 kPa and a minimum concentrated live load of 1.3 kN. These live loads are "use and occupancy loads" intended to provide for maintenance loadings, workmen and so forth. These live loads are not reduced as a function of area or as a function of the roof slope.

Commentary G

History of Snow Loads in the National Building Code

52. In the 1953 National Building Code of Canada, design snow loads were equal to the ground snow load, with reductions allowed for sloped roofs only. The load values were very approximate and resulted in over-design for some roofs and under-design for others, particularly in areas subject to high drift loads. Information on which to base a more refined assessment of the loads was not available until a countrywide survey of snow loads on roofs was undertaken by the Institute for Research in Construction with the help of many volunteer observers. This survey provided evidence on the relationship between ground and roof loads and enabled the committees responsible for the 1960 edition of the National Building Code of Canada to adjust the Code requirements. The roof load was set at 80% of the ground load and the ground load was based on a return period of 30 years and adjusted to allow for the increase in the load caused by rainwater absorbed by the snow.

53. With the introduction of the 1965 Code and the Commentary on Part 4, further changes made by the Revision Committee on Structural Loads and Procedures led to a more rational approach to design loads. The Committee concluded that all roof loads were directly related to the snow load on the ground; consequently, the roof snow loads were removed from the table of Design Data for Selected Locations in Canada. The basic design load remained at 80% of the ground load, except that a snow load of 60% of the ground load was allowed for roofs exposed to the wind. This reduction was made because at the same time allowance was made for a variety of influences causing the accumulation of snow on roofs. This was done by means of "snow load coefficients" or shape factors, which were shown in the form of simple formulas and diagrams similar to Figures G-1 to G-8. In addition, the slope reduction formula was changed from the step function used in 1960 to a linear function.

54. In the 1970 Code and Commentary, minor changes were made to the provisions for gable and arch roofs and more severe "full and partial loading provisions"—"full and zero loading" rather than "full and half"—were introduced.

55. In the 1975 Code and Commentary, few changes were made, except that the requirement for full and partial loading was considered too severe at "full and zero" and was changed back to "full and half" loading.

56. In the 1977 and 1980 Commentaries, the provisions for loads on arch roofs were changed and a number of rationalizations were made to help Code users better understand snow loads on roofs.

57. The 1985 Code and Commentary provisions were rewritten to simplify the presentation and to clarify the intent of the minimum roof loading of 1.0 kPa. Furthermore, the minimum roof loading was made independent of slope, the unit weight of snow on roofs was increased by 1.9% to give $\gamma = 2.4$ kN/m^3, "full and partial loading" was restricted to Case I loadings on buildings like the ones shown in Figures G-1, G-2 and G-3, and the unbalanced loading on arches was simplified.

58. In the 1990 Code and Commentary, a new slope reduction formula was given for unobstructed slippery sloped roofs, the unit weight of snow on roofs was increased to $\gamma = 3.0$ kN/m^3, the need for unbalanced snow loads on domes was emphasized, the minimum C_w was reduced to 0.5—rather than 0.75—for exposed roofs north of the treeline, and design roof snow loads were separated into snow and rain components consistent with the ground snow loads given in Chapter 1 of the 1990 Supplement.

59. In the 1995 Code and Commentary, new formulae were given for the accumulation factor, C_a, for the calculation of uniformly distributed snow loads on large flat upper or lower roofs. Additional information was also provided for snow loads on lower roofs and elongated spike drifts on high-low roof configurations.

References

[1]   D.A. Taylor, A Survey of Snow Loads on the Roofs of Arena-Type Buildings in Canada. Can. J. Civ. Eng., Vol. 6, No. 1, 1979, pp. 85-96.

[2]   M.J. Newark, L.E. Welsh, R.J. Morris and W.V. Dynes, Revised Ground Snow Loads for the 1990 National Building Code of Canada. Can. J. Civ. Eng., Vol. 16, No. 3, June 1989, pp. 267-278.

[3]   Geographical Names Board of Canada, The Canadian Geographical Names Data Base (CGNDB) 1997. Natural Resources Canada. Web site: http://geonames.nrcan.gc.ca/info/cgndb_e.php; E-mail: geonames@nrcan.gc.ca.

[4] B.R. Claus, S.O. Russell and P.A. Schaerer, Variation of Ground Snow Loads with Elevation in Southern British Columbia. Can. J. Civ. Eng., Vol. 11, No. 3, September 1984, pp. 480-493.

[5] D.A. Taylor, Snow on Two-level Flat Roofs – Measured vs 1990 NBC Loads, Can. J. Civ. Eng., Vol. 19, No. 1, 1992, pp. 59-67.

[6] Ontario Ministry of Municipal Affairs, Housing, Research and Development Section. Prevention of Excess Snow Accumulation due to Roof Mounted Solar Collectors. (Report prepared under contract by MHTR Ltd., Guelph, Ontario) Toronto, December 1981, 76 pp.

[7] D. Nixon, Solar Collectors – Briefing Document S-2. Public Works Canada, Design/Construction Branch, Sir Charles Tupper Building, Ottawa, March 1981, 25 pp.

[8] D.A.Taylor, Snow Loads on Sloping Roofs. Two Pilot Studies in the Ottawa Area. Can. J. Civ. Eng., Vol. 12, No. 2, 1985, pp. 334-343.

[9] D.A. Taylor, Sliding Snow on Sloping Roofs. CBD 228, Division of Building Research, National Research Council Canada, Ottawa, 1983, 4 pp.

[10] R.L. Sack, Snow Loads on Sloped Roofs. ASCE Journal of Structural Eng., Vol. 114, No. 3, March 1988, pp. 501-517.

[11] N. Isyumov, Roof Snow Loads – Their Variability and Dependence on Climatic Conditions. Symposium on the Structural Use of Wood in Adverse Environments, 15-18 May 1978, Vancouver, Van Nostrand Reinhold, 510 pp.

[12] N. Isyumov and M. Mikitiuk, Climatology of Snowfall and Related Meteorological Variables with Application to Roof Snow Load Specifications. Can. J. Civ. Eng., Vol. 4, No. 2, 1977, pp. 240-256.

[13] N. Isyumov and A.G. Davenport, A Probabilistic Approach to the Prediction of Snow Loads. Can. J. Civ. Eng., Vol. 1, No. 1, 1974, pp. 28-49.

[14] W.R. Schriever, Y. Faucher, and D.A. Lutes, Snow Accumulation in Canada: Case Histories: I. Division of Building Research, National Research Council Canada, Ottawa, January 1967. NRCC 9287.

[15] D.A. Lutes and W.R. Schriever, Snow Accumulation in Canada: Case Histories: II. DBR Technical Paper 339, Division of Building Research, National Research Council Canada, Ottawa, March 1971. NRCC 11915.

[16] J.T. Templin and W.R. Schriever, Loads due to Drifted Snow. Journal of Structural Division, Proc. Am. Soc. Civ. Eng., Vol. 108, No. ST8, August 1982, pp. 1916-1925.

[17] P.A. Irwin, S.L. Gamble, and D.A. Taylor, Effects of Roof Size, Heat Transfer and Climate on Snow Loads: Studies for the 1995 NBC. Can. J. Civ. Eng., Vol. 22, No. 4, 1995.

[18] M.J. O'Rourke and E. Wood, Improved Relationship for Drift Loads on Buildings. Can. J. Civ. Eng., Vol. 13, No. 6, 1986, pp. 647-652.

[19] D.A. Taylor, Roof Snow Loads in Canada. Can. J. Civ. Eng., Vol. 7, No. 1, 1980, pp. 1-18.

[20] N. Isyumov and M. Mikitiuk, Wind Tunnel Model Tests of Snow Drifting on a Two-level Flat Roof, J. of Wind Engineering and Industrial Aerodynamics. Elsevier Science, Publishers, N.Y. Vol. 36, 1990.

[21] D.J.L. Kennedy, N. Isyumov and M. Mikitiuk, The Effectiveness of Code Provisions for Snow Accumulations on Stepped Roofs. 2nd International Conf. on Snow Eng'g. Engineering Federation, Santa Barbara CA, June 1992.

[22] D.A. Taylor, Snow Loads for the Design of Cylindrical Curved Roofs in Canada 1953-1980. Can. J. Civ. Eng., Vol. 8, No. 1, 1981, pp. 63-76.

[23] T.H.R. Kennedy, D.J.L. Kennedy, J.G. MacGregor and D.A. Taylor, Snow Loads in the 1985 National Building Code of Canada: Curved Roofs. Can. J. Civ. Eng., Vol. 12, No. 3, 1985, pp. 427-438.

[24] D.A. Taylor, Snow Loads on Roofs in British Columbia – Results of a Survey, Proc. 1991 CSCE Annual Conference. Vol. 111, 1991, pp. 205-213.

[25] R.L. Booth and D.A. Taylor, Discussion, Design of Light Industrial Buildings. Can. J. Civ. Eng., Vol. 7, No. 4, 1980, pp. 660-661.

[26] Ontario Ministry of Transportation and Communications, Highway Engineering Division, 1983 Ontario Highway Bridge Design Code, Toronto, p. 46.

[27] CSA S37-01, Antennas, Towers, and Antenna-Supporting Structures. Canadian Standards Association, Mississauga, Ontario, 2001.

Commentary H

Rain Loads

1. In accordance with Sentence 4.1.6.4.(1) of Division B of the National Building Code of Canada 2005, any roof that can accumulate water must be designed for the load that results from a one-day rainfall on the horizontal projected area of the roof. This requirement applies whether or not the surface is provided with drainage, such as rainwater leaders. The distribution of rain load should be determined by the designer, who should take into account the shape of the roof, including camber, with or without creep deflection due to dead load, and also deflection due to rain.

2. Notwithstanding the above requirement, it is considered good practice when locating roof drains to take into account not only the roof slope but also deflection of the roof due to creep, snow and rain. Drains should be provided with suitable devices to prevent clogging by leaves or, where appropriate, suitable overflows should be provided through parapet walls.

3. In some areas of Canada, there is potential for the primary drainage system for a roof to become blocked due to freeze-thaw conditions. Roofs in these areas should be designed accordingly.

Ponding Instability

4. If a flat roof is too flexible, rainwater will not accumulate evenly over the roof but will flow to form ponds in a few local areas. This may lead to an instability similar to buckling, which can result in failure of the roof due to local overloading. In the case of one-way roof beams or decking simply supported on rigid supports, ponding instability will occur when the beam or decking stiffness is less than EI_{crit} given by

$$EI_{crit} = \rho g S \left(\frac{L}{\pi}\right)^4 \tag{1}$$

where
$\quad E$ = modulus of elasticity,
$\quad I$ = moment of inertia of the beam or decking,
$\quad L$ = span,
$\quad S$ = spacing of the beam or decking,
$\quad \rho$ = mass density of water, kg/m^3.

5. In the case of a two-way system of roof joists on girders, the critical stiffness can be approximated by

$$\frac{EI_{jcrit}}{EI_j} + \frac{EI_{gcrit}}{EI_g} = 1 \tag{2}$$

where EI_{jcrit} and EI_{gcrit} are given by Equation (1) for joists and girders, respectively.

6. Even if the roof system is stiffer than the critical values determined by Equation (1) and Equation (2), calculated moments and deflections may be amplified due to ponding effect. A practical criterion is to require roof stiffness to be at least twice the critical stiffness. In the case of a one-way system on rigid supports, in terms of existing deflection requirements, this can be expressed as follows:

$$w > 15.4L \left(\frac{\Delta}{L}\right)_{allowable} \tag{3}$$

Commentary H

where w is the design load in kilopascals specified for deflection calculation and $(\Delta/L)_{allowable}$ is the allowable deflection to span ratio (see Table D-1 of Commentary D, Deflection and Vibration Criteria for Serviceability and Fatigue Limit States). If, for a one-way system, the design load w is less than the critical value given in Table H-1, the effects of ponding should be considered. This applies particularly to large flat roofs in areas of heavy rainfall. Further information is given in References [1] to [7].

Table H-1
Critical Values of w for Ponding, kPa
(one-way system – Equation (3))

Deflection/Span Requirement	w, kPa			
	L = 5 m	L = 10 m	L = 20 m	L = 30 m
1:180	0.43	0.86	1.71	2.57
1:240	0.32	0.64	1.28	1.93

References

[1]   D.A. Sawyer, Ponding of Rainwater on Flexible Roof Systems. Journal of Structural Division, Proc., Am. Soc. Civ. Eng., Vol. 93, ST1, February 1967, p. 127.

[2]   R.W. Haussler, Roof Deflection Caused by Rainwater Pools. Civil Engineering, Vol. 32, October 1962, p. 58.

[3]   F.J. Marino, Ponding of Two-Way Roof Systems. Engineering Journal Am. Inst. of Steel Construction, Vol. 3, No. 3, July 1966, p. 93.

[4]   Commentary on the Specification for the Design, Fabrication and Erection of Structural Steel for Buildings. Am. Inst. of Steel Construction, New York, February 1969.

[5]   A.E. Salama and M.L. Moody, Analysis of Beams and Plates for Ponding Loads. Journal of Structural Division, Proc., Am. Soc. Civ. Eng., Vol. 93, ST1, February 1967, p. 109.

[6]   J. Chinn, A.H. Mansouri and S.F. Adams, Ponding of Liquids on Flat Roofs. Journal of Structural Division, Proc., Am. Soc. Civ. Eng., Vol. 95, ST5, May 1969, p. 797.

[7]   D.A. Sawyer, Roof-Structural Roof-Drainage Interactions. Journal of Structural Division, Proc., Am. Soc. Civ. Eng., Vol. 94, ST1, January 1969, p. 175.

Commentary I

Wind Load and Effects

Commentary I

Wind Load and Effects

Summary of Changes from the National Building Code of Canada 1995

Notable changes in the National Building Code of Canada 2005 (NBC):

- Introduction of an importance factor, I_w (see NBC Table 4.1.7.1.), in the expressions for calculating the wind pressures p and p_i
- Replacement of the three return periods of 10, 30 and 100 years by one of 50 years
- Provision of the exposure factor, C_e, for an added category of rough terrain under the Static Procedure
- Modification of the internal gust effect factor, C_{gi}, under the Static Procedure
- Addition of a new definition of the minimum effective width, w, given in NBC Sentence 4.1.7.2.(2)
- Requirement for a higher removal of wind load for partial loading stipulated in NBC Clauses 4.1.7.3.(1)(b) and (d)

Notable changes in this Commentary:

- Complete reorganization of the content to make the Commentary easier to use, as well as the addition of a flow chart (Figure I-1) to guide users to the Paragraphs and Figures that are applicable to the design job at hand
- Introduction of a transition formula given for C_e under Static Procedure for terrains that change from smooth to rough
- Revision of C_{gi} in accordance with NBC Clause 4.1.7.1.(6)(c) given in Paragraph 22, and of C_{pi} given in Paragraphs 30 to 34
- Correction of C_g for speed-up over hills and escarpments given in Paragraph 21 to take into account that only the mean wind speed is increased, not the gust wind speed
- Addition of new Table I-2 in Paragraph 29 to help users find the appropriate Figure in the Commentary for the coefficients C_pC_g, C_p, and C_p^*
- Replacement of the jump in wind load on the building structure from low-rise to high-rise building categories by the transition formulae in Figure I-15
- Change in the localized pressure coefficient, C_p^*, from –1.0 to ±0.9 in areas away from corners of the building, and to –1.2 near the corners
- Replacement of W and D by w and d, respectively, for the calculation of C_g under the Dynamic Procedure and of building vibration

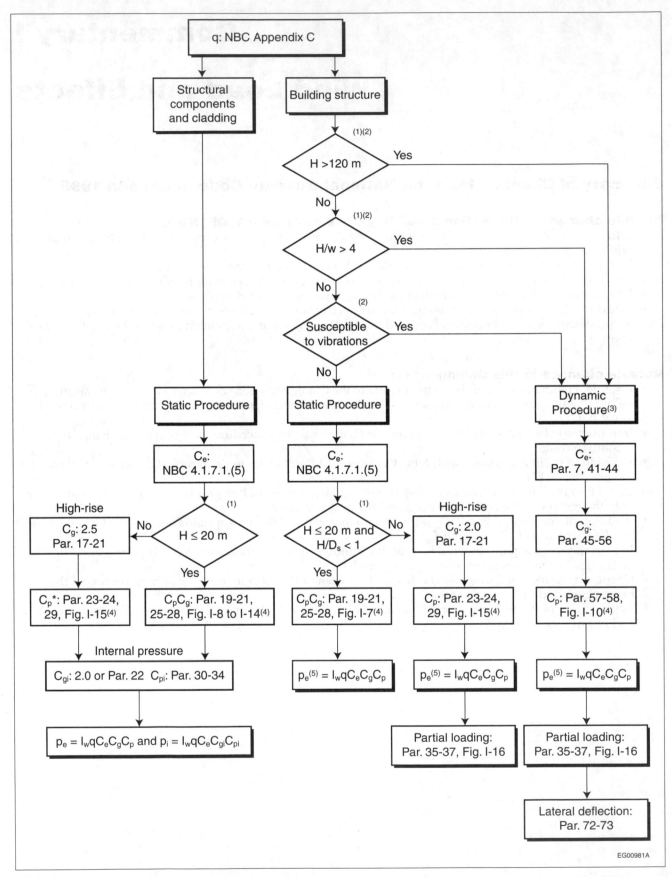

Figure I-1

Flow chart for calculating wind load and effects on buildings

Notes to Figure I-1:

(1) H is the height, D_s the smaller plan dimension, and w the effective width of the building as defined in Sentence 4.1.7.2.(2) of the National Building Code of Canada 2005 (NBC).

(2) See also NBC Sentence 4.1.7.2.(1).

(3) The Experimental Procedure is recommended for some cases—see Paragraph 4.

(4) For round buildings and spherical or curved roofs, see Figures I-24 to I-27.

(5) The internal pressure, p_i, should be considered where it could affect load on the building structure (e.g. roof uplift affecting axial load on columns).

Wind Load Calculation Procedure

1. Three different procedures of determining design wind load on buildings are indicated in NBC Subsection 4.1.7., Wind Load.[1]

2. The first procedure, called the Static Procedure, is appropriate for most cases, including the design of the structure of most low- and medium-rise buildings as well as the cladding of all buildings. The structure or element to be designed in these cases is relatively rigid. Detailed knowledge of the dynamic properties of these structures or elements is not required and dynamic actions of the wind can be represented by equivalent static loads.

3. The second procedure, called the Dynamic Procedure, is intended for determining the overall wind effects, including amplified resonant response, primarily for tall buildings and slender structures but not for cladding and secondary structural members.[5] Its format is the same as that of the Static Procedure except that the gust effect factor, C_g, and the exposure factor, C_e, are determined differently. C_g is derived from a series of calculations involving
    (a) the intensity of wind turbulence for the site as a function of height and of the surface roughness of the surrounding terrain, and
    (b) the properties of the building such as height, width, natural frequency of vibration and damping.
    When multiplied by the reference wind pressure, q, the importance factor, I_w, the exposure factor, C_e, and the pressure coefficient, C_p, this gust effect factor is expected to give a static design pressure that represents the same peak load effect as the dynamic resonant response to the actual turbulent wind. In addition to the calculation of wind load, the calculation of wind-induced lateral deflection and vibration can also be important for some buildings that are required to be treated by the Dynamic Procedure. These topics, as well as vortex shedding of rounded structures, are treated separately in this Commentary.

4. The third procedure, called the Experimental Procedure, consists of wind-tunnel testing or other experimental methods. It can be used as an alternative to the Static and Dynamic Procedures. It is especially recommended for buildings that may be subjected to buffeting or channeling effects caused by upwind obstructions, vortex shedding, or to aerodynamic instability. It is also suitable for determining external pressure coefficients for the design of cladding on buildings whose geometry deviates markedly from common shapes. Information on modern wind-tunnel techniques can be found in References [3], [4], [5] and [6].

5. The applicable exposure factors and some gust effect factors for the Static Procedure are specified in NBC Sentences 4.1.7.1.(5) and (6). The remaining gust effect factors and pressure coefficients for the Static Procedure, and all factors and coefficients for the Dynamic Procedure, are given in this Commentary. Figure I-1 shows the calculation procedure and provides references to applicable provisions in NBC Subsection 4.1.7. and this Commentary to help users determine wind load and effects for buildings.

Reference Wind Pressure

6. NBC Appendix C of Division B contains a description of the procedures followed in obtaining the reference wind pressures, q, based on mean hourly wind speed for the probability of being exceeded per year of 1 in 50, the values commonly referred to as having a return period of 50 years. These values of q are tabulated for many Canadian locations along with other climatic design data. Appendix C of the NBC and Equation (14) (see Paragraph 47) provide information on the conversion of reference wind pressure, q, to reference wind speed, $\bar{V}$, needed in Equation (13) (see Paragraph 47).

Commentary I

Reference Height

7. To calculate external pressure using both the Static and Dynamic Procedures, the reference height, h, for calculating C_e is defined as follows:
   (a) For low-rise buildings, as defined in Paragraph 26, h is the mean height of the roof or 6 m, whichever is greater. The height of the eaves may by substituted for the mean height if the slope of the roof is less than 7°.
   (b) For taller buildings,
       (i) h for the windward face is the actual height of that point above ground,
       (ii) h for the leeward face is half the height of the building, and
       (iii) h for the roof and side walls is the height of the building.
   (c) For any structural element of the building, h is the height of the element above ground.

8. To calculate internal pressure, h for calculating C_e is defined as half the height of the building, except that when a large opening is present, h should be taken as the height of the opening from the ground.

Static Procedure

Application

9. The Static Procedure can be used to calculate the wind loads on all buildings except those with the criteria defined in NBC Sentence 4.1.7.2.(1) and Figure I-1.

Exposure Factor, C_e

10. The exposure factor, C_e, reflects changes in wind speed with height, as well as the effects of variations in the surrounding terrain and topography.

11. The value of C_e to be used for the Static Procedure is given in NBC Sentence 4.1.7.1.(5). It is based on the profile (variation with height) of wind-gust pressure on two types of surrounding terrain, open and rough, which are illustrated in Figures I-2 to I-5. For open terrain, the profile is assumed to obey the 0.2 power law, which is equivalent to the 0.1 power law for wind-gust speeds. For rough terrain, the 0.3 power law is assumed for the wind-gust pressure profile (equivalent to the 0.15 power law for wind-gust speed). The wind gust referred to lasts about 3 to 5 s and represents a parcel of wind, which is assumed to have an effect over the whole structure of most ordinary buildings.

Figure I-2

Example of open terrain under the Static Procedure and of Exposure A under the Dynamic Procedure for determining the exposure factor, C_e. (See also Figure I-3.) (Reproduced with the permission of the National Capital Commission ©NCC/CCN)

Figure I-3
Example of open and rough terrains under the Static Procedure. Buildings located in the foreground near the road should be designed for open-terrain exposure. Buildings that are located away from the road and deeper into the built-up area should be designed for either an intermediate exposure as given in Paragraph 12, or a rough-terrain exposure as given in Paragraph 11, depending on the distance from the road. (See also Figure I-4.) (Reproduced with the permission of the National Capital Commission ©NCC/CCN)

Figure I-4
Example of rough terrain under the Static Procedure and of Exposure B under the Dynamic Procedure. Buildings located on the periphery of the lake and open area in the background may be required to be designed for an open-terrain exposure. (Reproduced with the permission of the National Capital Commission ©NCC/CCN)

Figure I-5
Example of Exposure C under the Dynamic Procedure. Buildings located on the periphery of the lake in the right background may be required to be designed for Exposure A. In addition, tall buildings in the foreground may be required to be designed by experimental methods to account for channeling, buffeting and vortex-shedding effects. (Reproduced with the permission of The Helicopter Company Inc., Toronto, Canada, 2003)

Changes in Terrain

12. The value of C_e given in Paragraph 11 for rough terrain can be used when the rough terrain extends in the upwind direction for at least 1 km or 10 times the building height, H, whichever is greater. When the rough terrain extends for less than 1 km (i.e. $x < 1$ km) and the building is less than 100 m tall, the value of C_e may be interpolated between those for the open and the rough terrain using the following formulae:

for x_r greater than 0.05 km and less than 1 km,

$$C_e = C_{er} \left(0.816 + 0.184 \log_{10} \left(\frac{10}{x_r - 0.05} \right) \right) \leq C_{eo} \tag{1}$$

and for x_r less than or equal to 0.05 km,

$$C_e = C_{eo} \tag{2}$$

where x_r is the upwind extent of rough terrain, C_{er} is the C_e for rough terrain, and C_{eo} is the C_e for open terrain.

Commentary I

Speed-up over Hills and Escarpments

13. Hills and escarpments can significantly amplify wind speeds near the ground and this should be reflected in the exposure factor for buildings located on a hill or escarpment. A method that can be used with both the Static and Dynamic Procedures to reflect this amplification is presented below.

14. Buildings on a hill or escarpment with a maximum slope greater than 1 in 10, particularly near a crest, may be subject to significantly higher wind speeds than buildings on level ground. The exposure factor at height z above the surrounding ground elevation is then equal to that over open level terrain multiplied by a factor $(1 + \Delta S(z))^2$, where $\Delta S(z)$ is the "speed-up factor" for the mean wind speed (this effect is illustrated in Figure I-6). Near the crest, and within a distance $|x| <$ kL, the exposure factor is modified as follows:

$$C_e^* = C_e \left\{ 1 + \Delta S_{max} \left(1 - \frac{|x|}{kL} \right) e^{(-\alpha z/L)} \right\}^2 \tag{3}$$

where
C_e^* = corresponding modified value for use on the hill or escarpment,
C_e = exposure factor over open level terrain given in Paragraphs 11 and 12 for the Static Procedure, and in Paragraph 41 for the Dynamic Procedure,
ΔS_{max} = relative speed-up factor at the crest near the surface, and
α = decay coefficient for the decrease in speed-up with height.

The values of α and ΔS_{max} depend on the shape and steepness of the hill or escarpment. Representative values for these parameters are given in Table I-1.

Table I-1
Parameters for Maximum Speed-up Over Hills and Escarpments

Shape of Hill or Escarpment	ΔS_{max}[1]	α	k $x < 0$	k $x > 0$
2-dimensional ridges (or valleys with negative H)	$2.2\ H_h/L_h$	3	1.5	1.5
2-dimensional escarpments	$1.3\ H_h/L_h$	2.5	1.5	4
3-dimensional axi-symmetrical hills	$1.6\ H_h/L_h$	4	1.5	1.5

[1] For $H_h/L_h > 0.5$, assume that $H_h/L_h = 0.5$ and substitute $2H_h$ for L_h in Equation (3).

15. The definitions of H_h, height, and L_h, length, shown in Figure I-6 are as follows: H_h is the height of the hill or or escarpment, or the difference in elevation between the crest and that of the terrain surrounding the hill or escarpment upwind; L_h is the distance upwind of the crest to where the ground elevation is half of H_h. The maximum slope for rounded hill shapes is roughly $H_h/(2L_h)$. In the expressions above, it is assumed that the wind approaches the hill along the direction of maximum slope, i.e. the direction giving the greatest speed-up near the crest.

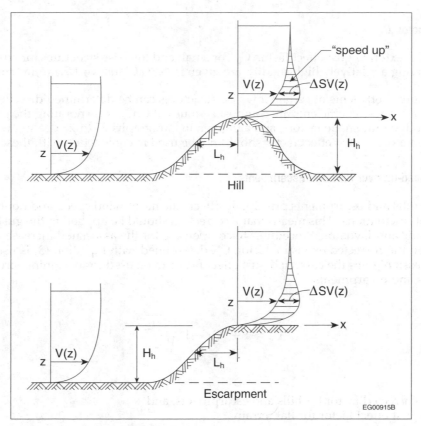

Figure I-6
Definitions for wind speed-up over hills and escarpments

16. Hills and escarpments with slopes less than 1 in 10 are unlikely to produce significant speed-up of the wind. A more detailed discussion of this issue and other simplified models for three-dimensional hills are given in Reference [7]. Background material may be found in References [8] and [9]. Wind tunnel tests and computational methods may be used to obtain design information in other cases.

Gust Effect Factors, C_g and C_{gi}

General

17. In this section, procedures are recommended for determining the external gust effect factor referred to in NBC Sentence 4.1.7.1.(1) and the internal gust effect factor referred to in NBC Sentence 4.1.7.1.(3). These two factors, denoted by C_g and C_{gi} respectively, are defined as the ratio of the maximum effect of the loading to the mean effect of the loading. They take into account:
  (a) random fluctuating wind forces caused by turbulence in the approaching wind and acting for short durations over all or part of the structure,
  (b) fluctuating forces induced by the wake of the structure itself,
  (c) additional inertial forces arising from motion of the structure itself as it responds to the fluctuating wind forces, and
  (d) additional aerodynamic forces due to alterations in the airflow around the structure caused by its motions (aero-elastic effects).

18. All structures are affected to some degree by these forces. The total response may be considered as a superposition of a "background component," which acts quasi-statically, and a "resonant component," which is due to inertial forces arising from excitation close to a natural frequency. For the majority of structures, the resonant component is small and the dynamic effect can be treated by considering only the background component using normal static methods. These structures are amenable to the Static Procedure. For structures that are particularly tall, long, slender, lightweight, flexible or lightly damped, the resonant component may be dominant: these structures should be treated by the Dynamic Procedure.

Commentary I

External Gust Effect Factor, C_g

19. The values of the external gust effect factor, C_g, for small and low-rise structures, or structures and components having a relatively high rigidity, are given in NBC Clauses 4.1.7.1.(6)(a) and (b).

20. The peak pressure coefficients of certain low-rise structures can be determined directly from wind-tunnel tests. These coefficients are composite values of C_pC_g, incorporating the gust effect in addition to aerodynamic shape factors, and are given in Paragraphs 25 to 28 dealing with pressure coefficients. Therefore, a gust effect factor should not be used in conjunction with these coefficients.

Correction of C_g for Speed-up over Hills and Escarpments

21. Speed-up over hills and escarpments principally affects the mean wind speed and not the amplitude of the turbulent fluctuations. This means that a correction should be applied to the gust effect factor for both the Static and Dynamic Procedures to compensate for the associated increase in gust amplitude when the corrected exposure factor, C_e^*, determined with Equation (3) is used. The following expression gives the corrected gust effect factor to be used for designing structures located on hills and escarpments:

$$C_g^* = 1 + (C_g - 1)\sqrt{\frac{C_e}{C_e^*}} \qquad (4)$$

where
C_g^* = the corrected factor for hills and escarpments, and
C_g = the gust effect factor for flat terrain.

When a combined C_pC_g value is used, the combined value can be adjusted for hills and escarpments by multiplying it by the ratio C_g^*/C_g, which is calculated using Equation (4) with a value of $C_g = 2.0$ for the building structure and $C_g = 2.5$ for cladding and secondary structural members.

Internal Gust Effect Factor, C_{gi}

22. As stipulated in NBC Clause 4.1.7.1.(6)(c), the default value of the internal gust effect factor, C_{gi}, should be taken as 2.0. However, for large structures enclosing a single unpartitioned volume, the internal pressure takes significant time to respond to changes in external pressure, thus reducing the gust factor. In such cases, the following expression for C_{gi} may be used in lieu of the default value:

$$C_{gi} = 1 + \frac{1}{\sqrt{1+\tau}} \qquad (5)$$

where τ is a parameter associated with the time it takes for the internal pressure to respond to changes in external pressure at openings, and τ is given by

$$\tau = \frac{V_0}{6950A}\left[1 + 1.42 \times 10^5 \frac{A_s}{V_0}\delta\right] \qquad (6)$$

where
V_0 = internal volume, in m³,
A = total area of all exterior openings of the volume, in m²,
A_s = total interior surface area of the volume (excluding slabs on grade), in m², and
δ = a measure of the flexibility of the building envelope and is the average outward deflection of the volumes envelope per unit increase in internal pressure, in m³/N.

A typical value of δ for buildings with sheet metal cladding is about 5×10^{-5} m³/N. Where δ is difficult to estimate, it may conservatively be taken as zero.

Example: Suppose a building's plan dimensions are 100 m × 50 m and it is 20 m high. It contains a single undivided volume, has a single opening of 5 m², and $\delta = 5 \times 10^{-5}$ m³/N. Then $V_0 = 100{,}000$ m³, $A = 5$ m², and $A_s = 6000 + 5000 = 11{,}000$ m². Hence

$$\tau = \frac{10^5}{6950 \times 5}\left[1 + 1.42 \times 10^5 \frac{1.1 \times 10^4}{10^5} 5 \times 10^{-5}\right]$$
$$= 2.88\left[1 + 0.78\right]$$
$$= 5.1$$

and

$$C_{gi} = 1 + \frac{1}{\sqrt{1 + 5.1}}$$
$$= 1.40$$

Pressure Coefficients, C_p, C_p^* and C_{pi}

General

23. Pressure coefficients are the non-dimensional ratios of actual wind-induced pressures on a building surface to the velocity pressure of the wind at the reference height. They account for the effects of aerodynamic shape of the building, orientation of the surface with respect to the wind flow, and profile of the wind velocity. Pressure coefficients are usually determined from wind-tunnel experiments on small-scale models, although measurements are occasionally made on full-scale buildings. It is very important to simulate the natural velocity profile and turbulence in the wind tunnel; experiments in uniform flow can be highly misleading.[10][11]

Directionality

24. At any geographical location, winds are the strongest in certain geographical directions. The probability is less than 100% that the direction of the strongest wind will align with the direction that produces the highest pressure on a given surface. Therefore, the actual wind load on a given surface will be less than that computed by combining the reference wind velocity pressure for the location with the peak pressure coefficient for the surface. Directionality effects have been accounted for in the factored loads, and no further reduction should be made to them.

External Pressure Coefficients for Low-Rise Buildings

25. Recommended external pressure coefficients for designing low-rise buildings are given in Figures I-7 to I-14. They are based on data obtained from systematic boundary-layer wind-tunnel studies. In several instances, these data have been verified against full-scale measurements. The coefficients are based on the maximum gust pressures lasting approximately 1 s and, consequently, include an allowance for the gust effect factor, C_g; they therefore represent the product $C_p C_g$. These coefficients apply to the tributary area associated with the particular element or member over which the wind pressure is assumed to act.

26. The external pressure-gust coefficients given in Figures I-7 to I-14 are most appropriate for buildings with height-to-width ratios of less than 0.5 and a reference height of less than 20 m, where the width is based on the smaller plan dimension, D_s. In the absence of more case-specific data, these Figures may also be used for buildings with height-to-width ratios of less than 1.0, provided that the reference height is less than 20 m. Beyond these limits, Figure I-15 should be used. These coefficients are based on References [12] and [13].

27. Figure I-7 presents values of $C_p C_g$ for the main wind force resisting system of the building affected by wind pressures on more than one surface, such as in frame buildings. The simplified load distributions in Figure I-7 were developed to represent as closely as possible the structural actions (horizontal thrust, uplift and frame moments) determined directly from experiment. These results make allowance for the partial loading of gusts referred to in NBC Sentence 4.1.7.3.(1).

28. Figures I-8 to I-14 are intended for those effects that are influenced mainly by wind acting over single surfaces, such as the design of cladding and secondary structural members such as purlins and girts. They should also be used for the design of structural elements with single surfaces, such as roofs for which moment connections are not provided at the roof/wall intersection. In this case, the edge region loads need not be included around the entire perimeter of the roof, but only adjacent to the windward edges. For roof slopes exceeding 7° where edge regions are also specified along the ridge, these increased loads need only be included on the downstream side. The loads on other edge regions can be reverted to the values specified for the interior regions.

External Pressure Coefficients for High-Rise Buildings

29. Figure I-15 contains the external pressure coefficients to be used for buildings that are rectangular in plan and whose height, H, is greater than 20 m or their smaller plan dimension, D_s. The coefficients are given as either time- and spatially-averaged pressure coefficients, C_p, or simply as time-averaged local pressure coefficients, C_p^*. A local pressure coefficient, $C_p^* = \pm 0.9$, applicable to the design of small cladding areas (about the size of a window), can occur almost anywhere at any elevation, except near corners where a local C_p^* of 1.2 is appropriate.

Table I-2 indicates which Figure to consult for deriving pressure coefficients.

Table I-2
Index of Figures Containing External Pressure Coefficients

Building Type	Structural Element	Roof slope (α) Limit	Figure Number	Coefficient Given
Low-rise buildings where $H/D_s < 1$ and $H \leq 20$ m	Primary structural action	—	I-7	
	Walls	—	I-8	
	Roofs			
	(a) general	$\alpha \leq 7°$	I-9	
	(b) stepped flat	$\alpha = 0°$	I-10	
	(c) gabled and hipped, single-ridge	$\alpha \leq 7°$	I-9	
		$\alpha > 7°$	I-11	$C_p C_g$
	(d) gabled, multiple-ridge	$\alpha \leq 10°$	I-9	
		$\alpha > 10°$	I-12	
	(e) monosloped	$\alpha \leq 3°$	I-9	
		$30° \geq \alpha > 3°$	I-13	
	(f) sawtoothed	$\alpha \leq 10°$	I-9	
		$\alpha > 10°$	I-14	
Buildings where $H/D_s \geq 1$ or $H > 20$ m	—	—	I-15	C_p and C_p^*

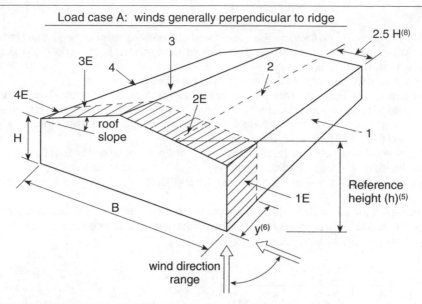

Load case A: winds generally perpendicular to ridge

Roof slope	Building surfaces							
	1	1E	2	2E	3	3E	4	4E
0° to 5°	0.75	1.15	−1.3	−2.0	−0.7	−1.0	−0.55	−0.8
20°	1.0	1.5	−1.3	−2.0	−0.9	−1.3	−0.8	−1.2
30° to 45°	1.05	1.3	0.4	0.5	−0.8	−1.0	−0.7	−0.9
90°	1.05	1.3	1.05	1.3	−0.7	−0.9	−0.7	−0.9

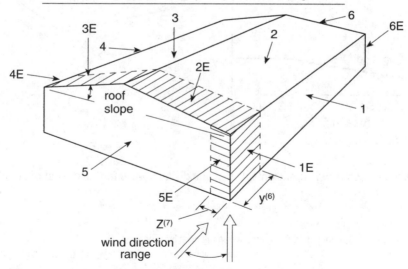

Load case B: winds generally parallel to ridge

Roof slope	Building surfaces											
	1	1E	2	2E	3	3E	4	4E	5	5E	6	6E
0° to 90°	−0.85	−0.9	−1.3	−2.0	−0.7	−1.0	−0.85	−0.9	0.75	1.15	−0.55	−0.8

EG00920B

Figure I-7

External peak composite pressure-gust coefficients, C_pC_g, for primary structural actions arising from wind load acting simultaneously on all surfaces

Notes to Figure I-7:

(1) The building must be designed for all wind directions. Each corner must be considered in turn as the windward corner shown in the sketches. For all roof slopes, Load Case A and Load Case B are required as two separate loading conditions to generate the wind actions, including torsion, to be resisted by the structural system.

(2) For values of roof slope not shown, the coefficient C_pC_g may be interpolated linearly.

(3) Positive coefficients denote forces toward the surface, whereas negative coefficients denote forces away from the surface.

(4) For the design of foundations, exclusive of anchorages to the frame, only 70% of the effective load is to be considered.

(5) The reference height, h, for pressures is mid-height of the roof or 6 m, whichever is greater. The eaves height, H, may be substituted for the mean height if the slope of the roof is less than 7°.

(6) End-zone width y should be the greater of 6 m or 2z, where z is the gable wall end zone defined for Load Case B below. Alternatively, for buildings with frames, the end zone y may be the distance between the end and the first interior frame.

(7) End-zone width z is the lesser of 10% of the least horizontal dimension or 40% of height, H, but not less than 4% of the least horizontal dimension or 1 m.

(8) For B/H > 5 in Load Case A, the listed negative coefficients on surfaces 2 and 2E should only be applied on an area that is 2.5 H wide measured from the windward eaves. The pressures on the remainder of the windward roof should be reduced to the coefficients specified for the leeward roof (i.e. those for 3 and 3E).

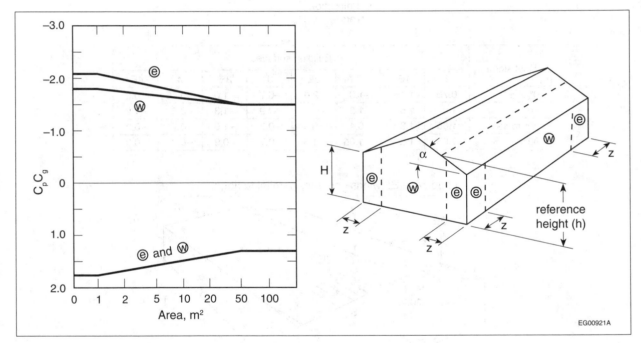

EG00921A

Figure I-8

External peak composite pressure-gust coefficients, C_pC_g, on individual walls for the design of structural components and cladding

Notes to Figure I-8:

(1) These coefficients apply for any roof slope, α.

(2) The abscissa area in the graph is the design tributary area within the specified zone.

(3) End-zone width z is the lesser of 10% of the least horizontal dimension and 40% of height, H, but not less than 4% of the least horizontal dimension or 1 m.

(4) Combinations of exterior and interior pressures must be evaluated to obtain the most severe loading.

(5) Positive coefficients denote forces toward the surface, whereas negative coefficients denote forces away from the surface. Each structural element must be designed to withstand the forces of both signs.

(6) Pressure coefficients may generally apply for facades with architectural features; however, when vertical ribs deeper than 1 m are placed on a facade, a local $C_pC_g = -2.8$ may apply to zone e.[35][36]

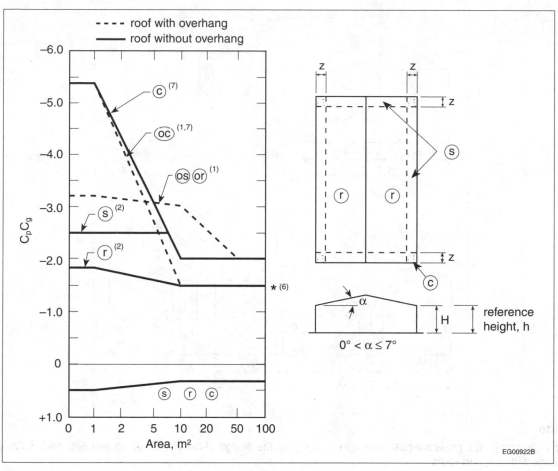

Figure I-9

External peak composite pressure-gust coefficients, C_pC_g, on roofs with a slope of 7° or less for the design of structural components and cladding

Notes to Figure I-9:

(1) Coefficients for overhung roofs have the prefix "o" and refer to the same roof areas as referred to by the corresponding symbol without a prefix. They include contributions from both upper and lower surfaces. In the case of overhangs, the walls are inboard of the roof outline.[37]

(2) s and r apply to both roofs and upper surfaces of canopies.

(3) The abscissa area in the graph is the design tributary area within the specified zone.

(4) End-zone width z is the lesser of 10% of the least horizontal dimension and 40% of height, H, but not less than 4% of the least horizontal dimension or 1 m.

(5) Combinations of exterior and interior pressures must be evaluated to obtain the most severe loading.

(6) Positive coefficients denote forces toward the surface, whereas negative coefficients denote forces away from the surface. Each structural element must be designed to withstand the forces of both signs.

(7) For calculating the uplift forces on tributary areas larger than 100 m² on unobstructed nearly-flat roofs with low parapets, and where the centre of the tributary area is at least two building heights from the nearest edge, the value of C_pC_g may be reduced to -1.1 at x/H = 2 and further reduced linearly to -0.6 at x/H = 5, where x is distance to the nearest edge and H is building height.[39]

(8) For roofs having a perimeter parapet that is 1 m high or greater, the corner coefficients C_pC_g for small tributary areas can be reduced from -5.4 to -4.4.[40][41]

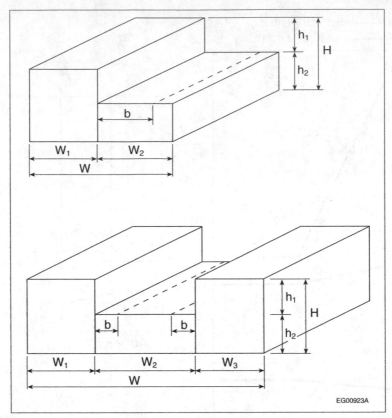

Figure I-10

External peak composite pressure-gust coefficients, C_pC_g, for the design of the structural components and cladding of buildings with stepped roofs

Notes to Figure I-10:

(1) The zone designations, pressure-gust coefficients and notes provided in Figure I-9 apply on both the upper and lower levels of flat stepped roofs, except that on the lower levels, positive pressure-gust coefficients equal to those in Figure I-8 for walls apply for a distance, b, where b is equal to $1.5h_1$ but not greater than 30 m. For all walls in Figure I-10, zone designations and pressure coefficients provided for walls in Figure I-8 apply.[42][43]

(2) Note (1) above applies only when the following conditions are met: $h_1 \geq 0.3H$, $h_1 \geq 3$ m, and W_1, W_2, or W_3 is greater than 0.25W but not greater than 0.75W

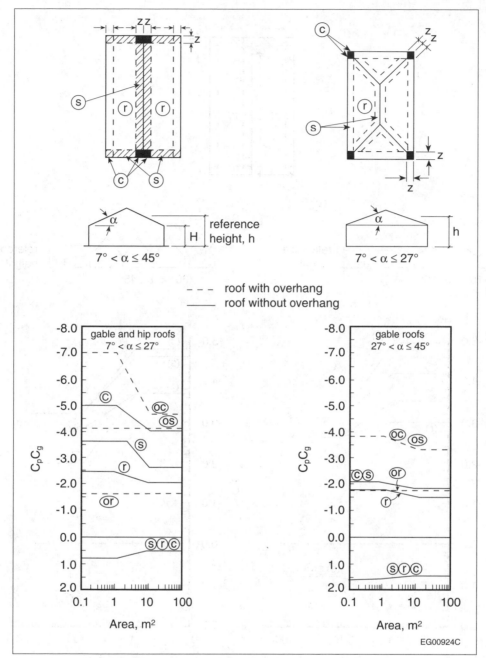

Figure I-11

External peak composite pressure-gust coefficients, C_pC_g, on single-span gabled and hipped roofs with a slope of 7° or greater for the design of structural components and cladding

Notes to Figure I-11:

(1) Coefficients for overhung roofs have the prefix "o" and refer to the same roof areas as referred to by the corresponding symbol without a prefix. They include contributions from both upper and lower surfaces.[24][44]

(2) The abscissa area in the graph is the design tributary area within the specified zone.

(3) End-zone width z is the lesser of 10% of the least horizontal dimension and 40% of height, H, but not less than 4% of the least horizontal dimension or 1 m.

(4) Combinations of exterior and interior pressures must be evaluated to obtain the most severe loading.

(5) Positive coefficients denote forces toward the surface, whereas negative coefficients denote forces away from the surface. Each structural element must be designed to withstand the forces of both signs.

(6) For hipped roofs with 7° < α ≤ 27°, edge/ridge strips and pressure-gust coefficients for ridges of gabled roofs apply along each hip.[45]

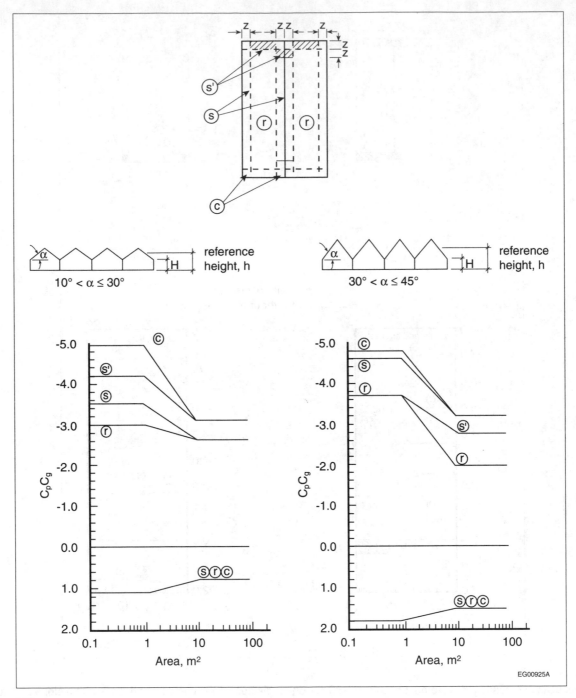

Figure I-12

External peak composite pressure-gust coefficients, C_pC_g, on multi-span gabled (folded) roofs with a slope greater than 10° for the design of structural components and cladding[46][47]

Notes to Figure I-12:

(1) The abscissa area in the graph is the design tributary area within the specified zone.

(2) End-zone width z is the lesser of 10% of the least horizontal dimension and 40% of height, H, but not less than 4% of the least horizontal dimension or 1 m.

(3) Combinations of exterior and interior pressures must be evaluated to obtain the most severe loading.

(4) Positive coefficients denote forces toward the surface, whereas negative coefficients denote forces away from the surface. Each structural element must be designed to withstand the forces of both signs.

(5) For $\alpha \leq 10°$, the coefficients given in Figure I-9 apply.

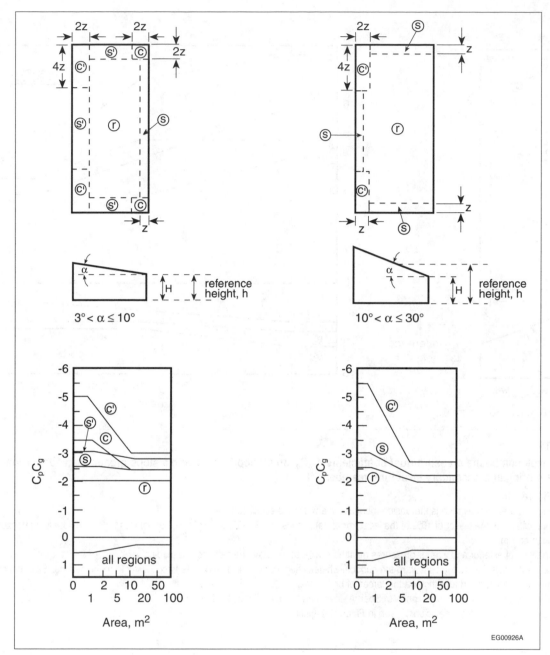

Figure I-13

External peak composite pressure-gust coefficients, C_pC_g, on monosloped roofs for the design of structural components and cladding[48][49]

Notes to Figure I-13:

(1) The abscissa area in the graph is the design tributary area within the specified zone.

(2) End-zone width z is the lesser of 10% of the least horizontal dimension and 40% of height, H, but not less than 4% of the least horizontal dimension or 1 m.

(3) Combinations of exterior and interior pressures must be evaluated to obtain the most severe loading.

(4) Positive coefficients denote forces toward the surface, whereas negative coefficients denote forces away from the surface. Each structural element must be designed to withstand the forces of both signs.

(5) For $\alpha \leq 3°$, pressure-gust coefficients given in Figure I-9 apply.

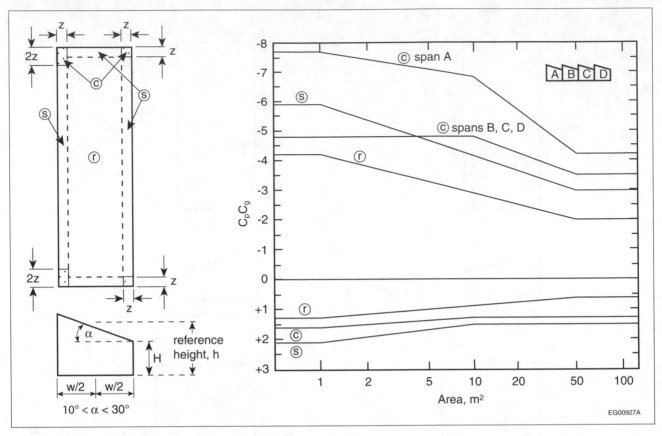

Figure I-14

External peak composite pressure-gust coefficients, C_pC_g, on sawtooth roofs with a slope greater than 10° for the design of roofing and secondary structural members[49]

Notes to Figure I-14:

(1) The abscissa area in the graph is the design tributary area within the specified zone.

(2) End-zone width z is the lesser of 10% of the least horizontal dimension and 40% of height, H, but not less than 4% of the least horizontal dimension or 1 m.

(3) Combinations of exterior and interior pressures must be evaluated to obtain the most severe loading.

(4) Positive coefficients denote forces toward the surface, whereas negative coefficients denote forces away from the surface. Each structural element must be designed to withstand the forces of both signs.

(5) Negative coefficients on the corner zones of Span A differ from those on Spans B, C and D.

(6) For $\alpha \leq 10°$, pressure-gust coefficients given in Figure I-9 apply.

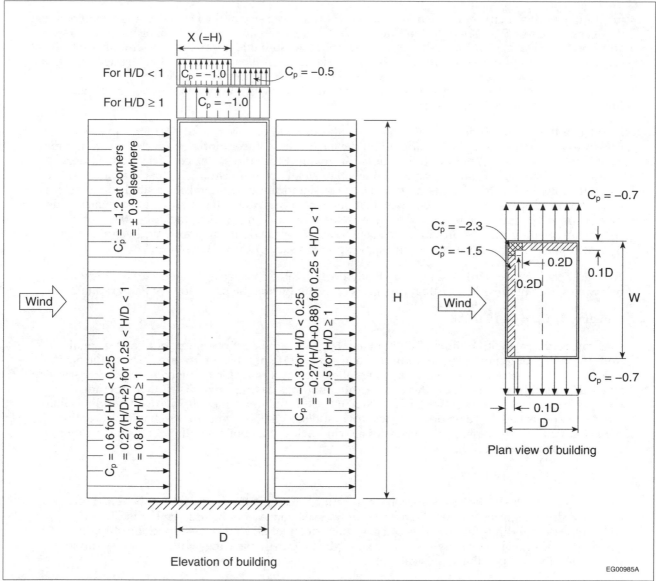

Elevation of building

EG00985A

Figure I-15

External pressure coefficients, C_p and C_p^*, for flat-roofed buildings

Notes to Figure I-15:

(1) D and W denote the building plan dimensions at the base in the along-wind and cross-wind directions, respectively.

(2) The coefficients C_p shown on the windward wall are applicable when the wind is perpendicular to the wall.

(3) The coefficients C_p^* account for high local suctions created by wind blowing at a slight angle to the wall. They should be used for designing small cladding and roofing areas, but need not be considered in conjunction with the C_p for overall loading.

(4) Combinations of exterior and interior pressures must be evaluated to obtain the most severe loading. Interior pressure coefficients, C_{pi}, are given in Paragraphs 30 to 34.

(5) Pressure coefficients as shown generally apply for facades that do not contain deep vertical ribs. In such facades, the C_p^* of -1.2 given for corners applies to an edge zone that is 0.1D wide. When vertical ribs deeper than 1 m are placed on a facade, a local $C_p^* = -1.4$ may apply to an edge zone that is 0.2D wide.[35][36]

(6) The value of C_p^* can be reduced from -2.3 to -2.0 for roofs with perimeter parapets that are higher than 1 m.[40][41]

(7) On lower level(s) of flat stepped roofs, positive pressure coefficients equal to those for the walls apply for a distance, b (see Figure I-9 for the definition of b). Segments of the walls above the lower roofs qualify for the same coefficients as the other walls similarly oriented to the wind flow.[42][43]

Internal Pressure Coefficient, C_{pi}

30. The internal pressure coefficient, C_{pi}, defines the effect of wind on the air pressure inside the building and is important in the design of both cladding elements and the primary structure. The magnitude of this coefficient depends on the distribution and size of the leakage paths and openings that vent the internal air space to the exterior. With very small and uniformly distributed cracks and pores, the leakage is slow. Although the internal pressure will approximately equilibrate to the average external pressure over the exposed surface, the influence of gusts will be attenuated. If the openings are larger and more significant—on the scale of doors or windows—the internal pressure will move closer to that prevailing externally at the largest dominant opening and gust pressures will be felt within the interior.

31. Because of the changeability and uncertainty of the size and distribution of openings, internal pressure coefficients can be wide ranging. In the face of these uncertainties, it is adequate to use the coefficients given below for both the Static and Dynamic Procedures. The coefficient depends on whether there are significant openings and whether small openings producing background leakage are uniformly distributed. In this context, a large or significant opening means a single opening or a combination of openings on any one wall that offers a passage to the wind and whose area exceeds by a factor of 2 or more the leakage area of the remaining building surface, including the roof. Such a significant opening may be provided by main doors, shipping doors, windows and ventilators if they are open during a storm, either through expected usage or through damage.

    To handle the range of circumstances that may prevail, three basic design categories are provided below. For each of these three categories, C_{gi} is calculated using the provisions of Paragraph 22:

    Category 1: C_{pi} = –0.15 to 0.0

    This category deals with buildings without any large or significant openings, but having small uniformly distributed openings amounting to less than 0.1% of total surface area. The value of C_{pi} should be −0.15, except where such openings alleviate an external load, in which case $C_{pi} = 0$ should be used. Internal pressure fluctuates even within buildings having small distributed openings, and the pressure fluctuations occasionally reach $C_{pi} = 0$. Such buildings include high-rise buildings that are nominally sealed, have no operable windows and screen doors, and are mechanically ventilated. Some less common low-rise buildings, such as windowless warehouses with door systems not prone to storm damage, also fall into this category.

    Category 2: C_{pi} = –0.45 to 0.3

    This category covers buildings in which significant openings, if there are any, can be relied on to be closed during storms but in which background leakage may not be uniformly distributed. Most low-rise buildings fall into this category provided that all elements—especially shipping doors—are designed to be fully wind-resistant. Most high-rise buildings with operable windows or balcony doors also fall into this category.

    Category 3: C_{pi} = –0.7 to 0.7

    This category covers buildings with large or significant openings through which gusts are transmitted to the interior. Examples of such buildings include sheds with one or more open sides as well as industrial buildings with shipping doors, ventilators or the like, which have a high probability of being open during a storm or not being fully resistant to design wind loads.

32. An ever-present threat in severe storms is the breakage of large unprotected glass areas and other vulnerable components by flying debris. Structures required in post-disaster services should be capable of withstanding all the consequences of failure of glass and conform to the requirements of Category 3. For other structures in which the glass is designed for wind and there is adequate protection against roof uplift, the contingency of glass damage due to debris is covered by normal load factors for wind.

33. In most cases, there is no need to consider non-uniform internal pressures except in the design of internal partitions (see NBC Sentence 4.1.7.4.(1)). Thus, for most structural design, the two limiting values of internal pressure can be considered separately unless interior compartments of the building are well sealed and wind damage or the like could expose one area of the building to Category 3 conditions while the rest of the building remains in Category 1 or 2, resulting in unbalanced internal pressures.

34. Internal pressures are also affected by mechanical ventilation systems and by the stack effect due to different inside and outside air temperatures. Under normal operation, mechanical ventilation

systems create a differential across walls of less than 0.1 kPa, but the stack effect due to differences in temperature of 40°C could amount to a differential of 0.2 kPa per 100 m of building height.[30]

Partial Loading

35. Partial wind loading can, in some cases, cause more severe effects than full loading. Pressure patterns observed in turbulent wind indicate reduced loading on portions of the building faces, which can produce additional torsion due to horizontal shifting of the wind-load vector. Reduced but simultaneous loading along both major axes can be induced by wind blowing diagonally to the building, which can produce higher stresses in some structural members than by wind blowing along any one major axis. Other structures, such as curved roofs, may undergo larger stresses under partial loading. NBC Sentence 4.1.7.3.(1) therefore requires all buildings to be designed for partial loading as well as full loading.

36. Low buildings designed by the Static Procedure to the specifications of Figure I-7 do not need to have further unbalanced loads (see Paragraph 27). Taller buildings, in addition to being designed for the full wind load along each of the principal axes as shown in Figure I-16, Case A, should be checked for maximum additional torsion arising from partial loadings created by applying the wind pressure to only a part of the building face areas as shown in Figure I-16, Case B, for rectangular plan buildings.

37. To account for the potentially more severe effects induced by diagonal wind, and also for the tendency of structures to sway in the across-wind direction, taller structures should be designed to resist 75% of the maximum wind pressures for each of the principal directions applied simultaneously as shown in Figure I-16, Case C. In addition, the influence of removing 50% of the Case C loads from parts of the face areas that maximizes torsion, as shown in Figure I-16, Case D, should be investigated. Further discussion of combined loading effects can be found in References [15] and [16].

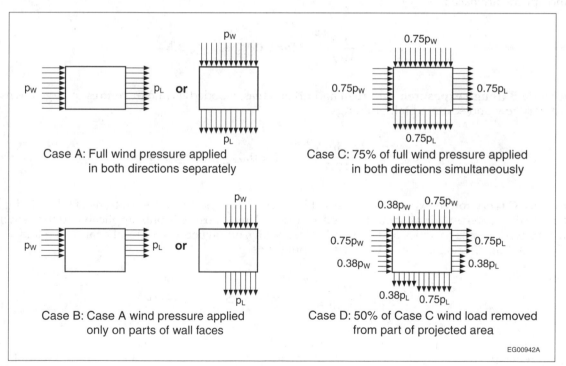

Figure I-16

Full and partial wind loads (see NBC Sentence 4.1.7.3.(1))

Notes to Figure I-16:

(1) p_W and p_L are the windward and leeward wind pressures, respectively, as calculated for the full wind load.

(2) In Case B, the full wind pressure should be applied only to parts of the wall faces so that the wind-induced torsion is maximized.

Commentary I

Dynamic Procedure

Application

38. NBC Sentence 4.1.7.2.(1) requires the use of the Dynamic or Experimental Procedure for buildings whose height is greater than 4 times their minimum effective width, or greater than 120 m, and other buildings whose properties make them susceptible to vibration. Minimum effective width is defined in NBC Sentence 4.1.7.2.(2).

39. In the Dynamic Procedure for calculating wind load on the building structure, the exposure factor, C_e, and external gust effect factor, C_g, are different from the factors used in the Static Procedure, but the pressure coefficient, C_p, is the same. See Figure I-1 for guidance on how the Dynamic Procedure for the structure is carried out in conjunction with the Static Procedure for the cladding.

40. In addition to the calculation of wind load, the calculation of wind-induced lateral deflection, vibration and vortex-shedding effect can also be important for some buildings that are required to be treated by the Dynamic Procedure. These topics are dealt with separately under the sections of this Commentary entitled Lateral Deflection of Tall Buildings, Building Vibration and Vortex Shedding.

Exposure Factor, C_e

41. In the Dynamic Procedure, the exposure factor, C_e, is based on the profile of mean wind speed, which varies considerably with the general roughness of the terrain over which the wind has been blowing before it reaches the building. To determine the exposure factor, three categories of terrain exposure have been established and are illustrated in Figures I-2 to I-5.

    Exposure A (open or standard exposure): open level terrain with only scattered buildings, trees or other obstructions, open water or shorelines thereof. This is the exposure on which the reference wind speeds are based.

$$C_e = \left(\frac{h}{10} \right)^{0.28} \quad \text{for } 1.0 \leq C_e \leq 2.5 \tag{7}$$

    Exposure B (rough exposure): suburban and urban areas, wooded terrain or centres of large towns with very few and scattered tall buildings.

$$C_e = 0.5 \left(\frac{h}{12.7} \right)^{0.50} \quad \text{for } 0.5 \leq C_e \leq 2.5 \tag{8}$$

    Exposure C (very rough exposure): centres of large cities with heavy concentrations of tall buildings. At least 50% of the buildings should exceed 4 storeys. This exposure is only applicable to the heavily built-up centres of large cities and should be used with caution because of local channeling and wake buffeting effects that can occur near tall buildings.

$$C_e = 0.4 \left(\frac{h}{30} \right)^{0.72} \quad \text{for } 0.4 \leq C_e \leq 2.5 \tag{9}$$

    In Equations (7) to (9), h is the reference height (see Paragraphs 7 and 8) above ground in metres. The exposure factor can be calculated using these Equations or can be obtained directly from Figure I-17.

42. Exposure B or C should not be used unless the applicable terrain roughness persists in the upwind direction for at least 1.0 km or 10 times the height of the building, H, whichever is larger, and the exposure factor should be recalculated if the roughness of the terrain differs from one direction to another.

43. In addition to being used to calculate pressures on building surfaces, the exposure factor is needed for calculating the hourly mean wind speed at the top of the building, V_H, and the gust effect factor, C_g (see Paragraphs 46 and 47).

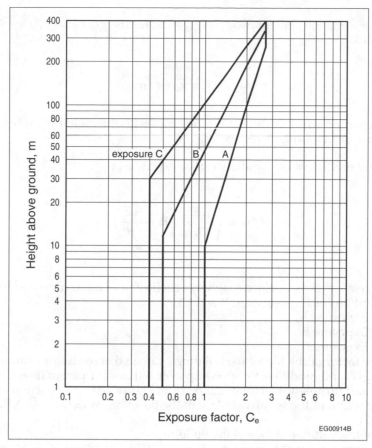

Figure I-17
Exposure factor as a function of terrain roughness and height above ground

Speed-up over Hills and Escarpments

44. The exposure factor must be modified for speed-up over hills and escarpments in both the Static and Dynamic Procedures as covered in Paragraphs 13 to 16. However, as the speed-up principally affects the mean wind speed and not the amplitude of the turbulent fluctuations, a correction also needs to be applied to the gust effect factor as shown in Paragraph 21.

Gust Effect Factor, C_g

General

45. The general discussion on the gust effect factor presented in Paragraphs 17 and 18 under the Static Procedure is also applicable to the Dynamic Procedure.

External Gust Effect Factor, C_g

46. A general expression for the maximum or peak loading effect, denoted by W_p, is as follows:

$$W_P = \mu + g_P \sigma \qquad (10)$$

where
$\quad \mu \quad$ = mean loading effect,
$\quad g_P \quad$ = statistical peak factor for the loading effect, and
$\quad \sigma \quad$ = "root-mean square" loading effect.

If this expression is rearranged, the following expression for the gust effect factor, C_g, which is equal to W_p/μ, is obtained:

$$C_g = 1 + g_p \left(\sigma/\mu \right) \tag{11}$$

The form of the fluctuating wind loading effect, σ, varies with the excitation, whether it is due to gusts, wake pressures or motion-induced forces.

47. The value of σ/μ, the coefficient of variation, can be expressed by

$$\sigma/\mu = \sqrt{\frac{K}{C_{eH}} \left(B + \frac{sF}{\beta} \right)} \tag{12}$$

where
- K = a factor related to the surface roughness coefficient of the terrain (see Paragraph 41 for the definitions of Exposures A, B and C),
  - = 0.08 for Exposure A,
  - = 0.10 for Exposure B,
  - = 0.14 for Exposure C,
- C_{eH} = exposure factor at the top of the building evaluated according to Paragraph 41 or Figure I-17, and modified for speed-up over hill or escarpment if required,
- B = background turbulence factor obtained from Figure I-18 as a function of w/H,
- w = effective width of the windward face of the building, as defined in NBC Sentence 4.1.7.2.(2),
- H = height of the windward face of the building,
- s = size reduction factor obtained from Figure I-19 as a function of w/H and the reduced frequency $f_{nD}H/V_H$,
- f_{nD} = natural frequency of vibration in the along-wind direction, in Hz,
- V_H = mean wind speed, in m/s, at the top of structure, H, evaluated using Equation (13) below,
- F = gust energy ratio at the natural frequency of the structure obtained from Figure I-20 as a function of the wave number, f_{nD}/V_H , and
- β = critical damping ratio in the along-wind direction.

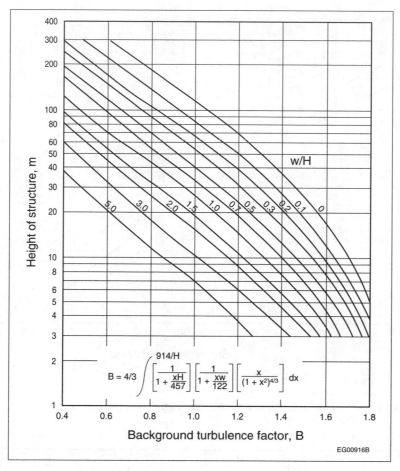

Figure I-18
Background turbulence factor as a function of width and height of structure

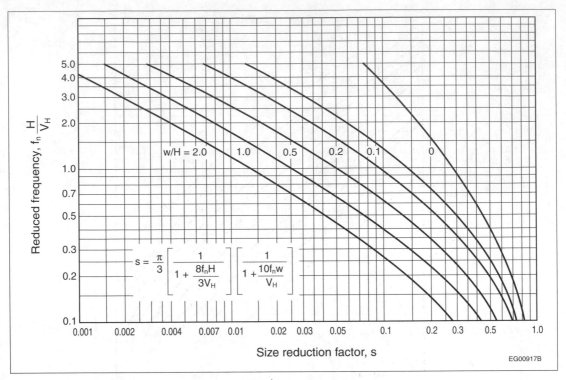

Figure I-19
Size reduction factor as a function of width, height and reduced frequency of structure

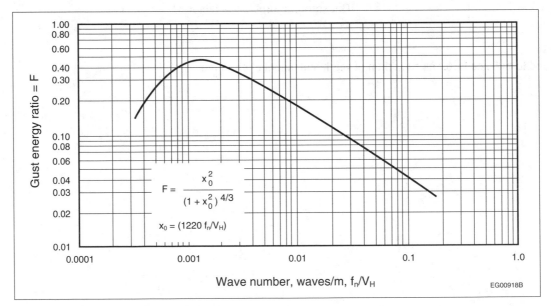

Figure I-20
Gust energy ratio as a function of wave number

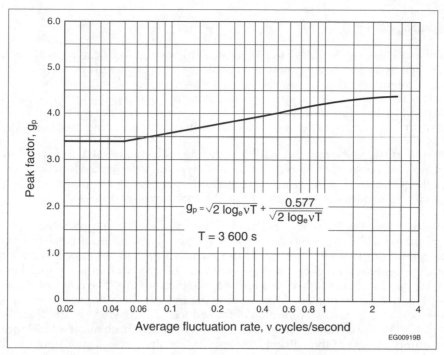

Figure I-21
Peak factor as a function of average fluctuation rate

The mean wind speed at the top of the structure, V_H in m/s, in Figures I-19 and I-20 is given by

$$V_H = \overline{V}\sqrt{C_{eH}} \tag{13}$$

where $\overline{V}$ (m/s), the reference wind speed at the height of 10 m, is determined from the reference velocity pressure, q (kPa), as follows (see NBC Appendix C of Division B):

$$\overline{V} = 39.2\sqrt{q} \tag{14}$$

48. The critical damping ratio, β, is based mainly on experiments on real structures. Expressed as a fraction of critical damping, values commonly used in the design of buildings with steel frames and concrete frames are 1% and 2%, respectively. Masts and stacks, on the other hand, may have much lower inherent or structural damping. Aerodynamic damping in the along-wind direction becomes significant at high wind speeds, but plays no useful role in limiting cross-wind motion induced by vortex shedding. Spread footings on soft or medium-stiff soil provide higher damping compared to pile foundations or spread footings on stiff soil and rock. Damping values measured from more than 20 stacks are tabulated in Reference [17] and the results from 5 more stacks are given in Reference [18]. The logarithmic decrement mentioned therein is 2π times the critical damping ratio. Sachs[17] concludes by stating a range of 0.2% to 0.8% for β for the total damping of closed circular and unlined welded steel stacks, and suggests that the minimum value be used in design. Corresponding ranges for lined welded steel stacks and for unlined reinforced concrete stacks are given as 0.5% to 1% and 1% to 2%, respectively.

49. The peak factor, g_p, in Equation (10) gives the number of standard deviations by which the peak load effect is expected to exceed the mean load effect, and is given in Figure I-21 as a function of the average fluctuation rate. The average fluctuation rate, ν, can be estimated as follows using the variables defined for Equation (12):

$$\nu = f_n\sqrt{\frac{sF}{sF + \beta B}} \tag{15}$$

Commentary I

50. The response of a tall, slender building to a randomly fluctuating force can be evaluated rather simply by treating it as a rigid, spring-mounted cantilever whose dynamic properties are specified by a single natural frequency and an appropriate damping value. The variance of the output quantity or loading effect is the area under the spectrum of the input quantity (the forcing function) after it has been multiplied by the transfer function. The transfer function is the square of the well-known dynamic load magnification factor for a one-degree-of-freedom oscillating mechanical system.

51. In the case of wind as the randomly fluctuating force, the spectrum of the wind speed must first be multiplied by another transfer function called the aerodynamic admittance function, which in effect describes how the turbulence in the wind is modified by its encounter with the building, at least insofar as its ability to produce a loading effect on the structure is concerned.

52. For the purpose of calculating σ/μ, the spectrum of the wind speed is represented by an algebraic expression derived from observations of real wind. The aerodynamic admittance function is also an algebraic expression, computed on the basis of somewhat simplified assumptions but appearing to be in reasonable agreement with experimental evidence. The spectrum of wind speed is a function of frequency having the shape of a rather broad hump (see Figure I-20). The effect of the aerodynamic admittance is to reduce the ordinates of the curve to the right of the hump more and more as the frequency increases. This is partly a reflection of the reduced effectiveness of small gusts in loading a large area. The effect of the dynamic load magnification factor or mechanical admittance is to create a new peak or hump centred at the natural frequency of the structure—usually well to the right of the broad peak—which represents the maximum density of fluctuating force of the wind.

53. The area under the loading effect spectrum, the square root of which is the coefficient of variation, σ/μ, is taken as the sum of two components: the area under the broad hump, which must be integrated numerically for each structure, and the area under the resonance peak, for which a single analytic expression is available. These components are represented in Equation (12) by B and sF/β, respectively. The factor K/C_{eH} can be thought of as scaling the result for the appropriate input turbulence level. If resonance effects are small, then sF/β will be small compared to the background turbulence B, and vice versa.

54. The peak factor, g_p, depends on the average number of times the mean value of the loading effect is surpassed during the averaging time of 1 hour (3600 s). The functional relationship in Figure I-21 holds when the probability distribution of the mean loading effect is normal (Gaussian).[19]

Correction of C_g for Speed-up over Hills and Escarpments

55. The correction applied under the Static Procedure in Paragraph 21 must also be applied under the Dynamic Procedure.

Sample Calculation of C_g

56. To illustrate the calculation of a gust effect factor, the following sample problem is worked out in detail:

Objective: To obtain the gust effect factor for a building with the following properties:

Height, H	183 m
Across-Wind Effective Width, w	30.5 m
Along-Wind Effective Depth, d	30.5 m
Fundamental natural frequency, f_{nD}	0.2 Hz
Critical damping ratio, β	0.015
Terrain for site	Exposure B
Reference wind speed, $\bar{V}$, at 10 m and in open terrain	27.4 m/s

Step 1: Calculate required parameters.

C_{eH} = 1.90 (from Figure I-17)

$V_H = \bar{V}\sqrt{C_{eH}}$ (Equation (13))

$= 27.4 \times \sqrt{1.90}$

= 37.8 m/s

w/H = aspect ratio

= 30.5/183

= 0.17

f_{nD}/V_H = wave number for calculation of F

= 0.2/37.8

= 0.0053

$f_{nD}H/V_H$ = reduced frequency for calculation of s

= 0.2 × 183/37.8

= 0.968

Step 2: Calculate σ/μ using Equation (12).

K = 0.10 for Exposure B

B = 0.62 (from Figure I-18)

s = 0.11 (from Figure I-19)

F = 0.28 (from Figure I-20)

β = 0.015 (given)

$$\sigma/\mu = \sqrt{\frac{K}{C_{eH}}\left(B + \frac{sF}{\beta}\right)}$$

$$= \sqrt{\frac{0.10}{1.90}\left(0.62 + \frac{0.11 \times 0.28}{0.015}\right)}$$

$$= 0.375$$

Step 3: Calculate v using Equation (15).

f_{nD} = 0.2 Hz (given)

$$v = f_{nD}\sqrt{\frac{sF}{sF + \beta B}}$$

$$= 0.2\sqrt{\frac{0.11 \times 0.28}{0.11 \times 0.28 + 0.015 \times 0.62}}$$

$$= 0.175/s$$

Step 4: Obtain peak factor, g_p.

g_p = 3.75 (from Figure I-21)

Step 5: Calculate C_g using Equation (11).

$C_g = 1 + g_p(\sigma/\mu)$

= 1 + 3.75(0.375)

= 2.41

Pressure Coefficients, C_p

General

57. The general discussion presented in Paragraphs 23 and 24 under the Static Procedure is also applicable to the Dynamic Procedure.

External Pressure Coefficient, C_p

58. The coefficients given in Figure I-15 under the Static Procedure are also applicable to the Dynamic Procedure (see Paragraph 29).

Commentary I

Partial Loading

Refer to Paragraphs 35 to 37 for partial loading requirements.

Wind Load on Miscellaneous Structures

Interior Walls and Partitions

59. If windows are broken during a storm, considerable pressure differences can result across interior walls and partitions in high-rise buildings, as well as in low-rise buildings in exposed locations. In certain locations, almost the full pressure difference between the windward and leeward sides of the building could be applied across interior walls or partitions. For example, when a large window in a small room on the windward side is broken by flying debris, the full positive pressure is exerted on the walls of that room. Similar conditions could prevail in an apartment building with operable windows or doors. This pressure difference could be aggravated by mechanical ventilation and winter-time stack effects in a tall building. On the other hand, experience does not indicate many failures of interior walls due to pressure differences, and thus interior walls and partitions are not required to be designed for the maximum possible pressure difference. An unfactored pressure difference of at least 0.25 kPa is suggested and a value of 0.5 kPa or higher may be appropriate in cases where the exterior wind pressures are likely to be transmitted to the interior walls and partitions through large openings in the exterior envelope.

Protected Membrane Roofs

60. In the case of a protected-membrane roof in which the insulation is not bonded to the waterproofing membrane, the insulation is not subjected to the same uplift pressure as is applied through the depth of the entire roof assembly, because of air leakage and partial pressure equalization between the top and bottom of the insulation boards. External pressure or uplift due to wind is, therefore, applied to the membrane, which acts as an air barrier between the inside and the outside and prevents pressure equalization. Further information can be found in References [20] and [21].

Unenclosed Parking Structures

61. For multi-level, unenclosed parking structures, the exposed exterior area is reduced compared with enclosed structures. However, internal parts of the structure, and vehicles parked there, are subject to additional wind forces not present in enclosed structures. In lieu of a detailed analysis of the specific structure under consideration, a reasonable and conservative assumption is to treat the unenclosed parking structure as though it were enclosed.

Structural Members and Frames, and Rounded Structures

62. Although the NBC deals primarily with building structures, the present Commentary has a long tradition of providing guidance on determining the wind load on various other structures. Figures I-22 and I-24 to I-33 at the end of the Commentary, which are derived from Standard No. 160 produced by the Swiss Association of Engineers and Architects Standards (SIA),[22] provide such guidance. The Figures are based on wind-tunnel experiments in which the correct velocity profile and wind turbulence were not simulated; they should therefore be regarded with caution. Note that many of these Figures provide formulae for the total wind load rather than the wind pressure as given by the NBC, and hence use a force coefficient rather than a pressure coefficient. The exposure and gust effect factors required in the Figures to calculate the wind load can be determined by using either the Static Procedure, the Dynamic Procedure, or Vortex Shedding of rounded structures described in this Commentary, as deemed appropriate.

63. Wind loads on standalone structural members, and frames, trusses and lattices made of such members can be calculated using Figures I-29 to I-33. The subscript ∞ in these Figures indicates that the coefficients apply to structural members of infinite lengths. The coefficients are multiplied by a reduction factor, k, for structural members of finite lengths. If a structural member cantilevers from a large plate or wall, k should be calculated for a slenderness based on twice the actual length. If a member terminates with both ends in large plates or walls, the reduction factors for infinite length should be used.

64. For framing members that are located behind each other in the direction of the wind, the shielding effect may be taken into account. The shielded parts of the leeward members should be designed with the reduced pressure, q_x, according to Figure I-31. A detailed discussion of the loads on unclad building frameworks is given in Reference [23].

65. As the shape of a structure may change during erection, the wind loads may be temporarily more critical during erection than after completion of the structure.[24] These increased wind loads should be taken into account using the appropriate coefficients from Figures I-7 to I-15 and I-22 to I-33.

66. For constructions made of circular sections with $D\sqrt{qC_e} < 0.167$ and $A_s/A > 0.3$, the shielding factors can be taken by approximation from Figure I-28. If $D\sqrt{qC_e} \geq 0.167$, the shielding effect is small and for a solidity ratio $A_s/A \leq 0.3$, it can be taken into account by a constant shielding factor $k_x = 0.95$.

67. For rounded structures (in contrast to sharp-edged structures), the cross-wind pressures vary with the wind velocity and depend strongly on the Reynolds Number. Pressure coefficients for some rounded structures are given in Figures I-24, I-25, I-28 and I-33, in which the Reynolds Number is expressed differently from the conventional one, by $D\sqrt{qC_e}$, where D is the diameter of the sphere or cylinder in m and q is the velocity pressure in kPa. To convert to the conventional Reynolds Number, multiply $D\sqrt{qC_e}$ by 2.7×10^6.

68. The roughness of rounded structures may be of considerable importance. With reference to Figure I-24, metal, concrete, timber and well-laid masonry without parging can be considered as having a "moderately smooth" surface. Surfaces with ribs projecting more than 2% of the diameter are considered "very rough." In case of doubt, coefficients that result in the greater forces should be used. For cylindrical and spherical objects with substantial stiffening ribs, supports and attached structural members, the pressure coefficients depend on the type, location and relative magnitude of these roughnesses. For vortex shedding of circular cylinders, see Reference [25].

Increased Wind Load due to Icing

69. In locations where the strongest winds and icing may occur simultaneously, forces on structural members, cables and ropes must be calculated assuming an ice covering based on climate and local experience. For the iced condition, values of C_f given in Figure I-28 for thick wire cables for a "rough" surface should be used. Information on icing loads can be obtained from the CSA standard on antennas and towers[26] and the ISO standard on icing load.[27]

Vortex Shedding

70. Slender, free-standing cylindrical structures such as chimneys, observation towers and in some cases, high-rise buildings, should be designed to resist the dynamic effect of vortex shedding. A structure may be considered slender in this context if the ratio of height to width or diameter exceeds 5. When the wind blows across slender prismatic or cylindrical structures, vortices are shed alternately from one side and then the other along the length of the structure, giving rise to a fluctuating force acting at right angles to the wind direction. The wind speed, V_{Hc}, at the top of the structure when the frequency of vortex shedding equals the natural frequency, f_n, is given by:

$$V_{Hc} = \frac{1}{S}f_n D \qquad (16)$$

where
    V_{Hc} = critical mean wind speed at the top of the structure, in m/s, when resonance due to vortex shedding occurs,
    S = Strouhal Number, which is dependent on the shape of the cross-section,
    f_n = frequency, in Hz, and
    D = width or diameter, in m.

For circular and near-circular cylinders, the Strouhal Number is approximately 1/6 for small-diameter structures such as chimneys, and 1/5 for large-diameter structures such as observation towers or buildings. For non-circular cylindrical structures, the Strouhal Number is approximately 1/7.

Commentary I

71. The dynamic effects of vortex shedding of circular and near-circular cylindrical structures, including tapered structures, can be estimated in accordance with Reference [25]. Wind-tunnel tests are recommended for non-circular cylindrical structures.

Lateral Deflection of Tall Buildings

72. Lateral deflection of tall buildings under wind loading may require consideration from the standpoints of serviceability or comfort. The general trend is toward more flexible structures, partly because adequate strength can now be achieved by using higher strength materials that may not provide a corresponding increase in stiffness.

73. One symptom of unserviceability may be the cracking of masonry and interior finishes. Unless precautions are taken to permit movement of interior partitions without damage, a maximum lateral deflection limitation of 1/250 to 1/1 000 of the building height should be observed. According to NBC Sentence 4.1.3.5.(3), 1/500 should be used unless other drift limits are specified in the design standards referenced in NBC Section 4.3. or a detailed analysis is made.

Building Vibration

74. While the maximum lateral wind loading and deflection are generally in the direction parallel to the wind (i.e. the along-wind direction), the maximum acceleration of a building leading to possible human perception of motion or even discomfort may occur in the direction perpendicular to the wind (i.e. the across-wind direction). Across-wind accelerations are likely to exceed along-wind accelerations if the building is slender about both axes, that is if $\sqrt{wd}/H$ is less than one-third, where w and d are the across-wind effective width and along-wind effective depth, respectively, and H is the height of the building. The along-wind effective depth, d, is calculated using the formula given in NBC Sentence 4.1.7.2.(2) by replacing w_i by d_i.

75. The accelerations in a building are very dependent on the building's shape, orientation and buffeting from surrounding structures. However, data on the peak across-wind acceleration at the top of the building from a variety of turbulent boundary-layer wind-tunnel studies exhibit much scatter around the following empirical formula:

$$a_W = f_{nW}^2 g_P \sqrt{wd} \left(\frac{a_r}{\rho_B g \sqrt{\beta_W}} \right) \tag{17}$$

76. In less slender structures or for lower wind speeds, the maximum acceleration may be in the along-wind direction and may be estimated from the following expression:

$$a_D = 4\pi^2 f_{nD}^2 g_P \sqrt{\frac{KsF}{C_{eH}\beta_D} \frac{\Delta}{C_g}} \tag{18}$$

The variables in the formulae given in Paragraphs 75 and 76 have the following definitions:
w, d = across-wind effective width and along-wind effective depth respectively, in m,
a_W, a_D = peak acceleration in across-wind and along-wind directions, respectively, in m/s²,
$a_r = 78.5 \times 10^{-3} \left[V_H / \left(f_{nW} \sqrt{wd} \right) \right]^{3.3}$, in N/m³,
ρ_B = average density of the building, in kg/m³,
β_W, β_D = fraction of critical damping in across-wind and along-wind directions, respectively,
f_{nW}, f_{nD} = fundamental natural frequencies in across-wind and along-wind directions, respectively, in Hz,
Δ = maximum wind-induced lateral deflection at the top of the building in along-wind direction, in m, and
g = acceleration due to gravity = 9.81 m/s².
The variables g_p, K, s, F, C_{eH}, and C_g are as defined previously in connection with Equations (10) to (12).

77. Although many additional factors such as visual cues, body position and orientation, and state of mind influence human perception of motion, when the amplitude of acceleration is in the range of 0.5% to 1.5% of g, movement of the building becomes perceptible to most people.[28][29][30]

78. Historically, Equations (17) and (18) have been used with one-in-ten-year wind acceleration limits of 1% to 3% of g for the preliminary assessment of tall buildings. In North America in the period 1975 to 2000, many of the tall buildings that underwent detailed wind tunnel studies were designed for a peak one-in-ten-year acceleration in the range of 1.5% to 2.5% of g. The lower end of this range was generally applied to residential buildings and the upper end to office towers; their performance based on these criteria appears to have been generally satisfactory. Other criteria have been published that depend on the building's lowest natural frequency. The ISO criterion[31] can be expressed as a peak acceleration not exceeding $0.928\,f^{-0.412}$ once every 5 years, where f is the lowest natural frequency in Hz. This results in a 5-year criterion of about 1.8% of g when $f = 0.2$ Hz, and 2% of g when $f = 0.1$ Hz.

79. Owing to the relative sensitivity of Equations (17) and (18) to the natural frequency of vibration, and of Equation (18) to the corresponding building stiffness, these properties should be determined using fairly rigorous methods, and approximate formulas should be used with caution. For example, the adoption of a natural frequency of 10/N, where N is the number of storeys, may not be consistent with the assumption that the displacement under wind loading is as large as H/500.

Sample Calculation of a_W and a_D

80. A detailed calculation of a_W and a_D using Equations (17) and (18) will be carried out using the sample problem worked out in Paragraph 56 to illustrate the calculation of gust effect factor. Although one-in-ten-year wind data should be used to determine a_W and a_D, the values of C_g and other parameters computed earlier will be used in this example to avoid repeating the computation.

Given that $f_{nW} = f_{nD} = 0.2$ Hz and $q_{10} = 0.49$ kPa

$$\beta_W = \beta_D = 0.015$$
$$\rho_B = 176 \text{ kg/m}^3$$

Step 1: Calculate a_r.

$$a_r = 78.5 \times 10^{-3} \left[V_H / \left(f_{nW} \sqrt{wd} \right) \right]^{3.3}$$
$$= 78.5 \times 10^{-3} \left[37.8 / (0.2 \times 30.5) \right]^{3.3}$$
$$= 32.3 \text{ N/m}^3$$

Step 2: Calculate a_W using Equation (17).

$$a_W = 0.2^2 \times 3.75 \times 30.5 \left(\frac{32.3}{176 \times 9.81\sqrt{0.015}} \right)$$
$$= 0.70 \text{ m/s}^2$$

Therefore, $a_W/g = 7.1\%$.

Step 3: Calculate a_D/g. a_D is given in Equation (18) as a function of Δ whose value is usually determined from a structural analysis. In this example, Δ_{10}, the value of Δ for one-in-ten-year wind, is assumed equal to 0.35 m.

$$a_D = 4\pi^2 \times 0.2^2 \times 3.75 \sqrt{\frac{0.1 \times 0.11 \times 0.28}{1.9 \times 0.015} \frac{0.35}{2.41}}$$
$$= 0.283$$

$$a_D/g = 0.283/9.81 = 2.9\%$$

Commentary I

81. In this example, the across-wind accelerations clearly overshadow the along-wind accelerations. A tall building erected in a waterfront location may be exposed to all three terrain conditions for different wind directions.

Tornadoes

82. Although the probability of any one particular building being hit by a tornado is very small (less than 10^{-5} per year[32]), tornadoes account for the greatest incidence of death and serious injury of building occupants due to structural failure and cause considerable economic loss. With some exceptions, such as nuclear power plants, it is generally not economical to design buildings for tornadoes beyond what is currently required by NBC Subsection 4.1.7. because of the low risk of loss to individual owners (insurance is cheaper). It is, however, important to provide key construction details for the safety of building occupants. Investigations of tornado-damaged areas in Eastern Canada[33][34] have shown that the buildings in which well over 90% of the occupants were killed or seriously injured by tornadoes did not satisfy the following two key details of building construction:
    (a) the anchorage of house floors into the foundation or ground (the floor takes off with the occupants on it), and
    (b) the anchorage of roofs down through concrete block walls (the roof takes off and the unsupported block wall collapses onto the occupants).

83. The first detail—the anchorage of house floors—is essentially covered by NBC Article 9.23.6.1. for typical housing with permanent foundations. CSA Z240.10.1[50] contains anchorage recommendations for protecting mobile homes against the effects of tornadoes. The second detail—roof anchorage in block walls—is essentially covered in CSA S304.1[51] through limit states requirements for wind uplift and, for the empirical method of masonry design, by Clause F.1.4 of the standard. Deficiency of this construction detail is especially serious for open assembly occupancies because there is nothing inside, such as stored goods, to protect the occupants from wall collapse. For such buildings in tornado-prone areas, it is recommended that the block walls contain vertical reinforcing linking the roof to the foundation.

84. For tornado protection, key details such as those indicated above should be designed on the basis of a factored uplift wind suction of 2 kPa on the roof, a factored lateral wind pressure of 1 kPa on the windward wall, and suction of 2 kPa on the leeward wall.

85. Guidance for determining if a given locality is prone to tornadoes may be obtained from Information Services Section, Environment Canada, 4905 Dufferin Street, Toronto, Ontario M3H 5T4; e-mail: climate.services@ec.gc.ca.

Figures

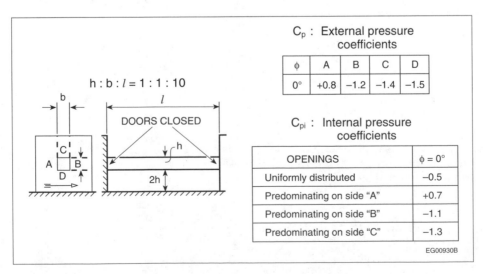

Figure I-22
Closed passage between large walls

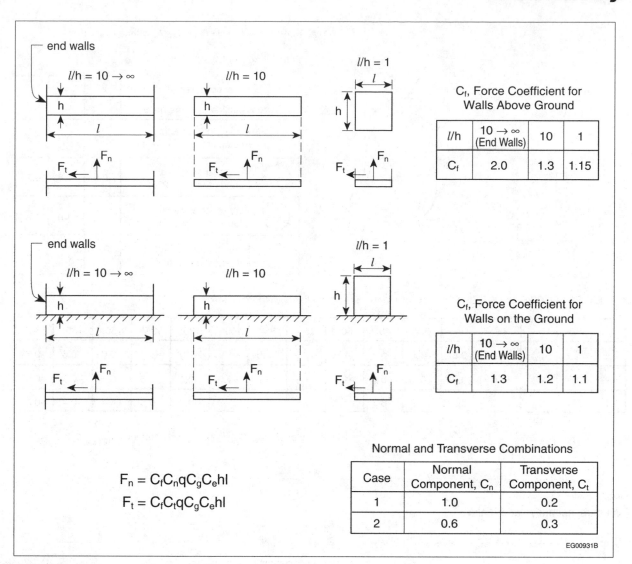

$$F_n = C_f C_n q C_g C_e hl$$
$$F_t = C_f C_t q C_g C_e hl$$

C_f, Force Coefficient for Walls Above Ground

l/h	10 → ∞ (End Walls)	10	1
C_f	2.0	1.3	1.15

C_f, Force Coefficient for Walls on the Ground

l/h	10 → ∞ (End Walls)	10	1
C_f	1.3	1.2	1.1

Normal and Transverse Combinations

Case	Normal Component, C_n	Transverse Component, C_t
1	1.0	0.2
2	0.6	0.3

EG00931B

Figure I-23
Free-standing plates, walls and billboards

Commentary I

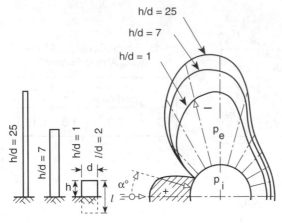

TOTAL FORCE $F = C_f \cdot q \cdot C_g \cdot C_e \cdot A$, where $A = d \cdot h$

C_f : FORCE COEFFICIENT FOR $\quad d\sqrt{qC_e} > 0.167$

Slenderness h/d = ⟶	25	7	1
Cross section and roughness	C_f	C_f	C_f
⭕ Moderately smooth, (metal, timber, concrete)	0.7	0.6	0.5
⚙ Rough surface (rounded ribs h = 2%d)	0.9	0.8	0.7
⚙ Very rough surface (sharp ribs h = 8%d)	1.2	1.0	0.8
⬡ Smooth and rough surface sharp edges	1.4	1.2	1.0

C_p : EXTERNAL PRESS. COEFF. FOR $\quad d\sqrt{qC_e} > 0.167$ and moderately smooth surface

h/d	l/d	α=	0°	15°	30°	45°	60°	75°	90°	105°	120°	135°	150°	165°	180°
25	50	C_p	+1.0	+0.8	+0.1	−0.9	−1.9	−2.5	−2.6	−1.9	−0.9	−0.7	−0.6	−0.6	−0.6
7	14	C_p	+1.0	+0.8	+0.1	−0.8	−1.7	−1.6	−2.2	−1.7	−0.8	−0.6	−0.5	−0.5	−0.5
1	2	C_p	+1.0	+0.8	+0.1	−0.7	−1.2	−1.6	−1.7	−1.2	−0.7	−0.5	−0.4	−0.4	−0.4

$\Delta p = p_i - p_e$

$p_i = C_{pi} \cdot q \cdot C_g \cdot C_e$

$p_e = C_p \cdot q \cdot C_g \cdot C_e$

Stack fully operating $C_{pi} = +0.1$; Stack throttled $C_{pi} = -0.8$

EG00932B

Figure I-24
Cylinders, chimneys and tanks

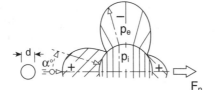

TOTAL FORCE $F = C_f \cdot q \cdot C_g \cdot C_e \cdot A; \quad A = \dfrac{\pi d^2}{4}$

for $\quad d\sqrt{qC_e} > 0.8$ and moderately smooth surface

C_f : FORCE COEFFICIENT

$C_f = 0.2$

$p = p_i - p_e \qquad p_i$ for closed tanks = working pressure

$\qquad\qquad\qquad p_e = C_p \cdot q \cdot C_g \cdot C_e$

C_p : EXTERNAL PRESS. COEFF. FOR $\quad d\sqrt{qC_e} > 0.8$ and moderately smooth surface

α=	0°	15°	30°	45°	60°	75°	90°	105°	120°	135°	150°	165°	180°
C_p	+1.0	+0.9	+0.5	−0.1	−0.7	−1.1	−1.2	−1.0	−0.6	−0.2	+0.1	+0.3	+0.4

EG00933B

Figure I-25
Spheres

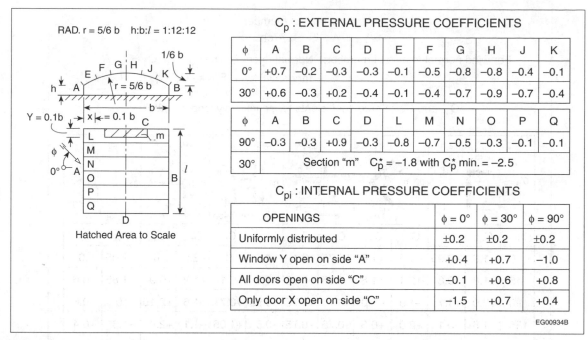

RAD. r = 5/6 b   h:b:*l* = 1:12:12

Hatched Area to Scale

Cp : EXTERNAL PRESSURE COEFFICIENTS

φ	A	B	C	D	E	F	G	H	J	K
0°	+0.7	−0.2	−0.3	−0.3	−0.1	−0.5	−0.8	−0.8	−0.4	−0.1
30°	+0.6	−0.3	+0.2	−0.4	−0.1	−0.4	−0.7	−0.9	−0.7	−0.4

φ	A	B	C	D	L	M	N	O	P	Q
90°	−0.3	−0.3	+0.9	−0.3	−0.8	−0.7	−0.5	−0.3	−0.1	−0.1
30°	Section "m" $C_p^* = -1.8$ with C_p^* min. $= -2.5$									

C_{pi} : INTERNAL PRESSURE COEFFICIENTS

OPENINGS	φ = 0°	φ = 30°	φ = 90°
Uniformly distributed	±0.2	±0.2	±0.2
Window Y open on side "A"	+0.4	+0.7	−1.0
All doors open on side "C"	−0.1	+0.6	+0.8
Only door X open on side "C"	−1.5	+0.7	+0.4

EG00934B

Figure I-26
Hangar, curved roof with moderately smooth surface

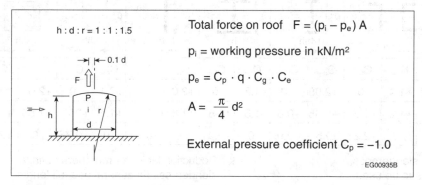

h : d : r = 1 : 1 : 1.5

Total force on roof $F = (p_i - p_e) A$

p_i = working pressure in kN/m²

$p_e = C_p \cdot q \cdot C_g \cdot C_e$

$A = \dfrac{\pi}{4} d^2$

External pressure coefficient $C_p = -1.0$

EG00935B

Figure I-27
Roof load on smooth closed tank

C_f = FORCE COEFFICIENTS

l/d > 100

Total force $F = C_f \cdot q \cdot C_g \cdot C_e \cdot A$

$A = d \cdot l$

		$d \sqrt{q\, C_e}$	
		< 0.167	> 0.167
Smooth wires, rods, pipes	○	1.2	0.5
Mod. smooth wires and rods	○	1.2	0.7
Fine wire cables	◉	1.2	0.9
Thick wire cables	◉	1.3	1.1

EG00936B

Figure I-28
Poles, rods and wires

l = Length of member

$A = h \cdot l$ = Area

For wind normal to axis of member: Normal force $F_n = k \cdot C_{n\infty} \cdot q \cdot C_g \cdot C_e \cdot A$

Tangential force $F_t = k \cdot C_{t\infty} \cdot q \cdot C_g \cdot C_e \cdot A$

$C_{n\infty}$ and $C_{t\infty}$: Force coefficients for an infinitely long member

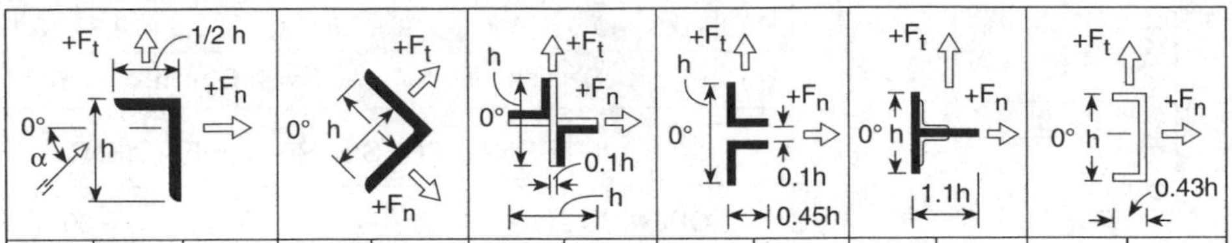

α	$C_{n\infty}$	$C_{t\infty}$	$C_{n\infty}$	$C_{t\infty}$	$C_{n\infty}$	$C_{t\infty}$	$C_{n\infty}$	$C_{t\infty}$	$C_{n\infty}$	$C_{t\infty}$	$C_{n\infty}$	$C_{t\infty}$
0°	+1.9	+0.95	+1.8	+1.8	+1.75	+0.1	+1.6	0	+2.0	0	+2.05	0
45°	+1.8	+0.8	+2.1	+1.8	+0.85	+0.85	+1.5	−0.1	+1.2	+0.9	+1.85	+0.6
90°	+2.0	+1.7	−1.9	−1.0	−0.1	+1.75	−0.95	+0.7	−1.6	+2.15	0	+0.6
135°	−1.8	−0.1	−2.0	+0.3	−0.75	+0.75	−0.5	+1.05	−1.1	+2.4	−1.6	+0.4
180°	−2.0	+0.1	−1.4	−1.4	−1.75	−0.1	−1.5	0	−1.7	±2.1	−1.8	0

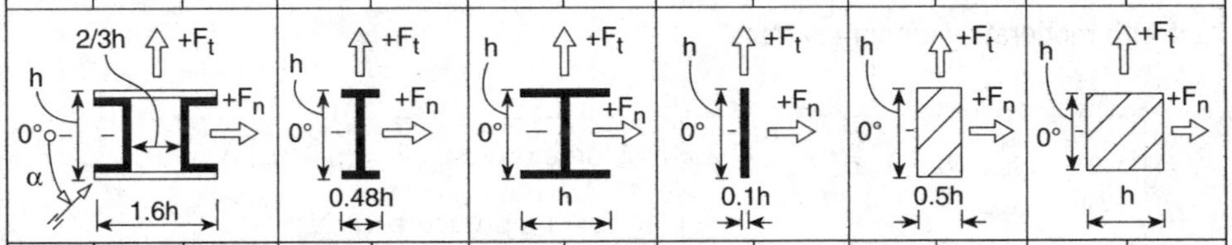

α	$C_{n\infty}$	$C_{t\infty}$	$C_{n\infty}$	$C_{t\infty}$	$C_{n\infty}$	$C_{t\infty}$	$C_{n\infty}$	$C_{t\infty}$	$C_{n\infty}$	$C_{t\infty}$	$C_{n\infty}$	$C_{t\infty}$
0°	+1.4	0	+2.05	0	+1.6	0	+2.0	0	+2.1	0	+2.0	0
45°	+1.2	+1.6	+1.95	+0.6	+1.5	+1.5	+1.8	+0.1	+1.4	+0.7	+1.55	+1.55
90°	0	+2.2	±0.5	+0.9	0	+1.9	0	+0.1	0	+0.75	0	+2.0

For slenderness, h_α is to be used:

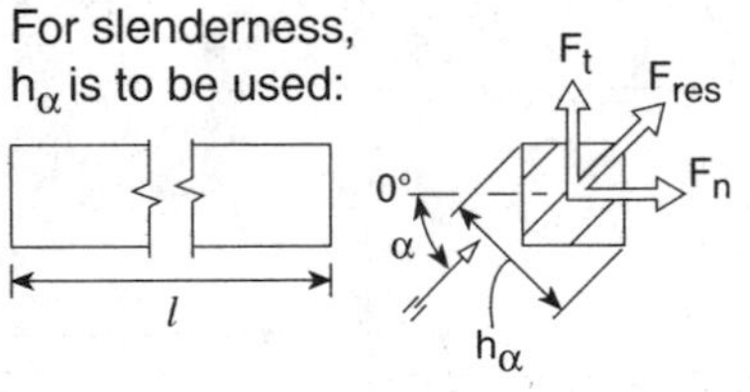

k : Reduction factor for members of finite slenderness (in general use full length not panel length)

l/h_α	5	10	20	35	50	100	∞
k	0.60	0.65	0.75	0.85	0.90	0.95	1.0

EG00937B

Figure I-29
Structural members, single and assembled sections

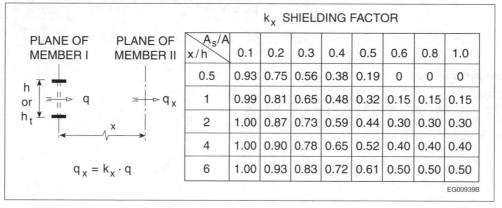

A_s = Section area

$A = h_t \cdot L$

A_s / A = Solidity ratio

For wind normal to surface A :   Normal force $F_n = k \cdot C_{n\infty} \cdot q \cdot C_g \cdot C_e \cdot A_s$

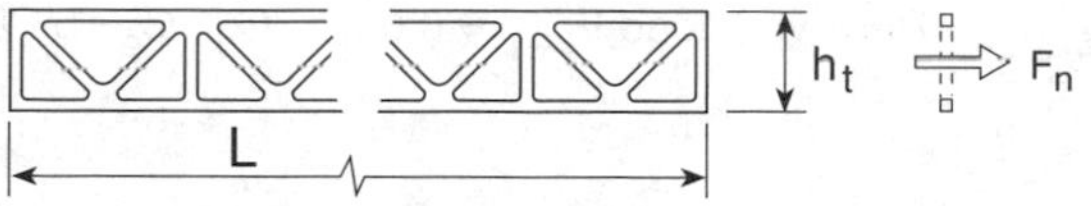

$C_{n\infty}$: Force coeff. for an infinitely long truss, $0 \le A_s/A \le 1$

A_s/A	0	0.1	0.15	0.2	0.3 to 0.8	0.95	1.0
$C_{n\infty}$	2.0	1.9	1.8	1.7	1.6	1.8	2.0

k : Reduction factor for trusses of finite length and slenderness

L/h_t \ A_s/A	0.25	0.5	0.9	0.95	1.0
5	0.96	0.91	0.87	0.77	0.60
20	0.98	0.97	0.94	0.89	0.75
50	0.99	0.98	0.97	0.95	0.90
∞	1.0	1.0	1.0	1.0	1.0

EG00938B

Figure I-30
Plane trusses made from sharp-edged sections

k_x SHIELDING FACTOR

x/h \ A_s/A	0.1	0.2	0.3	0.4	0.5	0.6	0.8	1.0
0.5	0.93	0.75	0.56	0.38	0.19	0	0	0
1	0.99	0.81	0.65	0.48	0.32	0.15	0.15	0.15
2	1.00	0.87	0.73	0.59	0.44	0.30	0.30	0.30
4	1.00	0.90	0.78	0.65	0.52	0.40	0.40	0.40
6	1.00	0.93	0.83	0.72	0.61	0.50	0.50	0.50

PLANE OF MEMBER I   PLANE OF MEMBER II

$q_x = k_x \cdot q$

EG00939B

Figure I-31
Shielding factors

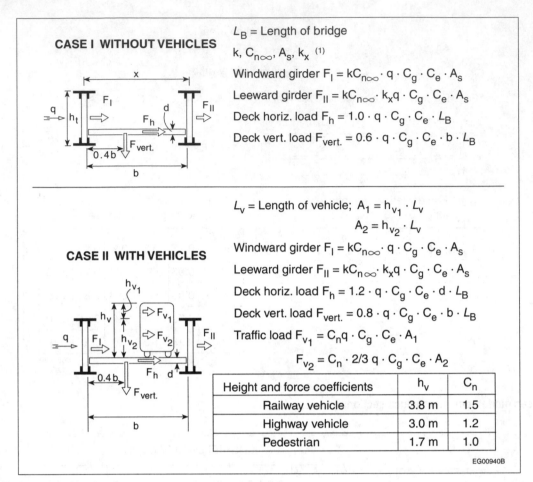

CASE I WITHOUT VEHICLES

L_B = Length of bridge

$k, C_{n\infty}, A_s, k_x$ [1]

Windward girder $F_I = kC_{n\infty} \cdot q \cdot C_g \cdot C_e \cdot A_s$

Leeward girder $F_{II} = kC_{n\infty} \cdot k_x q \cdot C_g \cdot C_e \cdot A_s$

Deck horiz. load $F_h = 1.0 \cdot q \cdot C_g \cdot C_e \cdot L_B$

Deck vert. load $F_{vert.} = 0.6 \cdot q \cdot C_g \cdot C_e \cdot b \cdot L_B$

CASE II WITH VEHICLES

L_v = Length of vehicle; $A_1 = h_{v_1} \cdot L_v$

$A_2 = h_{v_2} \cdot L_v$

Windward girder $F_I = kC_{n\infty} \cdot q \cdot C_g \cdot C_e \cdot A_s$

Leeward girder $F_{II} = kC_{n\infty} \cdot k_x q \cdot C_g \cdot C_e \cdot A_s$

Deck horiz. load $F_h = 1.2 \cdot q \cdot C_g \cdot C_e \cdot d \cdot L_B$

Deck vert. load $F_{vert.} = 0.8 \cdot q \cdot C_g \cdot C_e \cdot b \cdot L_B$

Traffic load $F_{v_1} = C_n q \cdot C_g \cdot C_e \cdot A_1$

$F_{v_2} = C_n \cdot 2/3 \, q \cdot C_g \cdot C_e \cdot A_2$

Height and force coefficients	h_v	C_n
Railway vehicle	3.8 m	1.5
Highway vehicle	3.0 m	1.2
Pedestrian	1.7 m	1.0

EG00940B

Figure I-32
Truss and plate girder bridges

Note to Figure I-32:
(1) The values for these coefficients are taken from Figures I-29 and I-30.

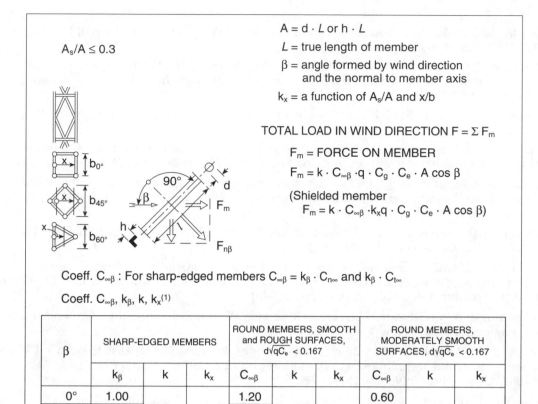

Figure I-33

Three-dimensional trusses

Notes to Figure I-33:
(1) See Figure I-29 for $C_{n\infty}$ and $C_{t\infty}$ values.
(2) See Figure I-29.
(3) See Figure I-31.

References

[1] Canadian Commission on Building and Fire Codes, National Building Code of Canada 2005. National Research Council of Canada, Ottawa, NRCC 47666.

[2] A.G. Davenport, Gust Loading Factors. Journal of Structural Division, Proc., Am. Soc. Civ. Eng., Vol. 93, June 1967, pp. 12-34.

[3] E. Simiu and R.H. Scanlan, Wind Effects on Structures: An Introduction to Wind Engineering. John Wiley & Sons, New York, 1986.

[4] ASCE Manuals and Reports on Engineering Practice No. 67, Wind Tunnel Studies of Buildings and Structures, American Society of Civil Engineers, 1999.

[5] J.E. Cermak, Application of Fluid Mechanics to Wind Engineering. Freeman Scholar Lecture, Journal of Fluid Engineering, ASME, Vol. 97, No. 1, March 1975.

[6] D. Surry and N. Isyumov, Model Studies of Wind Effects A Perspective on the Problems of Experimental Technique and Instrumentation. Int. Congress on instrumentation in Aerospace Simulation Facilities, 1975 Record, pp. 79-90.

[7] D.R. Lemelin, D. Surry and A.G. Davenport, Simple Approximations for Wind Speed-Up Over Hills. 7th International Conference on Wind Engineering, Aachen, West Germany, July 6-10, 1987.

Commentary I

[8]   P.S. Jackson and J.C.R. Hunt, Turbulent Wind Flow Over a Low Hill. Quart. Journal R. Met. Soc., Vol. 101, 1975, pp. 929-955.

[9]   J.L. Walmsley, P.A. Taylor and T. Keith, A Simple Model of Neutrally Stratified Boundary-Layer Flow Over Complex Terrain With Surface Roughness Modulations. Boundary-Layer Meteorology, Vol. 36, 1986, pp. 157-186.

[10]   M. Jensen and N. Franck, Model Scale Tests in Turbulent Wind, Part II. Danish Technical Press, Copenhagen, 1965.

[11]   D. Surry, R.B. Kitchen and A.G. Davenport, Design Effectiveness of Wind Tunnel Studies for Buildings of Intermediate Height. Can. J. Civ. Eng., Vol. 4, No. 1, 1977, pp. 96-116.

[12]   T. Stathopoulos, D. Surry, and A.G. Davenport, Internal Pressure Characteristics of Low-Rise Buildings Due to Wind Action. Proc. Fifth International Conference on Wind Engineering, Colorado State University, July 1979, Pergamon Press.

[13]   D. Surry, T. Stathopoulos and A.G. Davenport, The Wind Loading of Low Rise Buildings. Proc. Can. Struct. Eng. Conference, Toronto, 1978.

[14]   Y. Lee, H. Tanaka and C.Y. Shaw, Distribution of Wind and Temperature Induced Pressure Differences Across the Walls of a Twenty Story Compartmentalized Building. Journal of Wind Eng. and Indust. Aerodynamics, Vol. 10, 1982, pp. 287-301.

[15]   Wind Loading and Wind-Induced Structural Response, Wind Effects Committee, American Society of Civil Engineers. ASCE, New York, 1987.

[16]   N. Isyumov, The Aeroelastic Modelling of Tall Buildings. International Workshop on Wind Tunnel Modeling Criteria and Techniques in Civil Engineering Applications, Gaithersburg, Maryland, April 1982. Cambridge University Press, 1982.

[17]   P. Sachs, Wind Forces in Engineering. Second Edition, Pergamon Press, Toronto, 1978.

[18]   L. Christensen and S. Frandsen, A Field Study of Cross Wind Excitation of Steel Chimneys: Safety of Structures under Dynamic Loading. Norwegian Institute of Technology, Trondheim, June 1977, pp. 689-697.

[19]   A.G. Davenport, Note on the Distribution of the Largest Value of a Random Function with Application to Gust Loading. Proc., Inst. Civ. Eng., London, Vol. 28, June 1964, pp. 187-196.

[20]   R.J. Kind and R.L. Wardlaw, Model Studies of the Wind Resistance of Two Loose-Laid Roof-Insulation Systems. Laboratory Technical Report, LTR-LA-234, National Aeronautical Establishment, National Research Council of Canada, Ottawa, May 1979.

[21]   R.J. Kind and R.L. Wardlaw, Design of Rooftops Against Gravel Blow-Off. National Aeronautical Establishment, National Research Council of Canada, Ottawa, September 1976. NRCC 15544.

[22]   Normen fur die Belastungsannehmen, die Inbetriebnahme und die Uberwachung der Bauten (Standards for Load Assumptions, Acceptance and Inspection of Structures). Schweizerischer Ingenieur und Architekten Verein (Swiss Society of Engineers and Architects), SIA Standard 160: Actions on Structures, Zurich, 1989.

[23]   P.N. Georgiou and B.J. Vickery, Wind Loads on Building Frames. Proc. Fifth International Conference on Wind Engineering, Colorado State University, July 1979, Pergamon Press.

[24]   D.E. Walshe, Measurements of Wind Force on a Model of a Power Station Boiler House at Various Stages of Erection. NPL Aero Report 1165, National Physical Laboratory, Teddington, England, September 1965.

[25]   B.J. Vickery and R.I. Basu, Simplified Approaches to the Evaluation of the Across-Wind Response of Chimneys. Journal of Wind Eng. and Indust. Aerodynamics, Vol. 14, December 1983, pp. 153-166.

[26]   CSA S37-01, Antennas, Towers, and Antenna-Supporting Structures. Canadian Standards Association, Mississauga, Ontario, 2001.

[27]   International Organization for Standardization, ISO 12494: Atmospheric Icing of Structures, Geneva, 2001.

[28]   P.W. Chen and L.E. Robertson, Human Perception Thresholds of Horizontal Motion. Journal of Structural Division, Proc., Am. Soc. Civ. Eng., Vol. 98, August 1972, pp. 1681-1695.

[29]   F.K. Chang, Human Response to Motions in Tall Buildings. Journal of Structural Division, Proc., Am. Soc. Civ. Eng., Vol. 99, June 1973, pp. 1259-1272.

[30]   R.J. Hansen, J.W. Reed and E.H. Van Marcke, Human Response to Wind-Induced Motion of Buildings. Journal of Structural Division, Proc., Am. Soc. Civ. Eng., Vol. 99, July 1973, pp. 1587-1605.

[31]   International Organization for Standardization, ISO 10137: Bases for design of structures -- Serviceability of buildings against vibration, Geneva, 1992.

[32]   M.J. Newark, A Design Basis Tornado. Can. J. Civ. Eng., Vol. 18, 1991, pp. 521-524.

[33]   D.E. Allen, Tornado Damage at Blue Sea Lake and Nicabong. Building Research Note 222, Institute for Research in Construction, National Research Council of Canada, Ottawa, 1984.

[34]   D.E. Allen, Tornado Damage in the Barrie/Orangeville Area, Ontario, May 1985. Building Research Note 240, Institute for Research in Construction, National Research Council of Canada, Ottawa, 1986.

[35]   T. Stathopoulos and X. Zhu, Wind Pressures on Buildings with Appurtenances. Journal of Wind Eng. and Indust. Aerodynamics. Vol. 31, 1988, pp. 265-281.

[36]   T. Stathopoulos and X. Zhu, Wind Pressures on Buildings with Mullions. Journal of Structural Eng., ASCE, Vol. 116, No. 8, 1990, pp. 2272-2291.

[37]   T. Stathopoulos, Wind Loads on Eaves of Low Buildings. Journal of Structural Division, ASCE, Vol. 107, No. ST10, October 1981, pp. 1921-1934.

[38]   T. Stathopoulos and H.D. Luchian, Wind-Induced Forces on Eaves of Low Buildings. Journal of Wind Eng. and Indust. Aerodynamics, Vol. 52, 1994, pp. 249-261.

[39]   D. Surry and E.M.F. Stopar, Wind Loading of Large Low Buildings. Can. J. Civ. Eng., Vol. 16, 1989, pp. 526-542.

[40]   T. Stathopoulos and A. Baskaran, Wind Pressures on Flat Roofs with Parapets. Journal of Structural Division, ASCE, Vol. 113, No. 11, Nov. 1987, pp. 2166-2180.

[41]   T. Stathopoulos, Wind Pressures on Flat Roof Edges and Corners. Proc. of Seventh International Conference on Wind Engineering, Aachen, West Germany, July 6-10, 1987.

[42]   T. Stathopoulos and H.D. Luchian, Wind Pressures on Building Configurations with Stepped Roofs. Can. J. Civ. Eng., Vol. 17, No. 4, 1990, pp. 569-577.

[43]   T. Stathopoulos and H.D. Luchian, Wind Loads on Flat Roofs with Discontinuities. CSCE Annual Conf., Vancouver, May 1991.

[44]   D. Surry and T. Stathopoulos, The Wind Loading of Low Buildings with Mono-sloped Roofs. Final Report BLWT-SS38, University of Western Ontario, London, Ont., 1988.

[45]   D. Meecham, D. Surry and A.G. Davenport, The Magnitude and Distribution of Wind-Induced Pressures on Hip and Gable Roofs, 8th Coll. on Ind. Aerodynamics, Aachen, Germany, September 1989.

[46]   J.D. Holmes, Wind Loading on Multi-span Building. 1st National Structural Eng. Conf., Melbourne, Australia, August 1987.

[47]   T. Stathopoulos and P. Saathoff, Wind Pressures on Roofs of Various Geometries. Journal of Wind Eng. and Indust. Aerodynamics, Vol. 38, 1991, pp. 273-284.

[48]   T. Stathopoulos and A.R. Mohammadian, Wind Loads on Low Buildings with Monosloped Roofs. Journal of Wind Eng. and Indust. Aerodynamics, Vol. 23, 1986, pp. 81-97.

[49]   P. Saathoff and T. Stathopoulos, Wind Loads on Buildings with Sawtooth Roofs. Journal of Structural Eng., ASCE, Vol. 118, No. 2, 1992, pp. 429-446, Paper No. 675.

[50]   CSA Z240.10.1-94, Site Preparation, Foundation, and Anchorage of Mobile Homes. Canadian Standards Association, Mississauga, Ontario, 1994.

[51]   CSA S304.1-04, Design of Masonry Structures. Canadian Standards Association, Mississauga, Ontario, 2004.

Commentary J

Design for Seismic Effects

Commentary J

Design for Seismic Effects

Scope

1. The requirements of NBC Subsection 4.1.8. apply only to the seismic design of new buildings and should not be used for special structures such as bridges, towers, dams and storage tanks (for recommendations on free-standing storage tanks, see the Commentary section on NBC Article 4.1.8.17.). However, the effects of tanks within buildings are addressed in NBC Article 4.1.8.17. Subsection 4.1.8. is not specifically intended for the evaluation and upgrading of existing buildings but the concepts and methods of analysis and design presented therein are often applicable to that purpose as well, as discussed in Commentary L.

2. Even though design forces for wind may be greater than seismic design forces in some situations (i.e. wind "governs" the design), seismic detailing may be required. Even if wind forces do govern, the design must accommodate at least the type of lateral-load-resisting system and the detailing that correspond to the seismic forces calculated for the building.

Seismic Design Objectives and Expected Performance

3. Earthquakes may cause damage to buildings through any of the following: ground shaking, soil failures (liquefaction or landslides) caused by shaking, effects of surface fault ruptures on structures, or tsunamis. The only one of these hazards that is directly addressed by the NBC is ground shaking, although the potential for liquefaction and its consequences are taken into account in the design of foundations; the other hazards are addressed primarily through planning and site selection. Seismic design has the following intents, which are consistent with the overall objectives of the NBC:
   (1) to protect the life and safety of building occupants and the general public as the building responds to strong ground shaking,
   (2) to limit building damage during low to moderate levels of ground shaking, and
   (3) to ensure that post-disaster buildings can continue to be occupied and functional following strong ground shaking, though minimal damage can be expected in such buildings.

4. According to the NBC, strong ground shaking is considered to be a rare occurrence in Canada; indeed, NBC Article 4.1.2.1., Loads and Effects, defines earthquake loads as rare loads. As discussed in detail in the Commentary section titled Seismic Hazard, strong ground shaking is defined as having a probability of exceedance of 2% in 50 years at a median confidence level; this corresponds to a 0.04% annual probability of exceedance. Although stronger shaking than this could occur, in most situations it is typically economically impractical to design for such rare ground motions; hence the 2% in 50 year level may be termed the maximum earthquake ground motion to be considered, or more simply the design ground motion (DGM).

5. It is generally considered both unnecessary and uneconomical to design and construct buildings that will not be damaged during the DGM. The primary objective of seismic design is to provide an acceptable level of safety for building occupants and the general public as the building responds to strong ground motion; in other words, to minimize loss of life. This implies that, although there will likely be extensive structural and non-structural damage during the DGM, there is a reasonable degree of confidence that the building will not collapse nor will its attachments break off and fall on people near the building. This performance level is termed "extensive damage" because, although the structure may be very heavily damaged and may have lost a substantial amount of its initial strength and stiffness, it retains some margin of resistance against collapse.

6. A high degree of life safety protection that is consistent with the low probability of the "extensive damage" performance level is achieved through inelastic energy dissipation, which is the explicit seismic design approach used in the NBC seismic provisions. Inelastic energy dissipation leads to a

Commentary J

reduction of design forces. Seismic Force Resisting Systems (SFRS) that do not have a significant inelastic energy dissipation capacity, i.e. those with limited ductility, are subject to higher loads and have less stringent detailing requirements; in certain cases, systems with limited ductility may not be permitted in regions where the DGM is high. The capacity of various kinds of SFRS to resist the anticipated seismic loads is achieved by applying the design and detailing provisions contained in the NBC and in the referenced material standards. There is an enhanced confidence that the integrity of the overall structure will be maintained following strong ground shaking when limits on interstorey drift are imposed that are consistent with the "extensive damage" performance objective.

7. While the foregoing text describes the primary objective of seismic design, designers often wish to have more information on the performance expectations associated with that objective, particularly at levels of ground shaking that approach or exceed the DGM. Heidebrecht[1] discusses such objectives and describes a number of building design features that contribute significantly towards meeting the intended performance objectives. In addition to energy dissipation characteristics, the important features include: regularity of building configuration, susceptibility to sway effects because of earthquake-dominated design, overstrength, and reserve ductility capacity in structural elements and joints. Experience during recent earthquakes has shown that ductile structures with regular configurations in which the energy dissipation is distributed throughout the structure can sustain their integrity at ground motions considerably above the DGM level (Hall[2] and Park et al.[3]). On the other hand, irregular structures with limited ductility often perform poorly at the DGM level because the energy dissipation and damage is concentrated in one part of the structure (e.g. soft-storey structures). Heidebrecht[1] also discusses the important role of capacity design in improving performance expectations at unexpectedly high levels of earthquake ground motion.

8. Design that complies with the NBC provisions is also expected to limit damage at ground shaking levels that are well below the DGM level. When peak ground shaking is below one-half of the DGM level, well designed and detailed structures can be expected to sustain limited structural damage (Heidebrecht[1]). Because the primary design objective is based on inelastic energy dissipation, it is implicit that some structural damage can be expected when peak ground motions approach the DGM level. Damage can be reduced by selecting a structural system that has sufficient stiffness to ensure that drifts are below the specified drift limits, which are actually intended to prevent collapse rather than control damage. Damage to non-structural elements can be minimized by limiting their deflections, paying careful attention to detailing, providing adequate clearances from the structure, and protecting elements tied rigidly to the structure from deformations, which could cause cracking.

9. The performance objectives for post-disaster buildings differ from those stated above because such buildings must remain operational during and following an earthquake. Therefore, the performance objective for post-disaster buildings when subject to DGM-level shaking can best be described as "immediate occupancy:" there should be very little damage to the structural system so as not to impede the continued use and occupancy of the building and minor damage to non-structural systems; the structure is expected to retain most of its pre-earthquake strength and stiffness; mechanical, electrical, plumbing and other systems necessary for normal operation are expected to remain functional. This more stringent performance objective is achieved in two ways:
    (1) through the application of an importance factor (1.5 for post-disaster buildings and 1.3 for other buildings whose primary use is not post-disaster (e.g. schools and community centres) but that are likely to be used as post-disaster shelters) used to increase the design lateral load, and
    (2) through the establishment of a much lower interstorey drift limit.
Of course, other factors such as building configuration, type of structural framing, materials and as-built construction details have a significant effect on the ability of the building to achieve this performance objective. The NBC incorporates some of these considerations by prohibiting most structural irregularities in locations having moderate to high levels of DGM and by requiring that the SFRS have a minimum ductility capacity.

10. When considering performance objectives, it is important to recognize that the wide range of possible building characteristics, site conditions and earthquake characteristics will contribute to a very wide range of actual performance during any future earthquake. Although the NBC seismic provisions are intended to provide an acceptable level of protection, experience and observations during past earthquakes elsewhere in the world have shown that a wide variation in the extent of damage can be expected during any future earthquake event. Irregular structures and those with poor detailing can be expected to perform poorly while regular, well designed and detailed structures can be expected to perform well. Although the minimum requirements in these provisions are intended to provide an adequate level of protection, good performance can only be ensured if the

designer follows coherent design and detailing approaches that are consistent with the intent of the NBC seismic provisions and if the building is constructed according to that design.

Rationale for Updating the NBC 1995 Provisions

11. One of the major reasons for revising the NBC seismic provisions is to incorporate the ongoing improvement in knowledge on seismic hazard and its geographical distribution throughout the country. Table J-1 (Heidebrecht[1]) presents a brief summary on how seismic hazard information has been used in the determination of seismic design forces in the NBC from 1953 to the present. As Table J-1 indicates, this knowledge evolved from a general qualitative sense of seismicity based on historical earthquake activity to the expression of hazard using two ground motion parameters, peak ground velocity and acceleration, which are determined probabilistically. In addition to changes in the way in which seismic hazard is described, earthquake activity in Canada during the recent historical period has been used to produce more reliable estimates of seismic hazard.

Table J-1
History of How Seismic Hazard Information is Used for the Determination of Seismic Design Forces in the NBC

NBC Edition	Nature of Hazard Information	Manner in which Hazard Information is Used to Determine Seismic Design Forces
1953 through 1965	Four zones (0, 1, 2, 3) based on the qualitative assessment of historical earthquake activity	Base shear coefficients are prescribed for the design of buildings in zone 1; these are doubled for zone 2 and multiplied by 4 for zone 3
1970	Four zones (0, 1, 2, 3) with boundaries based on peak acceleration at 0.01 annual probability of exceedance	Base shear coefficient includes a non-dimensional multiplier (0 for zone 0, 1 for zone 1, 2 for zone 2, and 4 for zone 3)
1975 through 1980		Base shear coefficient includes factor A, which is numerically equal to the zonal peak acceleration (0 for zone 0, 0.02 for zone 1, 0.04 for zone 2 and 0.08 for zone 3); value of seismic response factor is adjusted so that base shear is approximately 20% below that in the NBC 1970
1985	Seven (0 to 6) acceleration- and velocity-related zones with boundaries based on 10% probability of exceedance in 50 years	Base shear coefficient includes zonal velocity, v, which is numerically equal to peak ground velocity in m/s (values are 0, 0.05, 0.10, 0.15, 0.20, 0.30 and 0.40); value of seismic response factor is adjusted by calibration process so that seismic forces are equivalent, on average across the country, to those in the NBC 1980 (see Heidebrecht et al.[9])
1990 and 1995		Elastic force coefficient includes zonal velocity, v, (as above) with total seismic force V calculated as elastic force divided by force reduction factor and then multiplied by a calibration factor of 0.6; the seismic response factor is modified to maintain the same design force for highly ductile systems as in the NBC 1985
2005	Site-specific spectral acceleration ordinates determined at 2% probability of exceedance in 50 years	Dynamic analysis or static elastic force coefficient, both using spectral acceleration ordinates as input; site coefficients and higher mode factor also dependent upon spectral acceleration ordinates

12. There are several other major reasons for updating the seismic provisions over and above those directly related to seismic hazard. First, studying and learning from the damage caused by major earthquakes around the world allows engineers to determine whether or not current NBC provisions can provide an adequate level of protection in buildings and other facilities being constructed in Canada. Each major earthquake provides one or more significant lessons that lead to further

Code improvements. For example, the 1989 Loma Prieta earthquake demonstrated the dramatic amplification of ground motions on soft soil sites; subsequent analysis of ground motions measured during that earthquake was used to improve Code provisions so that those effects will be taken into account in the design of structures located on soft soil sites (Borcherdt[4]).

13. Another reason for the periodic updating of seismic provisions arises directly from the results of broadly based earthquake engineering research being conducted in Canada and around the world. Such research, as reported in the literature and presented at conferences, often demonstrates the need to improve the Code's representation of seismic effects on structures. Many of the changes to the NBC seismic provisions during the past half-century have been made based directly on the results of earthquake engineering research carried out in Canada and elsewhere in the world.

14. Another reason for changing the NBC seismic provisions is so as to be responsive to the changes made in foreign codes. Canadians derive benefit from the experience and research used to make changes in other codes; when analysis of such developments shows that the NBC provisions could be improved, then they are adapted for use in the NBC.

Summary of Major Changes from the NBC 1995

Updated Hazard in Spectral Format

15. As indicated in Table J-1, seismic hazard in the 1985, 1990 and 1995 editions of the NBC was described in terms of peak ground velocity, v, and acceleration, a, determined at a probability of exceedance of 10% in 50 years. The period-dependent variation of seismic forces was obtained by multiplying v by a seismic response factor, denoted S in the NBC 1995, with the shape of S dependent upon the ratio of a to v. Uniform hazard spectra—i.e. spectral acceleration ordinates at different periods calculated at the same probability of exceedance—provide a much better period-dependent representation of earthquake effects on structures. In order for such information to be used in the NBC 2005 provisions, the Geological Survey of Canada is now calculating seismic hazard on that basis and providing selected spectral acceleration values for specific geographical locations in Canada (Adams and Halchuk,[5] Adams and Atkinson[6]). Because the spectral ordinates are determined directly at each geographical location, the differences in spectral shape across the country are reflected directly in the determination of design forces rather than being approximated by amplifying zonal values of peak ground velocity.

Change in Return Period (Probability of Exceedance)

16. In the NBC and in the seismic design provisions of many other countries (e.g. U.S.A. and New Zealand), it has been common during the past several decades to specify seismic hazard information at a 10% in 50 year probability of exceedance, which corresponds to a return period of 475 years. At the same time, it has been recognized that the contribution of various sources of conservatism (e.g. overstrength) in the design and construction processes leads to a much lower probability of structural failure or collapse due to strong seismic ground motion. However, the use of 10% in 50 year ground motions for design does not provide a uniform margin against collapse in all parts of Canada for reasons outlined below.

17. Calculations of seismic hazard at different probabilities of exceedance have demonstrated that the slopes of the hazard curve vary considerably in different parts of the country; the hazard curve is defined as the relationship between the level of ground shaking, e.g. a spectral ordinate at a specific period or peak ground acceleration or velocity, and the probability that that particular level of ground shaking will be exceeded (Adams and Atkinson[6]). Figure J-1 shows typical hazard curves for selected Canadian locations, normalized at a 10% in 50 year probability. The main variation occurs between regions that are near plate boundaries (e.g. Vancouver and Victoria) and intraplate regions (e.g. eastern Canada). In order to provide a more uniform margin of collapse, it is necessary to specify seismic hazard at a lower probability of exceedance, i.e. one that is much nearer to the probability of failure or collapse than 10% in 50 years.

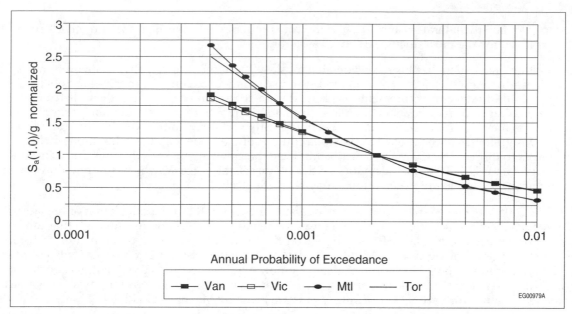

Figure J-1
$S_a(1.0)$ hazard curves for selected Canadian locations normalized for P = 0.0021

18. The 1997 National Earthquake Hazards Reduction Program (NEHRP) provisions (Building Seismic Safety Council[7]), which are based on the approach of providing a more uniform margin against collapse, specified the use of "maximum considered earthquake ground motion," which is defined as earthquake ground motion having a 2% in 50 year probability of exceedance (return period of approximately 2500 years). Appendix A4 of Adams and Halchuk[5] provides a rationale for using this level of probability in Canada. As a result, the seismic provisions in the NBC 2005 are based on the 2% in 50 year seismic hazard values.

Period-Dependent Site Factors

19. It has long been recognized that the amplification of seismic motions from rock to soil sites can be significant, especially at sites with soft soil conditions. The NBC 1995 included a foundation factor, F, which ranged from 1.0 to 2.0 but did not vary with period or with the intensity of the underlying rock motion; the type and depth of rock and soil in each of four categories were defined only in a qualitative manner.

20. As noted earlier, research by Borcherdt[4] and others has enabled the quantification for Code purposes of the effects of soil conditions on the seismic response of a site. The procedure involves the categorization of soil profiles using quantitative measures of soil properties (shear wave velocity, standard penetration resistance, or undrained shear strength), and recognizing the period-dependence of ground motions and the effects of the intensity of underlying rock motion. This work was incorporated into the seismic provisions of NEHRP 1997 (Building Seismic Safety Council[7]) with site effects represented by two site factors, one for short period response and the other for long period response. Those provisions are used as the basis for the site factors in the NBC 2005, as discussed by Finn and Wightman.[8] An important feature of the revised site factors in the NBC is the de-amplification of seismic motions at sites located on rock or hard rock, i.e. sites at which the shear wave velocity is greater than that of the reference site condition, which is described as "very dense soil and soft rock."

Delineation of Effects of Overstrength and Ductility

21. The NBC seismic provisions have long taken into account, either implicitly or explicitly, that seismic forces are reduced when structural response goes into the inelastic range. This is an important property that enables structures to resist strong earthquake shaking, provided they have the capacity to deform inelastically through several load reversals without a significant loss of strength. The NBC 1995 recognized this by including a force modification factor, R, in the denominator of the expression

used to calculate the lateral seismic force, V; the value of R ranged from 1.0 for non-ductile structural systems to 4.0 for the most ductile structural systems.

22. On the other hand, there has been considerable mystery about the property that is now referred to as "overstrength." Various features of structural systems and their design (e.g. material factors used in design, minimum design requirements, capacity design, load combinations and the redistribution of forces arising from redundancy) often lead to a lateral strength that is considerably larger than that used as the basis for design. This has been implicitly addressed in the NBC by calibrating the seismic design forces to those used in previous editions of the Code (e.g. the calibration of NBC 1985 forces to those in NBC 1980 as described in Heidebrecht et al.[9]). The NBC 1990 introduced a calibration factor U = 0.6 in the calculation of the lateral seismic force, V, which has sometimes been interpreted as an explicit representation of overstrength (Tso[10]).

23. The NBC 2005 introduces an explicit system overstrength factor, R_o, in the calculation of the lateral seismic force, V. This factor is intended to represent the minimum level of overstrength that can be counted on for each particular SFRS. It ranges from 1.0 to 1.7 and is applied as a reduction factor in the denominator of the expression used to calculate V. A ductility modification factor is also used in the denominator; it is now labelled R_d to denote a more explicit linkage to the ductility capacity of each SFRS. The rationale for the use of these two factors as well as the reasons for particular values or ranges of values for various structural systems are given by Mitchell et al.[11]

Period Calculations

24. The calculation of the fundamental lateral period, T_a, is significant because its value determines the spectral response acceleration, $S(T_a)$. On the one hand, the determination of T_a needs to be relatively simple; on the other hand, its value should not be overestimated. Values of T_a that are larger than can be realistically expected result in an underestimate of the seismic design force V and an overestimate of lateral deflection.

25. Although the formulae for calculating the periods of moment-resisting frames are the same as in the NBC 1995, the formula for shear walls and other structures has been simplified so that it is no longer dependent on the length D_s of those elements. This change was made because of the considerable confusion as to the appropriate value of D_s, which is often ill-defined. The rationale for the new formula is given by Saatcioglu and Humar.[12] A new formula for steel-braced frames has also been added.

26. Although the revised provisions continue to allow period calculations using other established methods of mechanics, the upper limit on calculated periods is now applied to moment-resisting frames, braced frames and shear walls rather than by placing a lower limit on the seismic force; the limit is now expressed as $1.5T_a$ for moment frames and $2.0T_a$ for braced frames and shear walls. The imposition of an upper limit on the periods for structures is justified because of the concern that structural models frequently overestimate the flexibility of a structural system (e.g. by neglecting non-structural stiffening elements), giving rise to an overestimate of the natural period.

Higher Mode Effects in the Equivalent Static Force Procedure

27. The static equivalent lateral seismic force calculated in the NBC provisions and in other codes is based on the assumption that the main features of the dynamic response of the structure can be represented by a single mode response at the fundamental period, T_a. Since many structures, particularly those with longer periods, have significantly higher mode effects, these are taken into account by modifications to both the value of the seismic design force and the distribution of the shears and moments along the height of the structure. In the NBC 1995, higher mode effects were simulated by an additional top force, F_t, by an overturning moment reduction factor, J, and by using $\sqrt{T}$ in the denominator of the seismic response factor, S, for periods of 0.5 s or greater. F_t and J are also used in the NBC 2005 provisions in lieu of using $\sqrt{T}$ in the denominator, but a higher mode factor, M_v, is applied in the determination of the lateral seismic force, V, in which the seismic hazard is represented directly by the spectral response acceleration, i.e. a single-degree-of-freedom response. The rationale for this factor and for the values prescribed in the NBC provisions is given by Humar and Mahgoub.[13]

28. The simulation of higher mode effects in an equivalent static procedure is not valid for structures with long periods because their response is dominated by the second or even third mode; the

equivalent static procedure only takes account of higher mode effects when the fundamental mode dominates response. Consequently, the NBC 2005 allows the Equivalent Static Force Procedure to be used for regular structures with periods of less than 2 s whose height is less than 60 m, for those located in regions of low seismicity, and for irregular structures, except torsionally sensitive ones, with a fundamental lateral period of less than 0.5 s whose height is less than 20 m. For all other structures, dynamic analysis must be used.

Irregularities

29. In the NBC 1995, the only specific requirement concerning structures with irregularities was that they be analyzed for torsional effects. General statements were made regarding discontinuous vertical resisting elements and the need to take into account the possible effects of setbacks, but the provisions contained no specific requirements. The NBC 2005 includes definitions of eight types of irregularities and specifications regarding analysis and design for each of those types. The kinds of specifications applicable to the different types of irregularities include the following: limitations on the use of the static analysis procedure, restrictions on irregularities permitted in relation to the extent of seismic hazard, restrictions applicable to post-disaster buildings, increases in seismic design forces, and specific design requirements (e.g. related to diaphragms, openings, and discontinuities). A detailed description of the rationale behind the provisions on irregularities is given by DeVall.[14] The NBC 2005 still contains specific requirements for taking torsional effects into account; a torsional sensitivity parameter, B, is used to determine whether or not dynamic analysis is required. The basis for the revisions to the torsional design requirements is given by Humar, Yavari and Saatcioglu.[15]

Dynamic Analysis Requirements

30. Dynamic analysis played a very small role in the NBC 1995; designers were given the option (see Clause 4.1.9.1.(13)(b) of the NBC 1995) of using it to determine the distribution of seismic forces within the structure, but these had to be scaled so that the lateral seismic force, V, was the same as that determined using the normal static method. As indicated in Commentary J of the 1995 edition of the Structural Commentaries, the dynamic option was primarily applicable to buildings with significant irregularities and to buildings with setbacks or major discontinuities in stiffness or in mass. The main reason for using dynamic analysis in these cases would be to obtain a better distribution of forces within such buildings; this would also apply to tall buildings in which the dynamic analysis included higher mode effects, which cannot be well represented by static equivalent loads. Designers were also allowed to use dynamic analysis for the determination of torsional moments, with the proviso that the effects of accidental torsion had to be determined statically and added to the effects of a three-dimensional dynamic analysis. To facilitate the use of dynamic analysis, Commentary J of the 1995 Structural Commentaries included a normalized design spectrum and a very brief procedure for conducting an elastic dynamic modal analysis.

31. Dynamic analysis plays a very prominent role in the NBC 2005 seismic provisions. The general rationale for this radical change is that Linear Dynamic Analysis—particularly modal analysis—is now a straightforward procedure that simulates the effects of earthquakes on a structure much better than the Equivalent Static Force Procedure. It is stated as the required method of analysis, except for the following structures for which the Equivalent Static Force Procedure may be used:
    (a) structures in areas of relatively low seismicity, as defined by the short period (0.2 s) design spectral acceleration,
    (b) regular structures less than 60 m in height and with a fundamental lateral period of less than 2 s, and
    (c) certain irregular structures less than 20 m in height and with a fundamental lateral period of less than 0.5 s.
    These exceptions recognize that:
    (a) there is not likely to be any significant negative consequence to allowing the static procedure in areas of low seismic hazard,
    (b) the equivalent static loads can simulate dynamic effects for medium-height regular structures provided that the fundamental period is not too long, and
    (c) both overall force and distributional effects are determined quite well by the static force method for relatively squat, short period, irregular structures, except for those that are torsionally sensitive.

Commentary J

32. Conducting dynamic analysis in accordance with the NBC 2005 provisions is also facilitated by the fact that seismic hazard is now specified in terms of spectral acceleration. Design spectral acceleration values are specified for all fundamental periods; these values are determined directly from 5% damped spectral response acceleration values, $S_a(T)$, multiplied by site amplification factors for periods T of 0.2 s, 0.5 s, 1.0 s and 2.0 s. This means that the input to a dynamic analysis is based directly on the best available estimates of ground motion, at the specified probability of exceedance. The NBC 2005 requires that the spectral acceleration values used in the Modal Response Spectrum Method be the design spectral acceleration values (which are also used as the basis for determining the minimum lateral seismic force, V, in the Equivalent Static Force Procedure) and that, if a Numerical Integration Linear Time History Method of dynamic analysis is used, the ground motion histories shall be compatible with a response spectrum constructed from the design spectral acceleration values. Saatcioglu and Humar[12] discuss the different methods of dynamic analysis and the necessary considerations for modelling structures for such analysis.

33. Although the NBC 2005 establishes dynamic analysis as the default procedure, there is still concern that the resultant seismic forces may be too low because the parameters used in the analysis (e.g. structural stiffness) are entirely at the designer's discretion rather than being specified by the Code. For example, while there are limitations on the maximum value of the fundamental lateral period, T_a, that can be used in the Equivalent Static Force Procedure, there are no such limitations in the specifications for dynamic analysis. To guard against inappropriate choices of design parameters, the NBC 2005 requires that the dynamically determined base shear be not less than 80% of that determined using the static method and that, in the case of irregular structures for which dynamic analysis is required (rather than being optional), the minimum dynamic base shear be 100% of the statically determined value. In this situation, the static base shear can be calculated using the dynamically determined fundamental period, provided that this period is not larger than:
    (a) 1.5 times the value determined using the simplified formulae for moment-resisting frames, and
    (b) 2.0 times the value determined using the simplified formulae for braced frames and shear walls.

Special Provisions

34. The NBC 1995, primarily Article 4.1.9.3., contained a number of special provisions that imposed certain restrictions when the velocity- or acceleration-related seismic zone was at a certain level or higher. These special provisions dealt with limiting the kind of structural system that could be used, restricting the height of buildings with structural systems having limited ductility capacity, ensuring that reinforcement was provided in certain kinds of masonry elements, and requiring that the design of foundations meet specific criteria.

35. In the NBC 2005, many of the restrictions on structural systems are grouped in the same table (NBC Table 4.1.8.9.), which specifies values of the force modification factor, R_d, and the system overstrength factor, R_o, for each Seismic Force Resisting System (SFRS). The restrictions are now governed by the design spectral acceleration values—including both the site coefficient and the earthquake importance factor, I_E—determined at periods of 0.2 s and 1.0 s. NBC Table 4.1.8.9. simplifies the design process in that the designer can immediately see the consequences of choosing a particular SFRS, both in terms of the factors R_d and R_o and any restrictions that may be applicable to a particular system.

36. The NBC 2005 provisions also contain other restrictions, including some on structures with particular structural irregularities and some on foundation design requirements. The rationale for the different restrictions is discussed in more detail in the sections of this Commentary that deal directly with individual restrictions.

Seismic Hazard

37. This section of the Commentary summarizes the primary aspects associated with the determination of seismic hazard to be used in the NBC 2005 seismic provisions. More detailed discussions are presented by Adams and Halchuk[5] and Adams and Atkinson[6] as well as in the other references cited.

Reasons for Recalculation of Hazard

Improved seismicity information

38. The 1985, 1990 and 1995 editions of the NBC relied on the 1982 seismic zoning maps developed between 1979 and 1982 using the catalogue of earthquakes, which comprised the data acquired up to 1977. There have been many earthquakes since 1977; this additional seismicity data has improved understanding of the geographical patterns of earthquake occurrence in many regions of Canada and the ability to estimate earthquake occurrence rates as a function of earthquake magnitude (Adams and Halchuk[5]). For example, large earthquakes have occurred in regions where earthquakes of such magnitudes had not been expected: the 1985 Nahanni, Northwest Territories, and the 1988 Saguenay, Quebec earthquakes being cases in point.

Improved understanding of seismotectonics

39. Discoveries since the early 1980s have lead to an improved understanding of the relationship between earthquake occurrence and the geological structure of the earth's crust. Examples of these discoveries are:
  (a) evidence concerning prehistoric large earthquakes on the Cascadia subduction zone off British Columbia, Washington and Oregon (Adams[16], Satake et al.[17]), and
  (b) the hypothesis concerning the correlation between the larger earthquakes in eastern North America and the relatively young rift faults that break the integrity of the continental crust (Basham[18]).
Findings such as these have a significant influence on the determination of seismic hazard in western and eastern Canada.

Improved estimates of strong seismic ground motion

40. Up to the 2005 edition, the NBC seismic provisions had used hazard parameters specified in terms of peak ground motions; the 1982 seismic zoning maps used peak ground acceleration and velocity. Direct specification of spectral acceleration ordinates provides a much better representation of earthquake-induced loading than the approach of amplifying peak ground motions does. Considerable research conducted in the 1980s and 1990s provided ground motion relations for spectral ordinates, which are applicable to the various kinds of earthquakes that influence seismic hazard in Canada (e.g. Atkinson and Boore,[19] Atkinson,[20][21] and Boore et al.[22]). These ground motion relations allow seismic hazard to be determined in the form of Uniform Hazard Spectra (UHS), which are plots of spectral acceleration ordinates at different periods, each ordinate having the same probability of exceedance.

Improved seismic hazard computation

41. The 1982 maps depicting peak horizontal acceleration and velocity were developed by applying the Cornell-McGuire probabilistic method (Cornell[23]) to 32 earthquake source zones in Canada and adjacent regions. More recent adaptations of the Cornell-McGuire method include the treatment of uncertainty in all of the significant input parameters such as seismicity rates, upper bound magnitudes, focal depth, ground motion relations and source zone models (McGuire[24]). Two kinds of uncertainty can be distinguished:
  (1) aleatory uncertainty arising from the physical variability that is inherent in the unpredictable nature of future events, and
  (2) epistemic uncertainty arising from differences in modelling assumptions, unknown or partially known parameters, and extrapolation beyond the range of observed data.
Realistic values of the various uncertainties can therefore be used to compute seismic hazard results at a desired level of confidence, e.g. median or median plus one standard deviation.

Need for hazard at a lower probability of exceedance

42. The 1982 maps portrayed peak ground acceleration and velocity at a 10% probability of being exceeded in a 50-year period, a level that has been commonly used for the geographical distribution of seismic hazard in both national and foreign building codes. However, this probability level is well above that at which well designed and detailed structures are expected to maintain their integrity, i.e. suffer extensive damage but not collapse. Consequently, it is desirable to calculate seismic

Commentary J

hazard at a much lower probability level, one that is consistent with the "rare events" for which extensive damage, short of collapse, is tolerable. A level of 2% in 50 years has been chosen for the data in the NBC 2005 and the maps in this Commentary (referred to as the 2003 maps); this level is consistent with recent developments in the U.S. (Building Seismic Safety Council,[25] International Code Council[26]). As discussed previously in the Summary of Major Changes from the NBC 1995, the major regional differences in the slope of the seismic hazard curve (see Figure J-1) resulted in significant differences in the level of protection among the different regions of the country. The use of the 2% in 50 year probability level should substantially reduce these differences in level of protection, which were unintentionally provided in previous editions of the NBC.

Brief Description of the Parameters Used in the Probabilistic Approach

Seismic source zones

43. The 1982 maps were based on a single set of 32 source zones and on historical seismicity. The 2003 maps used as the basis for the seismic data in the NBC 2005 incorporate two distinct models, which are distinguished primarily as historical and regional models, designated H and R respectively. In contrast to the historically based source zones used in the H model, the R model uses larger regional zones based on seismotectonic/geological considerations.

44. The source zone models mentioned above are applicable to the more seismically active parts of Canada. However, about one-half of the Canadian land mass has too few earthquakes to reliably define seismic source zones (see Figure J-2). Because large earthquakes can occur anywhere in Canada—albeit rarely in the more tectonically stable, less active regions—it is important to have reliable estimates of seismic hazard in these regions as well. Estimates of so-called "floor levels" of seismic hazard (designated as F) in these stable regions are based on considerations described by Adams and Halchuk.[5]

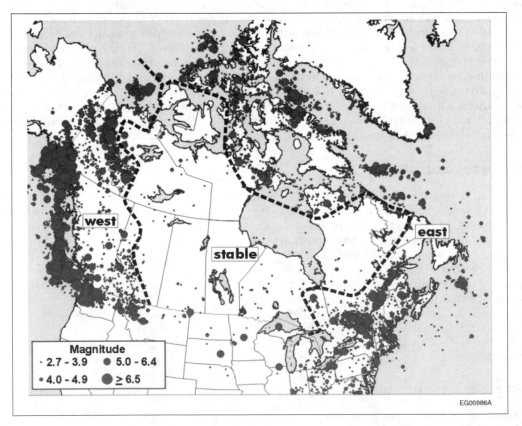

Figure J-2
Seismicity of Canada to 2001 delineating eastern and western seismic regions and the stable, low seismicity continental region

Table J-2 (Continued)

City	NBC 2005 Design Ground Motion Values[1]								NBC 1995 Peak Ground Motion Values[1]	
	$S_a(0.2)$		$S_a(0.5)$		$S_a(1.0)$		$S_a(2.0)$		PGA		PGA	PGV
Vancouver	0.96	H	0.66	R	0.34	R	0.18	R	0.48	H	0.23	0.21
Victoria	1.2	H	0.83	H	0.38	H	0.19	R	0.62	H	0.34	0.29
Tofino	1.2	C	0.93	C	0.47	C	0.21	C	0.52	C	0.38	0.33
Prince Rupert	0.38	R	0.25	R	0.17	R	0.096	R	0.18	R	0.13	0.27
Queen Charlotte	0.66	R	0.63	R	0.50	R	0.26	R	0.36	R	0.57	0.80
Inuvik	0.12	F	0.067	H	0.039	R	0.025	R	0.060	H	0.060	0.083

The letters in the Table indicate which results govern each value:

H = historical source zone   R = regional source zone   C = Cascadia scenario   F = floor level

(1) All values are in decimal percentages of g.

62. Figures J-3 through J-6 are maps of DGM spectral acceleration values at periods of 0.2 s and 1.0 s for southwestern and eastern Canada, which are heavily populated regions having a significant seismic hazard. All values are for Class C ground, i.e. very dense soil and soft rock. The purpose of providing these maps is to show how the pattern of hazard varies in different geographical regions; they should not be used to obtain the DGM values for specific locations.

63. DGM values (i.e. median confidence level at a probability of exceedance of 2% in 50 years) of spectral acceleration for periods of 0.1 s, 0.5 s, 1.0 s and 2.0 s and values of PGA for towns and cities throughout Canada are presented in NBC Table C-2, Design Data for Selected Locations in Canada, in Appendix C of Division B; they can also be found on the Web site of the Geological Survey of Canada (http://earthquakescanada.nrcan.gc.ca). DGM values at locations not listed can be obtained from this Web site by specifying the latitude and longitude of a particular location. This Web site also contains maps of all these parameters.

Seismicity parameters

45. The 2003 maps use the information contained in the Canadian earthquake catalogue up to 1990 for the east and up to 1991 for the west; this adds a significant amount of data to the pre-1977 catalogue, which was used for the 1982 maps, particularly for the Arctic. Magnitude-recurrence relations for each zone include uncertainty through the use of upper and lower curves, which approximate standard deviation error bounds. Estimates of upper-bound magnitude for each source zone were made by considering the largest earthquakes observed in similar seismotectonic regions around the world. Earthquake depth was included in the estimates even though probabilistic hazard for most of Canada is relatively insensitive to the exact depths used, the exception being southwestern B.C.

Strong ground motion relations

46. Strong ground motion relations are the most important component of the seismic hazard calculations as they govern the amplitudes of ground motion estimated for any magnitude and distance. The different physical properties of the earth's crust in eastern and western Canada require that separate strong ground motion relations be used for different regions. Also, in western Canada different relations were used for shallow source zones and for the deeper sub-crustal zones under Puget Sound. Various methods were used to determine upper and lower relations to represent the effects of uncertainty (Adams and Atkinson[6]).

Deterministic Approach for Cascadia Subduction Earthquake

47. The Cascadia subduction zone generated great prehistoric earthquakes off Vancouver Island. These earthquakes were large in magnitude and had ground motions of much longer duration than expected from nearby crustal and sub-crustal earthquakes. Geological records indicate a mean recurrence interval of about 600 years with a standard deviation of about 170 years; the last such earthquake occurred about 300 years ago. The nature of these earthquakes and their recurrence intervals make it difficult to treat them probabilistically, yet it is important that their potential effects be considered in the design of building structures. Consequently the Geological Survey of Canada has chosen to adopt a Cascadia scenario earthquake and to use this to provide a deterministic rather a probabilistic estimate of the resulting ground motions (Adams and Halchuk[5]).

48. Although current evidence indicates that the next Cascadia earthquake can be expected to have a magnitude of up to about 9, its location and exceedingly long rupture length indicate that much of the energy release would be too far from any Canadian location to significantly contribute to spectral accelerations. Rather, a magnitude of 8.2 was chosen for the Cascadia earthquake scenario, which was modelled as an offshore line source for the purpose of computing distances to various sites. Because the median values of ground motions (e.g. spectral accelerations) from this deterministic scenario have a probability of exceedance of about 10% in 50 years, it is inappropriate to use the median value to represent a 2% in 50 year probability level; 2% in 50 year level ground motions are deemed to be comparable to the median plus one standard deviation response.

49. Further information on the handling of the Cascadia subduction earthquake can be found in Adams and Halchuk[5] and Adams and Atkinson.[6] The effects of the long-duration Cascadia ground motions are addressed by Tremblay[27] and Tremblay and Atkinson.[28]

Calculated Hazard Results and Design Ground Motions

50. Complete probabilistic calculations of seismic hazard were done for each of the two seismic source zone models in western and eastern Canada; the UHS defined over a range of periods for the historical and regional models are referred to as the H and R results respectively. At each location considered, the higher of the two spectral values at any period is used to specify the DGM. The mapped DGM values are probabilistic for a particular period at any one location in that they are derived from an identifiable probabilistic hazard calculation based on a particular source model. However, the overall map of DGM values is "quasi-probabilistic" in that the model that produces the maximum value varies from location to location and even from period to period at a particular location. For the purpose of design, the DGM values are often referred to as UHS, even though they do not describe "uniform hazard" in a truly probabilistic sense.

51. An extension of this approach is used in areas that would be affected by earthquakes originating in the Cascadia subduction zone. In these areas, the largest of the deterministic Cascadia (C) , H and

R model results is chosen for the DGM. Similarly, when the probabilistically calculated H and R values are below the F (floor level) values, then the F values are specified as the DGM. Note that, as specified in NBC Article 4.1.8.1., seismic design is not required when the design spectral acceleration (including site coefficient) at a period of 0.2 s is at the floor level (0.12g on a Class C site). See the Commentary section on NBC Article 4.1.8.1.

52. The rationale for choosing this "maximizing" approach for the determination of design spectral values is that it preserves the levels of protection in areas that are historically highly seismic while providing increased protection in areas that have been less seismic in recent times but that are deemed likely to have large earthquakes in the future. An example of such an area is the St. Lawrence Valley near Trois-Rivières (Adams and Halchuk[5]).

Choice of Confidence Level

53. The Geological Survey of Canada has calculated hazard results at two confidence levels, the 50th percentile (median) and 84th percentile, which include a measure of epistemic uncertainty. These levels indicate a degree of confidence that the true ground motion parameter values for the 2% in 50 year probability are not greater than the specified values. These confidence levels were determined based on uncertainties in the model parameters input into the hazard calculations, Although the 84th percentile is on occasion referred to as the median plus one standard deviation, this description is not entirely valid when dealing with seismic hazard because it is applicable only to symmetrical normal or lognormal distributions. Due to the asymmetric nature of epistemic uncertainty, the distributions of ground motions about the median are quite asymmetric.

54. The median value is chosen for specifying DGMs because it can be expected to remain relatively stable as scientific opinion and knowledge change over a period of time; these changes contribute primarily to changes in epistemic uncertainty, which significantly affect the 84th percentile results but have less influence on the median values.

55. Mean values can also be determined but because of the asymmetric nature of the distribution due to epistemic uncertainty (i.e. uncertainty due to modelling, unknown or partially known parameters, or extrapolation beyond observed ranges of data), they will fluctuate somewhat with time. Mean values are not associated with a particular confidence level; for Canadian seismic hazard, mean values typically lie between the 70th and 90th percentile of the distribution (Adams and Atkinson[6]). It should be noted that spectral values currently being calculated by the U.S. Geological Survey for the U.S. codes are mean values; however, differences in modelling approaches are such that the relationship between the American (mean) and Canadian (median) DGM is neither consistent nor easy to quantify. Consequently, direct comparison of Canadian and American DGM values—e.g. at or near the Canada-U.S. border—has limited value and should be treated with considerable caution.

56. The use of median results clearly implies that there is a 50% chance that the actual ground motions for 2% in 50 years may be larger than the specified values. Results in the 84th percentile provide some sense of the range of variability of ground motions about the median value. The ratio of 84th percentile to median value results in ranges from about 1.5 to 3 (see the values in Table 3 of Adams and Halchuk[5]).

57. Choosing the median as the confidence level at which the DGM is specified means that there is one chance in two that the actual ground motion for the specified probability of exceedance will exceed the specified design value and a lower possibility that the actual ground motion will greatly exceed it. This means that designers should not place the same level of reliance on the forces and deformations determined from a seismic analysis as they would on the results due to dead and live loads. To provide an adequate level of protection against earthquakes, it is desirable that building structures have a substantial capacity for nonlinear deformation so as to be able to resist ground motions in excess of the DGM; the use of systems with such characteristics increases the likelihood that the structure, as designed and built, will perform well, even when ground motions exceed the DGM level.

Choice of Reference Ground Condition

58. It is essential that mapped values of seismic hazard be specified on the same reference ground condition for all of Canada to ensure that hazard values are comparable in different parts of the country, even when computed using different source zone models and strong ground motion relations.

59. The reference ground condition chosen for the seismic hazard values in the NBC 2005 is very dense soil and soft rock, or Site Class C, with an average shear wave velocity (in the upper 30 m) between 360 and 760 m/s (see NBC Table 4.1.8.4.A.). This ground condition is roughly comparable to the reference soil condition inferred in previous editions of the NBC (1985 through 1995), which was simply referred to as "rock or firm soil."

60. Another advantage of choosing Class C is that it closely corresponds to the ground conditions used in determining the strong ground motion relations that are used in western Canada. The strong ground motion relations used in eastern Canada were determined for hard rock conditions, which necessitated the use of an amplification factor in the seismic hazard computations (Adams and Halchuk[5]).

Hazard Values and Maps

61. Adams and Atkinson[6] show hazard results for a number of selected locations throughout Canada. Table J-2, which is based on information provided in their publication, shows median values (i.e. DGM at a probability of exceedance of 2% in 50 years) of spectral acceleration for periods of 0.1 s, 0.5 s, 1.0 s and 2.0 s as well as values of PGA (peak ground acceleration). Table J-2 also identifies the model that provides the maximum values in each case. To facilitate comparison, the Table also includes location-specific values of PGA and PGV (peak ground velocity) at a 10% in 50 year probability of exceedance, which is what the seismic zones in the NBC 1995 were based on.

Table J-2
NBC 2005 Design Ground Motion Values (median, 2% in 50 year probability of exceedance) and NBC 1995 Peak Ground Motion Values (10% in 50 year probability of exceedance)

City	NBC 2005 Design Ground Motion Values[1]										NBC 1995 Peak Ground Motion Values[1]	
	$S_a(0.2)$		$S_a(0.5)$		$S_a(1.0)$		$S_a(2.0)$		PGA		PGA	PGV
St. John's	0.18	R	0.11	R	0.060	R	0.016	R	0.090	R	0.054	0.052
Halifax	0.23	R	0.13	R	0.070	R	0.019	R	0.12	R	0.056	0.056
Moncton	0.30	H	0.16	H	0.068	H	0.021	H	0.21	H	0.085	0.061
Fredericton	0.39	R	0.20	R	0.086	R	0.027	H	0.27	R	0.096	0.066
La Malbaie	2.3	H	1.2	H	0.60	H	0.19	H	1.1	H	0.71	0.44
Quebec	0.59	R	0.29	H	0.14	H	0.048	H	0.37	R	0.19	0.14
Trois-Rivières	0.64	R	0.31	R	0.12	R	0.043	R	0.40	R	0.12	0.092
Montreal	0.69	R	0.34	R	0.14	R	0.048	R	0.43	R	0.18	0.097
Ottawa	0.67	R	0.32	R	0.14	R	0.045	R	0.42	R	0.20	0.098
Niagara Falls	0.41	H	0.20	H	0.073	H	0.021	H	0.30	H	0.084	0.039
Toronto	0.28	R	0.14	R	0.055	R	0.016	H	0.20	R	0.056	0.038
Windsor	0.18	R	0.087	R	0.040	R	0.011	R	0.12	R	0.029	0.026
Winnipeg	0.12	F	0.056	F	0.023	F	0.006	F	0.059	F	0	0
Calgary	0.15	H	0.084	H	0.041	H	0.023	H	0.088	H	0.019	0.040
Kelowna	0.28	H	0.17	R	0.089	R	0.053	R	0.14	R	0.053	0.069
Kamloops	0.28	H	0.17	R	0.10	R	0.060	R	0.14	H	0.056	0.076
Prince George	0.13	H	0.080	H	0.041	R	0.026	R	0.071	H	0.035	0.081

Seismicity parameters

45. The 2003 maps use the information contained in the Canadian earthquake catalogue up to 1990 for the east and up to 1991 for the west; this adds a significant amount of data to the pre-1977 catalogue, which was used for the 1982 maps, particularly for the Arctic. Magnitude-recurrence relations for each zone include uncertainty through the use of upper and lower curves, which approximate standard deviation error bounds. Estimates of upper-bound magnitude for each source zone were made by considering the largest earthquakes observed in similar seismotectonic regions around the world. Earthquake depth was included in the estimates even though probabilistic hazard for most of Canada is relatively insensitive to the exact depths used, the exception being southwestern B.C.

Strong ground motion relations

46. Strong ground motion relations are the most important component of the seismic hazard calculations as they govern the amplitudes of ground motion estimated for any magnitude and distance. The different physical properties of the earth's crust in eastern and western Canada require that separate strong ground motion relations be used for different regions. Also, in western Canada different relations were used for shallow source zones and for the deeper sub-crustal zones under Puget Sound. Various methods were used to determine upper and lower relations to represent the effects of uncertainty (Adams and Atkinson[6]).

Deterministic Approach for Cascadia Subduction Earthquake

47. The Cascadia subduction zone generated great prehistoric earthquakes off Vancouver Island. These earthquakes were large in magnitude and had ground motions of much longer duration than expected from nearby crustal and sub-crustal earthquakes. Geological records indicate a mean recurrence interval of about 600 years with a standard deviation of about 170 years; the last such earthquake occurred about 300 years ago. The nature of these earthquakes and their recurrence intervals make it difficult to treat them probabilistically, yet it is important that their potential effects be considered in the design of building structures. Consequently the Geological Survey of Canada has chosen to adopt a Cascadia scenario earthquake and to use this to provide a deterministic rather a probabilistic estimate of the resulting ground motions (Adams and Halchuk[5]).

48. Although current evidence indicates that the next Cascadia earthquake can be expected to have a magnitude of up to about 9, its location and exceedingly long rupture length indicate that much of the energy release would be too far from any Canadian location to significantly contribute to spectral accelerations. Rather, a magnitude of 8.2 was chosen for the Cascadia earthquake scenario, which was modelled as an offshore line source for the purpose of computing distances to various sites. Because the median values of ground motions (e.g. spectral accelerations) from this deterministic scenario have a probability of exceedance of about 10% in 50 years, it is inappropriate to use the median value to represent a 2% in 50 year probability level; 2% in 50 year level ground motions are deemed to be comparable to the median plus one standard deviation response.

49. Further information on the handling of the Cascadia subduction earthquake can be found in Adams and Halchuk[5] and Adams and Atkinson.[6] The effects of the long-duration Cascadia ground motions are addressed by Tremblay[27] and Tremblay and Atkinson.[28]

Calculated Hazard Results and Design Ground Motions

50. Complete probabilistic calculations of seismic hazard were done for each of the two seismic source zone models in western and eastern Canada; the UHS defined over a range of periods for the historical and regional models are referred to as the H and R results respectively. At each location considered, the higher of the two spectral values at any period is used to specify the DGM. The mapped DGM values are probabilistic for a particular period at any one location in that they are derived from an identifiable probabilistic hazard calculation based on a particular source model. However, the overall map of DGM values is "quasi-probabilistic" in that the model that produces the maximum value varies from location to location and even from period to period at a particular location. For the purpose of design, the DGM values are often referred to as UHS, even though they do not describe "uniform hazard" in a truly probabilistic sense.

51. An extension of this approach is used in areas that would be affected by earthquakes originating in the Cascadia subduction zone. In these areas, the largest of the deterministic Cascadia (C), H and

Commentary J

R model results is chosen for the DGM. Similarly, when the probabilistically calculated H and R values are below the F (floor level) values, then the F values are specified as the DGM. Note that, as specified in NBC Article 4.1.8.1., seismic design is not required when the design spectral acceleration (including site coefficient) at a period of 0.2 s is at the floor level (0.12g on a Class C site). See the Commentary section on NBC Article 4.1.8.1.

52. The rationale for choosing this "maximizing" approach for the determination of design spectral values is that it preserves the levels of protection in areas that are historically highly seismic while providing increased protection in areas that have been less seismic in recent times but that are deemed likely to have large earthquakes in the future. An example of such an area is the St. Lawrence Valley near Trois-Rivières (Adams and Halchuk[5]).

Choice of Confidence Level

53. The Geological Survey of Canada has calculated hazard results at two confidence levels, the 50th percentile (median) and 84th percentile, which include a measure of epistemic uncertainty. These levels indicate a degree of confidence that the true ground motion parameter values for the 2% in 50 year probability are not greater than the specified values. These confidence levels were determined based on uncertainties in the model parameters input into the hazard calculations. Although the 84th percentile is on occasion referred to as the median plus one standard deviation, this description is not entirely valid when dealing with seismic hazard because it is applicable only to symmetrical normal or lognormal distributions. Due to the asymmetric nature of epistemic uncertainty, the distributions of ground motions about the median are quite asymmetric.

54. The median value is chosen for specifying DGMs because it can be expected to remain relatively stable as scientific opinion and knowledge change over a period of time; these changes contribute primarily to changes in epistemic uncertainty, which significantly affect the 84th percentile results but have less influence on the median values.

55. Mean values can also be determined but because of the asymmetric nature of the distribution due to epistemic uncertainty (i.e. uncertainty due to modelling, unknown or partially known parameters, or extrapolation beyond observed ranges of data), they will fluctuate somewhat with time. Mean values are not associated with a particular confidence level; for Canadian seismic hazard, mean values typically lie between the 70th and 90th percentile of the distribution (Adams and Atkinson[6]). It should be noted that spectral values currently being calculated by the U.S. Geological Survey for the U.S. codes are mean values; however, differences in modelling approaches are such that the relationship between the American (mean) and Canadian (median) DGM is neither consistent nor easy to quantify. Consequently, direct comparison of Canadian and American DGM values—e.g. at or near the Canada-U.S. border—has limited value and should be treated with considerable caution.

56. The use of median results clearly implies that there is a 50% chance that the actual ground motions for 2% in 50 years may be larger than the specified values. Results in the 84th percentile provide some sense of the range of variability of ground motions about the median value. The ratio of 84th percentile to median value results in ranges from about 1.5 to 3 (see the values in Table 3 of Adams and Halchuk[5]).

57. Choosing the median as the confidence level at which the DGM is specified means that there is one chance in two that the actual ground motion for the specified probability of exceedance will exceed the specified design value and a lower possibility that the actual ground motion will greatly exceed it. This means that designers should not place the same level of reliance on the forces and deformations determined from a seismic analysis as they would on the results due to dead and live loads. To provide an adequate level of protection against earthquakes, it is desirable that building structures have a substantial capacity for nonlinear deformation so as to be able to resist ground motions in excess of the DGM; the use of systems with such characteristics increases the likelihood that the structure, as designed and built, will perform well, even when ground motions exceed the DGM level.

Choice of Reference Ground Condition

58. It is essential that mapped values of seismic hazard be specified on the same reference ground condition for all of Canada to ensure that hazard values are comparable in different parts of the

country, even when computed using different source zone models and strong ground motion relations.

59. The reference ground condition chosen for the seismic hazard values in the NBC 2005 is very dense soil and soft rock, or Site Class C, with an average shear wave velocity (in the upper 30 m) between 360 and 760 m/s (see NBC Table 4.1.8.4.A.). This ground condition is roughly comparable to the reference soil condition inferred in previous editions of the NBC (1985 through 1995), which was simply referred to as "rock or firm soil."

60. Another advantage of choosing Class C is that it closely corresponds to the ground conditions used in determining the strong ground motion relations that are used in western Canada. The strong ground motion relations used in eastern Canada were determined for hard rock conditions, which necessitated the use of an amplification factor in the seismic hazard computations (Adams and Halchuk[5]).

Hazard Values and Maps

61. Adams and Atkinson[6] show hazard results for a number of selected locations throughout Canada. Table J-2, which is based on information provided in their publication, shows median values (i.e. DGM at a probability of exceedance of 2% in 50 years) of spectral acceleration for periods of 0.1 s, 0.5 s, 1.0 s and 2.0 s as well as values of PGA (peak ground acceleration). Table J-2 also identifies the model that provides the maximum values in each case. To facilitate comparison, the Table also includes location-specific values of PGA and PGV (peak ground velocity) at a 10% in 50 year probability of exceedance, which is what the seismic zones in the NBC 1995 were based on.

Table J-2
NBC 2005 Design Ground Motion Values (median, 2% in 50 year probability of exceedance) and NBC 1995 Peak Ground Motion Values (10% in 50 year probability of exceedance)

City	NBC 2005 Design Ground Motion Values[1]										NBC 1995 Peak Ground Motion Values[1]	
	$S_a(0.2)$		$S_a(0.5)$		$S_a(1.0)$		$S_a(2.0)$		PGA		PGA	PGV
St. John's	0.18	R	0.11	R	0.060	R	0.016	R	0.090	R	0.054	0.052
Halifax	0.23	R	0.13	R	0.070	R	0.019	R	0.12	R	0.056	0.056
Moncton	0.30	H	0.16	H	0.068	H	0.021	H	0.21	H	0.085	0.061
Fredericton	0.39	R	0.20	R	0.086	H	0.027	H	0.27	R	0.096	0.066
La Malbaie	2.3	H	1.2	H	0.60	H	0.19	H	1.1	H	0.71	0.44
Quebec	0.59	R	0.29	H	0.14	H	0.048	H	0.37	R	0.19	0.14
Trois-Rivières	0.64	R	0.31	R	0.12	R	0.043	R	0.40	R	0.12	0.092
Montreal	0.69	R	0.34	R	0.14	R	0.048	R	0.43	R	0.18	0.097
Ottawa	0.67	R	0.32	R	0.14	R	0.045	R	0.42	R	0.20	0.098
Niagara Falls	0.41	H	0.20	H	0.073	H	0.021	H	0.30	H	0.084	0.039
Toronto	0.28	H	0.14	H	0.055	R	0.016	H	0.20	H	0.056	0.038
Windsor	0.18	R	0.087	R	0.040	R	0.011	R	0.12	R	0.029	0.026
Winnipeg	0.12	F	0.056	F	0.023	F	0.006	F	0.059	F	0	0
Calgary	0.15	H	0.084	H	0.041	H	0.023	H	0.088	H	0.019	0.040
Kelowna	0.28	H	0.17	H	0.089	R	0.053	R	0.14	H	0.053	0.069
Kamloops	0.28	H	0.17	H	0.10	R	0.060	R	0.14	H	0.056	0.076
Prince George	0.13	H	0.080	H	0.041	R	0.026	R	0.071	H	0.035	0.081

Table J-2 (Continued)

City	NBC 2005 Design Ground Motion Values[1]										NBC 1995 Peak Ground Motion Values[1]	
	$S_a(0.2)$		$S_a(0.5)$		$S_a(1.0)$		$S_a(2.0)$		PGA		PGA	PGV
Vancouver	0.96	H	0.66	R	0.34	R	0.18	R	0.48	H	0.23	0.21
Victoria	1.2	H	0.83	H	0.38	H	0.19	R	0.62	H	0.34	0.29
Tofino	1.2	C	0.93	C	0.47	C	0.21	C	0.52	C	0.38	0.33
Prince Rupert	0.38	R	0.25	R	0.17	R	0.096	R	0.18	R	0.13	0.27
Queen Charlotte	0.66	R	0.63	R	0.50	R	0.26	R	0.36	R	0.57	0.80
Inuvik	0.12	F	0.067	H	0.039	R	0.025	R	0.060	H	0.060	0.083

The letters in the Table indicate which results govern each value:

H = historical source zone   R = regional source zone   C = Cascadia scenario   F = floor level

[1] All values are in decimal percentages of g.

62. Figures J-3 through J-6 are maps of DGM spectral acceleration values at periods of 0.2 s and 1.0 s for southwestern and eastern Canada, which are heavily populated regions having a significant seismic hazard. All values are for Class C ground, i.e. very dense soil and soft rock. The purpose of providing these maps is to show how the pattern of hazard varies in different geographical regions; they should not be used to obtain the DGM values for specific locations.

63. DGM values (i.e. median confidence level at a probability of exceedance of 2% in 50 years) of spectral acceleration for periods of 0.1 s, 0.5 s, 1.0 s and 2.0 s and values of PGA for towns and cities throughout Canada are presented in NBC Table C-2, Design Data for Selected Locations in Canada, in Appendix C of Division B; they can also be found on the Web site of the Geological Survey of Canada (http://earthquakescanada.nrcan.gc.ca). DGM values at locations not listed can be obtained from this Web site by specifying the latitude and longitude of a particular location. This Web site also contains maps of all these parameters.

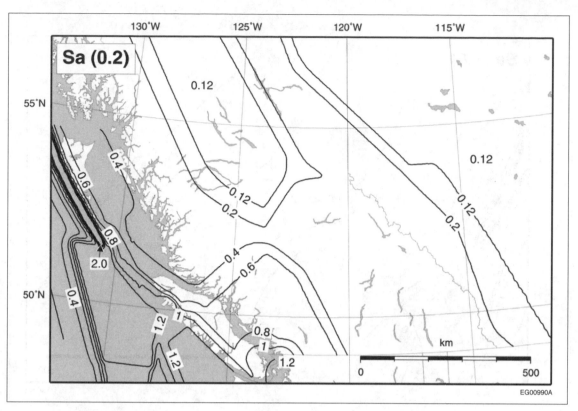

Figure J-3
5% damped spectral accelerations $S_a(0.2)$ in southwestern Canada

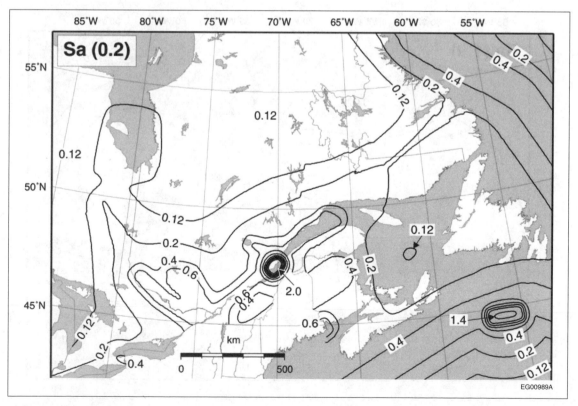

Figure J-4
5% damped spectral accelerations $S_a(0.2)$ in eastern Canada

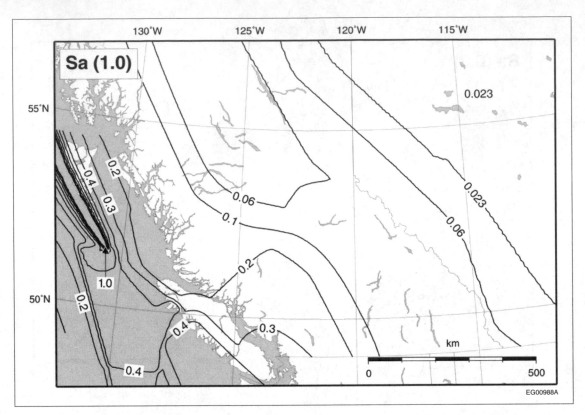

Figure J-5
5% damped spectral accelerations S$_a$(1.0) in southwestern Canada

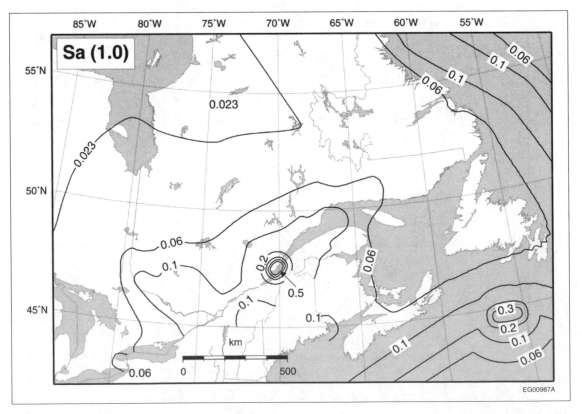

Figure J-6
5% damped spectral accelerations S$_a$(1.0) in eastern Canada

Site Response Effects

Site Amplification

64. Site conditions play a major role in establishing the damage potential of incoming seismic waves from large earthquakes. Damage patterns in Mexico City caused by the 1985 Michoacan earthquake conclusively demonstrated the significant effects of local site conditions on the seismic response of the ground (Seed[29]). Peak accelerations of incoming motions in rock were generally less than 0.04g and had predominant periods of around 2 s. Many clay sites in the dried lake bed on which the original city was founded had site periods also around 2 s and were excited into resonant response by the incoming motions. As a result, the bedrock outcrop motions were amplified about 5 times. The amplified motions had devastating effects on structures with periods close to site periods. In the 1989 Loma Prieta earthquake, major damage occurred on soft soil sites in the San Francisco-Oakland region where the spectral accelerations were amplified 2 to 4 times over adjacent rock sites (Housner[30]). It is clear that seismic design should incorporate the amplification effects of local soil conditions; this must be done effectively without unduly complicating the structural design process. Site amplification or foundation factors are the preferred means used in seismic codes to capture the amplification effects of local soil conditions on ground motions, and hence, on seismic design forces.

Theoretical Basis of Site Amplification

65. The effects of site conditions on seismic ground motions usually refer to how the waves from the underlying rock are affected by the geometrical and geological structures of the softer surface deposits during wave transmission to the surface. An elementary theory on wave propagation (i.e. how ground conditions affect the waves) and its application to site response for code purposes is given by Finn and Wightman.[8] The basic mechanism of amplification is best illustrated by examining the effect of a damped elastic surface layer on an incoming harmonic wave of period T_w from bedrock. Consider the elastic layer shown in Figure J-7, which is characterized by a thickness, H, a shear wave velocity, V_{ss}, and a density, ρ_s. The density and shear wave velocity in the bedrock is denoted by V_{sr} and ρ_r. The fundamental period of the elastic soil layer is $T_s = 4H/V_{ss}$.

66. Most strong motion instruments are located on rock or stiff soil sites and provide the database for predicting ground motions on such sites. Ground motions for seismic design on softer sites are determined by first estimating what the motions would be at the site on a rock or stiff soil outcrop and then estimating how much these motions would be amplified on passing through the soft overlying soils. The amplification ratio, A, between the outcrop acceleration, a_o, and the surface acceleration, a_t, shown in Figure J-7 when $T_w = T_s$ is

$$A = 1/\left(\kappa + \beta_s \pi/2\right)$$

where β_s is the critical damping ratio and $\kappa = \rho_s V_{ss}/\rho_r V_{sr}$ is the impedance ratio. These theoretical results show that the important parameters controlling ground motion amplification in elastic surface soil layers are:
   (a) the relationship between the predominant period of the outcrop motions and the fundamental period of the surface layer,
   (b) the impedance between the surface layer and the base material, and
   (c) the damping in the surface layer.
Therefore, the key site parameters controlling the amplification of the outcrop motions are H, V_{ss}, κ and β_s.

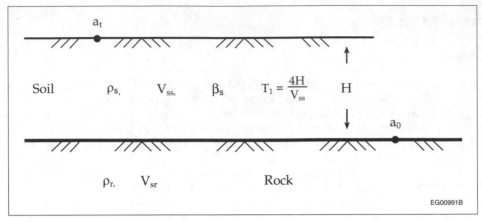

Figure J-7
Elastic layer on elastic half-space

Nonlinear Site Amplification

67. Under strong shaking, the response of the soil will be nonlinear. The shear modulus and damping are strain dependent and therefore the larger strains, associated with strong shaking, reduce the effective shear moduli and increase the damping. The shear strength of the soil also puts a limitation on the magnitude of the surface acceleration because the seismic waves cannot generate shear stresses greater than the mobilized shearing resistance of the soil. Field evidence shows that the nonlinear behaviour of soils causes the ground motion amplification factors to be dependent on the intensity of shaking.

68. In Figure J-8, Idriss[31] has conveniently summarized the nonlinear relationship between peak accelerations on soft soil sites and those on associated bedrock sites . The median curve is based on data recorded in Mexico City during the 1985 Michoacan earthquake and on strong motion data from the 1989 Loma Prieta earthquake. The part of the median curve for peak rock accelerations greater than 0.2g is based on 1-D site response analyses using the SHAKE computer program (Schnabel et al.[32]). The curve suggests that, on average, the bedrock accelerations are amplified in soft soils until the peak rock accelerations reach about 0.4g. The higher amplification ratios between rock and soil sites, in the range of 1.5 – 4, are associated with rock acceleration levels of less than 0.10g, when the response is closer to being elastic. The increased nonlinearity of soft soil response at the higher accelerations reduces the amplification ratios because of the increase in hysteretic damping and the reduction in effective shear moduli.

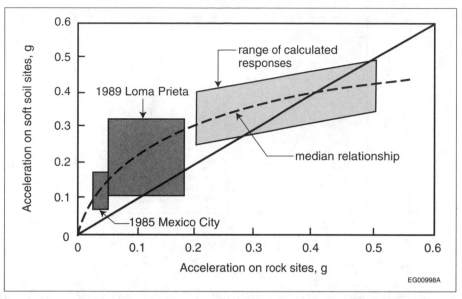

Figure J-8
Accelerations on soft soil and associated rock sites (after Idriss[31])

Foundation Factors

69. The properties of the soils in the database used by Idriss[31] vary significantly and the sites differ in geological structure. Thus, although the curve in Figure J-8 is useful for preliminary site evaluation, it is too general for estimating amplification factors for the different classes of soft soil sites encountered in practice. In many building codes, including the previous edition of the NBC (Associate Committee on the National Building Code 1995[33]), the amplification effects of local soil conditions are represented by foundation factors. The variety of soil conditions is condensed into four distinct site categories and an amplification factor for long period motions—termed a foundation or site factor—is associated with each site category. One advantage of using broad and well defined soil categories is that rather distinct patterns of ground response are associated with each category; however, one disadvantage is that it is sometimes difficult to decide which category a complex site condition should be assigned to.

70. There are two key elements to establishing a reliable foundation or site amplification factor:
    (1) the site conditions must be quantitatively characterized into soil categories, and
    (2) a numerical amplification factor must be assigned to each soil category that is dependent on the frequency and intensity of shaking.
    NEHRP (Building Seismic Safety Council[34]) adapted the research of Borcherdt[35][36][39] and others (Dobry et al.[37]) and developed an approach using two amplification factors, F_a and F_v, to describe the amplification of outcrop motions in the short and long period ranges, respectively. The use of this approach to construct the free-field acceleration response spectrum is shown in Figure J-9. NEHRP defined new site categories that are specified primarily in terms of the average shear wave velocity, V_{30}. To facilitate the use of these new site categories in practice, complementary descriptions were developed relating to their standard penetration resistance and undrained shear strength.

71. Values of F_a and F_v for each site category are specified for different levels of spectral ground accelerations. The values for F_a are mean values. The values of F_v derived from the research studies were highly variable depending on site conditions and input motions; the F_v values are therefore given at the mean plus one standard deviation level.

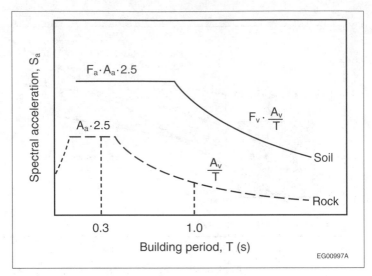

Figure J-9
Design spectra based on period-dependent site amplification factors (after Building Seismic Safety Council[34])

NBC 2005 Site Coefficients

72. The site amplification approach used in the NBC 2005 is the same as the one used in the original and current NEHRP (Building Seismic Safety Council[34][25]) provisions with the modifications noted below. The site classifications, as shown in NBC Table 4.1.8.4.A., are identical except that the descriptions of Site Classes E and F differ slightly. The short and long period amplification factors, F_a and F_v respectively, were adopted with some minor modifications and are given in NBC Tables 4.1.8.4.B. and 4.1.8.4.C. where the intensity of shaking is defined by the short and long period spectral accelerations, $S_a(0.2)$ and $S_a(1.0)$ respectively. NEHRP (Building Seismic Safety Council[34]) originally used peak ground acceleration and velocity but the most recent version of NEHRP (Building Seismic Safety Council[25]) also uses spectral accelerations.

73. As previously discussed in this Commentary, the reference ground condition used for the determination of seismic hazard is Site Class C, whereas NEHRP uses Site Class B as its reference. Site Class C is very similar to the reference site used in the NBC 1995. For all intensities of earthquake shaking, the site factor for Site C is 1.0; the site coefficients for the other site classes in the NBC 2005 were determined by maintaining the relative amplifications between each class and Site Class C, as found in NEHRP (Building Seismic Safety Council[25]).

Implications

74. The amplification factors specified by NEHRP were based on Borcherdt's analysis of 35 instrumented sites using data obtained during the 1989 Loma Prieta earthquake. Amplification was determined with respect to the Franciscan rock formation in California, which has a shear wave velocity of less than 1100 m/s; recorded rock motions during the Loma Prieta earthquake had peak ground accelerations less than 0.10g, which corresponds to $S_a(0.2) = 0.25$g. These empirical amplifications are in good agreement with those determined independently using numerical modelling and parametric studies of several hundred soil profiles (Dobry et al.[38]). Extrapolations of amplification levels beyond the 0.10g level were based on laboratory and theoretical modelling considerations because there were very few strong motion recordings at higher levels of ground motion, particularly through soft soil deposits. Amplification factors for the softest site class—Class E—were determined from hundreds of dynamic response analyses for mapped peak ground accelerations ranging from 0.10g to 0.5g ($S_a(0.2)$ from 0.25g to 1.25g); factors for Site Classes C and D for the same range were obtained by interpolation.

75. Since the form of the site classes and the specifications for the site amplification factors were determined in 1992, much new field data has become available that is still being processed. The Northridge earthquake in 1994 provided much data on the seismic response of the stiffer site classes at very high levels of shaking. Borcherdt[39] evaluated site amplification from that data and concluded that "regression coefficients as implied by current (NEHRP) code provisions for Site

Classes D and C cannot be inferred to be significantly different from those implied by the Northridge data at the 5 percent significance level (95 percent confidence level)."

76. The NBC 2005 provisions that deal with determining amplification factors are an improvement over the provisions in the NBC 1995. The major benefit is the way in which the new site classes are defined. Through the use of values of soil parameters such as shear wave velocity, penetration resistance and shear strength to define site classes, many of the troublesome ambiguities associated with the descriptive definitions in the 1995 Code are eliminated. The new foundation factors are intensity-dependent and reflect the effects of nonlinearity during strong shaking by a reduction in amplification. Because Site Class C was selected as the reference site for the NBC 2005, the maximum values of the new amplification factors on soft soil sites are not significantly different from the values in the 1995 Code. Also, the de-amplification of response on rock and hard rock sites gives a realistic representation of how ground motions for reference site conditions are modified for other site conditions.

Seismic Design Not Included in NBC 2005 Provisions

Seismic Design with Base Isolation

77. Base isolation is an alternative structural design concept for buildings, particularly suited to those in regions of high seismicity. Many buildings have been built using this approach, which is also used for retrofitting and upgrading existing buildings. The seismic design of buildings using base isolation is not a standard technique and requires a peer-reviewed special study or investigation tailored to the particularities of each building. The concept and basic approach are described below as well as the general requirements that must be met so that such seismic design is compatible with the intent of the NBC seismic provisions. Because base isolation requires that the fundamental period be much longer than that of a building on a fixed base, it is not suitable for tall building structures, i.e. those with long fundamental periods.

78. The concept of base isolation is to interpose a layer with low horizontal stiffness between the ground and the building so that the layer deforms rather than the building. The layer's low horizontal stiffness results in a modified structure that has a fundamental period that is much longer than that of a building structure on a fixed base and than the predominant periods of the seismic ground motion. As a consequence, the first dynamic mode of the isolated system involves the deformation of only the isolating layer while the structure above that layer remains essentially undeformed. The higher modes of the structure, which would produce deformation in the structural system, have very low participation factors so they are not excited even if the ground motion has high energy at the periods corresponding to those modes. This type of isolation system does not require damping in the isolators to function effectively but some damping is beneficial to suppress any possible resonance at the fundamental period of the isolated structure.

79. Most of the approaches used to provide the isolating layer can be categorized as one of two types (Kelly[40]). The most common type uses elastomeric bearings, the elastomer being made of either natural rubber or neoprene. Typical systems are made of natural rubber bearings with mechanical dampers or lead-rubber bearings; high-damping natural rubber isolators are also common. The second type is a sliding system, which works by limiting the transfer of shear across the isolation interface. Examples of this type of isolation system include the following: a lead-bronze plate sliding on stainless steel and a friction-pendulum system using a special interfacial material sliding on stainless steel.

80. Detailed information on the seismic design of buildings using base isolation, including both theory and examples of practical applications, is given by Naiem and Kelly.[41] The NEHRP 2000 Commentary also includes a chapter on design requirements for seismically isolated structures. Although the base isolation requirements in the Canadian Highway Bridge Design Code (Canadian Standards Association[42]) are not specifically intended for buildings, they are a useful complement to other information on base isolation. The following considerations are important to ensure that the design of isolation systems meets the objectives of the NBC 2005:

The response of such systems needs to be evaluated using a dynamic response approach in which the excitation is consistent with that required in the NBC 2005 provisions. This approach would normally comprise ground motion time-histories having spectra that are compatible with the specified design spectral acceleration values for the particular location, including both site effects and the appropriate importance factor.

The dynamic properties of the isolated system must be based on building properties that are appropriate for the anticipated response of the building. In particular, since the building itself is expected to respond elastically with very small deformations, the low-deformation elastic properties should be used rather than those appropriate for large inelastic deformations, which would be the case in normal seismic design.

Since the performance of the isolated system depends on large lateral deformations within the isolating layer, it is essential to ensure that the devices constituting the layer are designed to have the capacity to continue supporting the building while they undergo a number of cycles of such deformation. The devices must be tested to ensure that they are self-centring, i.e. that they return to the original equilibrium position after shaking.

Seismic Design with Supplemental Energy Dissipation Devices

81. Supplemental energy dissipation devices, often referred to as dampers (even if damping is not the primary dissipation mechanism), may be inserted into a structural system with the express objective of reducing the response of the overall building by absorbing or dissipating energy within the devices. The most common of these devices can be grouped into two categories, hysteretic and viscoelastic, according to the primary dissipation mechanism. Hysteretic devices are the most common; they rely on relative displacements within the device for the dissipation of energy and are typically based on either metallic yielding or frictional sliding. Viscoelastic devices dissipate energy in either solid or fluid devices and depend upon both relative velocities and displacements within the devices. The dynamic response of systems containing such devices is affected both by the energy dissipation introduced and by the strength and stiffness that the devices add to the structure. Hanson and Soong[43] present detailed information on such devices, their analysis and design.

82. The following considerations are important for the design of such systems to meet the objectives of the NBC 2005:

The linear methods of analysis—dynamic or static—specified in the NBC 2005 provisions cannot take into account the inclusion of energy dissipation devices. Consequently, special studies using Nonlinear Dynamic Analysis are required to determine the behaviour of the structure, since both the structural members and the devices will respond nonlinearly during design level ground motions. Anderson et al.[44] provide guidelines for the nonlinear analysis and design of hysteretic devices based on the case study of a building designed for Vancouver.

The excitation used in the dynamic analysis must be consistent with that required in the NBC 2005 provisions. This would normally comprise ground motion time-histories having spectra that are compatible with the specified design spectral acceleration values for the particular location, including both site effects and the appropriate importance factor.

It is also important that the devices be capable of sustaining the deformations (number of cycles and amplitudes) determined from the dynamic analysis without deterioration of their function.

Evaluation and Rehabilitation of Existing Buildings

83. Although the NBC 2005 seismic provisions are primarily intended for new buildings, they can also be used for the evaluation of the seismic adequacy of existing buildings. Commentary L contains general considerations for the structural evaluation and upgrading of existing buildings as well as some discussion on earthquake considerations, including difficulties in applying the NBC seismic provisions for this purpose.

84. The 1997 NEHRP guidelines (Applied Technology Council[45]) contain more detailed earthquake-specific information including a comprehensive approach to the seismic rehabilitation of existing buildings. These guidelines present a performance-based design approach and use simplified deformation-based analysis procedures that explicitly recognize the nonlinear behaviour of building components and elements; they also address the use of seismic isolation and energy dissipation devices. The Applied Technology Council[46] developed a recommended procedure for the seismic evaluation and retrofit of concrete buildings; the conceptual basis for this procedure is also performance-based design using nonlinear static structural analysis.

NBC Subsection 4.1.8., Earthquake Load and Effects

Analysis (4.1.8.1.)

85. Earthquake loading and deformation need not be considered in design if the design spectral response acceleration, $S(0.2)$, is less than or equal to 0.12g, which is the floor level value of $S_a(0.2)$ on a Class C site in the low seismicity regions of Canada (see Figure J-1). The design spectral response acceleration, $S(0.2)$, as specified in Sentence 4.1.8.4.(6), takes into account the effects of site conditions by multiplying the location-specific spectral response acceleration, $S_a(0.2)$, by the acceleration-based site coefficient, F_a. For $S_a(0.2)$ equals 0.12g, F_a ranges from 0.7 to 2.1, depending on the site class. Consequently seismic design is required for all sites for which $F_a > 1.0$ but is not required in low seismicity regions (i.e. where $S_a(0.2)$ is at the floor level) for sites for which $F_a \le 1.0$ (i.e. all sites at Class C or better).

General Requirements (4.1.8.3.)

Sentence 4.1.8.3.(1)

86. This Sentence is included to ensure that designers use both the requirements of Subsection 4.1.8. and those of the applicable CSA design standards referenced in Section 4.3. when developing both the concept for how the building structure will resist earthquake ground motions and the details of the seismic design of the building structure.

Sentence 4.1.8.3.(2)

87. This Sentence introduces the concept of transferring earthquake-induced inertial forces to the supporting ground through clearly defined load paths. This concept entails designing the structure so that it incorporates a systematic approach for transferring inertial forces generated in the more massive portions of the building (e.g. floor slabs) to columns or walls that are continuous to the foundation of the structure. Where there are discontinuities in the load path, other provisions must be satisfied (e.g. Article 4.1.8.15.) to ensure that these discontinuities do not become zones of weakness.

Sentence 4.1.8.3.(3)

88. The designer of a building is required to clearly define the Seismic Force Resisting System (SFRS), which is that part of the overall structural system of the building that is intended to provide earthquake resistance by being the load path through which inertial forces are transferred to the ground. The SFRS has two primary functions:
    (1) sufficient strength to transfer loads to the ground, and
    (2) sufficient stiffness to maintain lateral deformation within acceptable limits.
    Some elements of the building's structural system may not be part of the SFRS (e.g. slender perimeter columns); although these are not intended to resist earthquake loads, they will be affected by such loads and must take those effects into account, as per Sentence 4.1.8.3.(5).

Sentence 4.1.8.3.(4)

89. This Sentence ensures that only the SFRS is counted on to resist the specified earthquake loads. Although there may be some implicit lateral load resisting capability in other structural components, none of the earthquake-induced loads can be assigned to such components as they are only designed to maintain their vertical load-carrying capability and not to maintain lateral stiffness or capacity. For example, if the SFRS comprises a core-wall system, no earthquake-induced loads should be assigned to perimeter columns, which are designed to carry gravity loads but which may have nominal lateral load resistance.

Sentence 4.1.8.3.(5)

90. This Sentence requires that the behaviour of structural framing elements that are not part of the SFRS be investigated when subject to earthquake-induced deformations associated with the lateral deflections calculated in Article 4.1.8.13. Under these conditions, such elements must retain their integrity while supporting the gravity loads for which they were designed; their integrity is assured by requiring that the elements behave elastically, or if their deformations are inelastic, that their

load-carrying capacity not be at risk. For example, slender columns at the perimeter of a building whose SFRS comprises a core wall must be investigated to demonstrate that they retain their capability of supporting their tributary dead and live loads while subject to the lateral interstorey drift associated with the maximum expected earthquake-induced deflections.

Sentence 4.1.8.3.(6)

91. Stiff elements such as concrete, masonry, brick or precast walls or panels are often not intended to be part of the SFRS. However, if such elements are not adequately separated from other structural elements (not just those that are part of the SFRS), then they can have major effects on the behaviour of the building during an earthquake. First, they can significantly change the dynamic characteristics of the building structure (natural period and mode shapes) by stiffening it, which will normally increase the inertial forces in the building structure and possibly lead to its collapse. Second, these stiff elements will be subject to loads for which they were not designed, making them vulnerable to failure, particularly since they are often relatively brittle and not capable of undergoing earthquake-induced deformation without failing. Third, such stiff elements can cause the failure of components of the SFRS by inducing forces for which those components are not designed. Sentence 4.1.8.3.(6) requires that stiff elements be separated from all structural elements in the building so that no interaction can take place, or that they be specifically made part of the SFRS. Separation to prevent interaction requires that the gap between a stiff element and another structural element be greater than the maximum earthquake-induced deformation in that part of the structure. For example, an infill masonry wall would have to be separated from adjacent columns by at least the amount of the computed maximum interstorey drift. If the designer chooses to make a stiff element part of the SFRS, e.g. by connecting a precast exterior wall panel to perimeter columns, then all of the requirements of Subsection 4.1.8. would be applicable to the analysis and design of that specific element. In particular, the effect of any stiff elements on the structural period and on the deflection of the structure when subject to earthquake-induced inertial load would need to be taken into account by appropriate modelling (see Sentence 4.1.8.3.(8)). Sentence 4.1.8.3.(6) is not meant to apply to gypsum wallboard and stucco.

92. It is important that stiff elements identified in Sentence 4.1.8.3.(6) be treated as specified in Subsection 4.1.8. and as such it is important that they not be added to the structure after the seismic design has been completed. It may be prudent for designers to address this issue by including a note on the structural drawings that clearly states that "such stiff elements, that are not separated, must not be added without the written permission of the designer."

93. Gypsum wallboard and stucco walls are not required to be separated from the SFRS in wood-frame buildings. The effect of gypsum wallboard on the SFRS is addressed in the provisions of CAN/CSA-086[47] (background information for the CSA provisions is given by Ceccotti and Karacabeyli[48]).

Sentence 4.1.8.3.(7)

94. This Sentence is concerned with the effects of structural members that are not designed for seismic resistance, in other words, that are not part of the SFRS. Although such elements often contribute stiffness to the building structure, they are not considered as contributing to the earthquake resistance of the structure. However, even though they are not considered part of the earthquake resisting system, their presence can contribute significantly to the overall behaviour of the building structure during an earthquake. Sentence 4.1.8.3.(7) identifies three particular situations involving such elements, which must be accounted for in the design process:

    Clause (a): The presence of these elements adds stiffness, which decreases the structural period; when the decrease is more than 15%, then the modified period must be used in determining the design forces. This is particularly important in low- to medium-rise building structures because the reduction in period results in a disproportionate increase in inertial forces.

    Clause (b): The irregularity of the structure may be affected by the presence of these elements and so they must be considered in determining the irregularity (as described in Table 4.1.8.6.). However, the additional stiffness contributed by such elements cannot be used to make an irregular structure regular or to reduce the effects of torsion. For example, the stiffness of a wall element or a gravity frame that is not part of the SFRS cannot be used to eliminate or decrease an eccentricity that exists due to the SFRS alone. Consider the case of an offset core whose SFRS comprises a braced frame or wall; a stiff gravity frame on the opposite face of the building cannot be used to reduce the torsional eccentricity unless it is made part of the SFRS, and designed accordingly.

Clause (c): The inclusion of structural elements that are not part of the SFRS may have an adverse effect on the SFRS, for example, by changing the load path and causing some parts of the SFRS to be subject to higher forces and/or deformations than would otherwise be the case. The design of the SFRS must take such adverse effects into account. For example, the SFRS may consist of moment frames along the perimeter in one direction and a central wall in the other direction. However, there may be a gravity frame along the perimeter parallel to the central wall that has a column in common with the SFRS moment frame. Due to the frame action in the gravity frame, this column will be subject to axial forces, shears and moments during lateral deformation; these additional forces must be accounted for in the design of the column as part of the SFRS moment frame.

Sentence 4.1.8.3.(8)

95. This Sentence requires that the structural modelling of the SFRS incorporate a realistic representation of the magnitude and distribution of building mass and structural stiffness; it specifically requires that modelling include the effects of unseparated elements that are deemed to be part of the SFRS as stated in Sentence 4.1.8.3.(6). Such modelling is required for:
    (i) the determination of lateral deflections, as specified in Article 4.1.8.13.,
    (ii) the calculation of torsional sensitivity, as specified in Sentence 4.1.8.11.(9), and
    (iii) the determination of the fundamental period of the structure, as specified in Clause 4.1.8.11.(3)(d).

96. The modelling for each of these purposes must be consistent, i.e. it must use the same assumptions regarding structural properties and behaviour.

97. The following modelling considerations are specifically identified as being important to take into account:
    (a) The effects of cracked sections must be modelled in determining the stiffness and strength of reinforced concrete and reinforced masonry elements. CSA A23.3[49] specifies the stiffness reduction due to cracking, which depends on the kinds of loads carried by such elements and can be as high as 65%.
    (b) Modelling must include the finite sizes of members and joints; a model that overlooks this feature can result in a significant underestimation of the stiffness of the structure. The extent of underestimation will depend on the type of structural framing system and the relationship between member sizes and span lengths. It is particularly important to include finite member and joint sizes when beams frame into shear walls; using a line representation of the shear wall and considering the beams joined at the shear wall centre line—rather than at the edge of the shear wall—will result in a structural model that is significantly more flexible than the actual structure.
    (c) The effects of the interaction of gravity loads with the displaced configuration of the structure will increase lateral displacements and moments throughout the structure; these additional moments reduce the capacity of the structure to resist lateral loads. These effects, which are commonly known as P-delta effects, can be particularly significant in ductile structures, which tend to have large displacements because there is a tendency for displacement to increase during each incursion into the inelastic range.

    P-delta effects have only a small influence on the response of buildings to seismic forces when the storey shear capacities exceed certain minimum values and the slopes of the storey shear-displacement curves, including P-delta effects, remain positive for the anticipated seismic displacements. When shear capacities fall below the minimum values and the slopes of the storey shear-displacement curves become negative, the displacements during earthquakes can become unacceptably large. Consequently, it is important that P-delta effects be modelled and taken into account if significant. Although considerable research has been done on how to take P-delta effects into account (e.g. Paulay and Priestley,[50] MacRae et al.,[51] Tremblay et al.,[52] Bernal,[53][54] Montgomery,[55] and Gupta and Krawlinker[56]), there is no widely accepted method to estimate seismically induced P-delta effects that takes inelastic deformation into account. The following procedure, which is similar to that recommended by Paulay and Priestley,[50] is recommended.

Earthquake-induced forces, shears, overturning moments and torsional moments calculated at each storey level are to be multiplied by an amplification factor of $(1 + \theta_x)$ to allow for P-delta effects, where θ_x is a stability factor. The stability factor at level x is equal to

$$\theta_x = \frac{\sum\limits_{i=x}^{n} W_i}{R_o \sum\limits_{i=x}^{n} F_i} \frac{\Delta_{mx}}{h_s}$$

In the above expression

$\sum\limits_{i=x}^{n} F_i$ is the seismic design shear force at the level under consideration, which is equal to the sum of the design lateral forces acting at and above the storey under consideration as determined in Sentence 4.1.8.11.(6),

$\sum\limits_{i=x}^{n} W_i$ is that portion of the factored dead plus live load above the storey under consideration,

Δ_{mx} is the maximum inelastic interstorey deflection as defined in Sentence 4.1.8.13.(2),

h_s is the interstorey height,

R_o is the overstrength-related force modification factor, and

$R_o \sum\limits_{i=x}^{n} F_i$ is a measure of the capacity at the level under consideration.

The amplification factor of $(1 + \theta_x)$ need not be applied to displacements.

The procedure recommended to allow for P-delta effects is equivalent to proportioning the structure at each level x to resist an increased seismic shear force $\sum\limits_{i=x}^{n} F_i^*$ calculated from

$$\sum_{i=x}^{n} F_i^* = R_o \sum_{i=x}^{n} F_i + \sum_{i=x}^{n} W_i \frac{\Delta_{mx}}{h_s}$$

$$= R_o \sum_{i=x}^{n} F_i (1 + \theta_x)$$

In calculating $\sum\limits_{i=x}^{n} W_i$, the dead load factor and companion-load factors given in Load Case 5 of Table 4.1.3.2. should apply. The live load may be reduced for large tributary areas in accordance with Article 4.1.5.9. $\sum\limits_{i=x}^{n} W_i$ is an estimate of the actual gravity load acting at the storey under consideration at the time of an earthquake.

With the seismic shear capacities at each storey increased to allow for P-delta effects, the ability of the strengthened structure to absorb inelastic energy during an earthquake is also increased. The interstorey deflections of the strengthened structure should be about the same as the deflections of the original structure with the P-delta effects taken to be zero.

If the stability factor, θ_x, calculated as described above is less than about 0.10, then P-delta effects can often be ignored. When the stability factor is more than 0.40, the structure should be redesigned to guard against potentially unstable buildings during extreme earthquakes.

Although the method described above is conservative in most cases, it cannot guard against the risk of dynamic instability when large inelastic deformations are expected, particularly when ductility demand is concentrated in a few storeys.

(d) Modelling must take into account any other effects that might influence the lateral stiffness of the building, e.g. panel zone deformation in steel moment frames (Krawinkler, Bertero and Popov[57]). Lateral stiffness is a particularly important parameter for two reasons:

(i) the earthquake-induced load on the building is a direct function of the natural period, which itself is a direct function of lateral stiffness, and

(ii) lateral stiffness is a major determinant of lateral displacement, which governs structural performance.

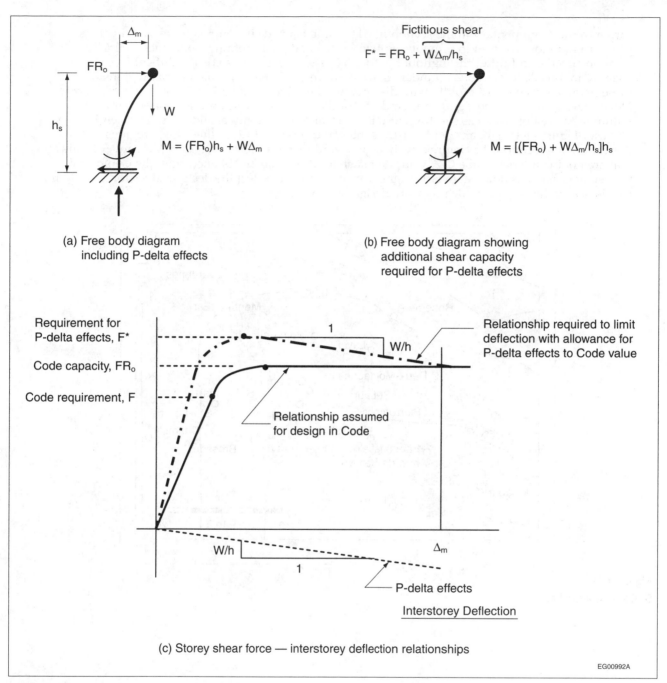

Figure J-10
P-delta effects for single-storey buildings

Site Properties (4.1.8.4.)

Sentence 4.1.8.4.(1)

98. Peak ground acceleration values and the 5% damped spectral response acceleration values $S_a(0.2)$, $S_a(0.5)$, $S_a(1.0)$ and $S_a(2.0)$ for the reference ground condition (Site Class C in Table 4.1.8.4.A.) for most towns and cities in Canada can be found in NBC Table C-2, Design Data for Selected Locations in Canada, in Appendix C of Division B. Values at locations not within the towns and cities listed can be obtained from the Geological Survey of Canada (at http://earthquakesCanada.nrcan.gc.ca or by mail at either 7 Observatory Crescent, Ottawa, Ontario K1A 0Y3, or at P.O. Box 6000, Sidney, B.C. V8L 4B2) by specifying the required latitude and longitude. The methodology for determining these values, which are median results at a 2% in 50 year probability of exceedance, is described earlier in this Commentary in the section titled Seismic Hazard. In contrast to the zonal values of peak ground motions used in previous editions of the National Building Code, these values are location-specific and differ throughout the country. This approach avoids the difficulty of sharp changes in force levels at zone boundaries, which were particularly problematic in regions where these parameters changed rapidly with distance or where the boundaries ran through urban areas. Nevertheless, there can be significant gradients of the values of these ground motion parameters within urban regions such as southwestern British Columbia, Montreal and the western end of Lake Ontario. Figures J-11, J-12 and J-13 illustrate the variations of $S_a(0.2)$ in these three regions. Also, there are some locations having relatively high hazard (e.g. on the west coast of Vancouver Island) that are not included in Table C-2; values for such locations can be obtained from the Geological Survey of Canada as noted above. Designers are cautioned to select the design values for a location that is near to the site for which they are designing a building.

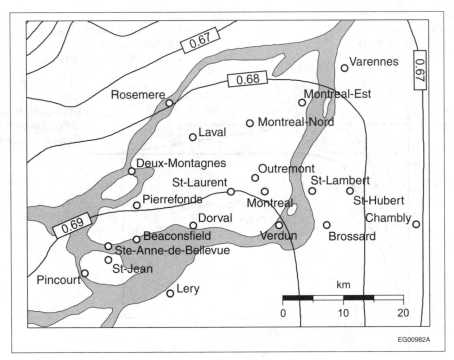

Figure J-11
$S_a(0.2)$ – Montreal area

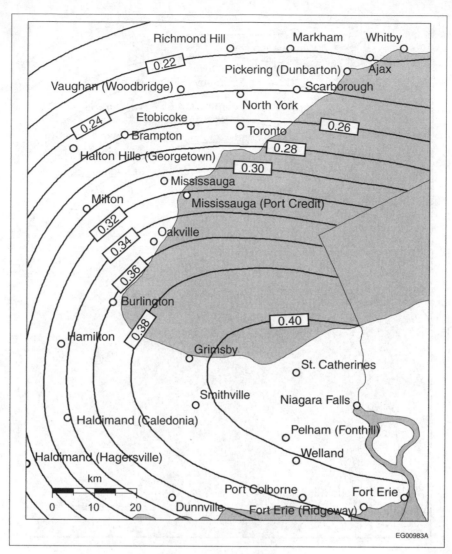

Figure J-12
$S_a(0.2)$ – Lake Ontario west

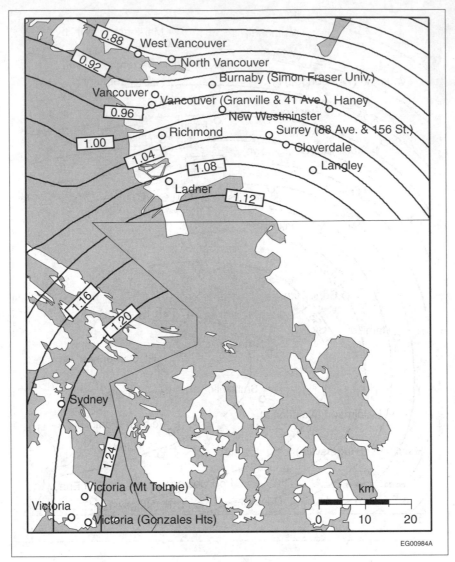

Figure J-13
S$_a$(0.2) – Southwestern British Columbia

Sentence 4.1.8.4.(2)

99. The rationale for using the site classifications given in Table 4.1.8.4.A. is described earlier in this Commentary in the section titled Site Response Effects. Although the brief qualitative description of the ground profile associated with each site class may be used for determining the appropriate site class, the standard penetration resistance, N$_{60}$, for sand sites and undrained shear strength, s$_u$, for clay sites are normally used to distinguish between Site Classes C, D and E. The preferred approach to determine whether a rock site is Class A or B is to use the time-averaged shear wave velocity, $\bar{V}_s$. In each of the above, the properties are to be averaged over a 30 m depth immediately below the bottom of the basement or the top of the piles. The allocation of a site to Class E is also based on the plasticity index, moisture content or undrained shear strength. With this approach, the difficulties associated with selecting a site class based solely on a qualitative description, as was the case in previous editions of the NBC, are avoided. The adjectives "very dense," "stiff," and "soft" used in Table 4.1.8.4.A. are general descriptions and do not necessarily correspond to standard geotechnical usage as defined in the Canadian Foundation Engineering Manual for example. The important properties are the ones presented in the last three columns of the Table.

100. The use of the hard rock or rock categories, i.e. Site Class A or B, requires that the shear wave velocity be measured either on site or on profiles of the same rock in the same formation with an equal or greater degree of weathering and fracturing. Where hard rock conditions are known to be

continuous to a depth of 30 m, shear wave velocity measurements at the surface may be extrapolated if the site contains softer and more highly fractured and weathered rock than profiles known to be Site Class B; either the shear wave velocity shall be measured on the site or the site shall be classified as Site Class C. The two rock categories, Site Classes A and B, are not to be used if there is more than 3 m of soil between the rock surface and the bottom of the spread footing or mat foundation, even if the computed average shear wave velocity (see below) is greater than 760 m/s.

101. Shear wave velocity can be determined using seismic cone, cross-hole or down-hole testing techniques (Kramer[58]). Where the top 30 m consists of a number of distinctly different soil layers, the shear wave velocity for each layer shall be determined and the average shear wave velocity, $\bar{V}_s$, should be computed using the following equation:

$$\bar{V}_s = \frac{\text{total thickness of all layers}}{\sum \left(\dfrac{\text{layer thickness}}{\text{layer shear wave velocity}} \right)}$$

Sentence 4.1.8.4.(3)

102. Although it is preferable to determine site class for non-rock sites on the basis of $\bar{V}_s$, it is permissible to use the energy-corrected Average Standard Penetration Resistance, $\bar{N}_{60}$, for sand sites, or the average undrained shear strength, s_u, for clay sites (averaged over the top 30 m of the site) in lieu of $\bar{V}_s$. The specification of the alternate site class definitions based on these geotechnical parameters should not be used to infer any specific numerical correlation between shear wave velocity and standard penetration resistance or undrained shear strength. Where the top 30 m is composed of a number of distinctly different soil layers, the parameters should be averaged as follows:

$$\bar{N}_{60} = \frac{\text{total thickness of all layers}}{\sum \left(\dfrac{\text{layer thickness}}{\text{layer standard penetration resistance}} \right)}$$

$$s_u = \frac{\text{total thickness of all layers}}{\sum \left(\dfrac{\text{layer thickness}}{\text{layer undrained shear strength}} \right)}$$

103. If the site contains more than 3 m of soft soil (which is defined by a plasticity index (PI) > 20, a moisture content of 40% or more, and an undrained shear strength (s_u) < 25 kPa), then the site is required to be assessed as Site Class E, even if the averaged parameters would otherwise qualify it as a better class. The rationale for this requirement is that soft soil layers as thin as 3 m can produce a high amplification of the underlying rock motion, somewhat analogous to large deflections due to the presence of a soft storey in a building structure.

104. Site Class F includes profiles of soils for which the determination of site amplification is problematic, e.g. liquefiable soils, highly sensitive clays, organic clays, highly plastic clays and thick soft to medium stiff clays. If the site corresponds to any of the four conditions described in the note to Table 4.1.8.4.A., then it is required to be assessed as Site Class F, and site amplification factors are to be determined by site response analyses, as specified in Sentence 4.1.8.4.(5).

Sentence 4.1.8.4.(4)

105. The site amplification approach described earlier in this Commentary in the section titled Site Response Effects was used to derive the site factors F_a and F_v specified in Tables 4.1.8.4.B. and 4.1.8.4.C., which are to be used to modify the ground motions for different site classes. Values of F_a and F_v are given for specific values of $S_a(0.2)$ and $S_a(1.0)$ in order to take into account the nonlinearity of site amplification with the intensity of ground motion. Linear interpolation is to be used for the determination of F_a and F_v for intermediate values of $S_a(0.2)$ and $S_a(1.0)$.

Sentence 4.1.8.4.(5)

106. As previously noted, Site Class F comprises soil profiles for which the determination of site amplification is problematic; the computation of F_a and F_v for this site class requires site-specific

Commentary J

geotechnical investigations and dynamic site response analyses. The site-specific geotechnical investigations required to determine data for site response analyses should include borings with sampling, standard penetration tests, cone penetrometer tests, and/or other subsurface investigations as well as laboratory soil tests to establish soil types, properties and thicknesses of layers down to rock or rock-like material. Dynamic site response analyses require modelling of the soil profile, selecting rock motions that are compatible with the spectral response acceleration values at the site, and conducting a nonlinear or equivalent linear dynamic analysis of the soil profile subjected to the selected rock motions. Further information on dynamic site response analyses is given in the Commentary of NEHRP 2000 (Building Seismic Safety Council[25]).

Sentence 4.1.8.4.(6)

107. This Sentence defines how the site coefficients are used to modify the 5% damped spectral response acceleration values, $S_a(0.2)$, $S_a(0.5)$, $S_a(1.0)$ and $S_a(2.0)$, to obtain the design spectral acceleration, $S(T)$, at $T = 0.2$ s, 0.5 s, 1.0 s, 2.0 s and 4.0 s, with linear interpolation used for intermediate values of T. The short period site factor, F_a, is used as an amplification factor for spectral values of 0.2 s and less; the long period site factor, F_v, applies for periods of 1.0 s and above. For $T = 0.5$ s, the construction used by NEHRP in formulating the two-factor approach (see Figure J-9) suggests F_v would be the appropriate multiplier. However, for some locations and site classes, the product $F_vS_a(0.5)$ is larger than the amplified motion $F_a S_a(0.2)$, which would produce an inappropriate spectral shape. Consequently, it is the smaller of these two products that is to be used to define $S(0.5)$. Figure J-14 shows an example of determining design spectral accelerations for this situation as well as the values that would be obtained using the incorrect formulation, i.e. $F_v S_a(0.5)$ instead of the smaller value $F_a S_a(0.2)$ at $T = 0.5$ s.

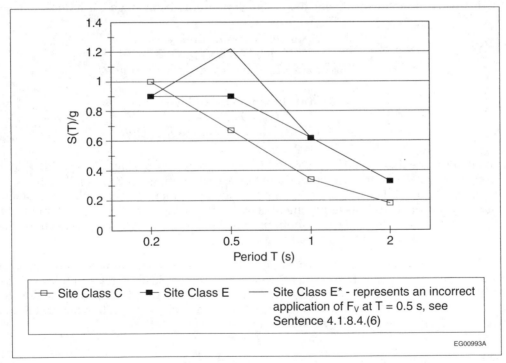

Figure J-14
Example of determining design spectral acceleration values (Vancouver)

108. Although spectral accelerations at very short periods are typically about the same or slightly less than the $S_a(0.2)$, the design values of $S(T)$ for $T < 0.2$ s are specified to be the same as $S(0.2)$. This degree of conservatism reflects the imprecision associated with the determination of periods for very stiff structures, since the period may well be somewhat longer than computed or damage to the structure may cause the period to lengthen and move into the higher response region.

109. Although insufficient data precludes the determination of spectral response acceleration values for periods longer than 2.0 s, it is necessary to specify design values for that period range. The design

acceleration, S(T), for T ≥ 4.0 s is specified to be one-half of that at T = 2.0 s, which is deemed to be conservative given available information on the drop-off gradient of spectral accelerations with increasing period.

110. To illustrate the combined effect of using two coefficients and nonlinearity, Figures J-15, J-16 and J-17 show the design spectral acceleration curves for three site classes (A, C and E) in Vancouver, Montreal and Toronto. These locations were chosen to represent high to low values of seismic ground motion; representative values of $S_a(0.2)$ for the greater Vancouver, Montreal and Toronto areas have been set at 1.00g, 0.69g and 0.28g respectively. For the purpose of comparing shapes only, all curves have been normalized to S(0.2) for Site Class C. To facilitate understanding of the impact of changes in the approach to site effects from the NBC 1995, Figures J-15, J-16 and J-17 include the comparable shapes of the product F·S·v, which represents amplified ground motions, for F = 1 and F = 2 in the NBC 1995, each normalized to the value of this product for F = 1 at T = 0.2 s. For the purpose of comparing shapes, note that F = 1 would apply to both Site Classes A and C while F = 2 would apply to Site Class E.

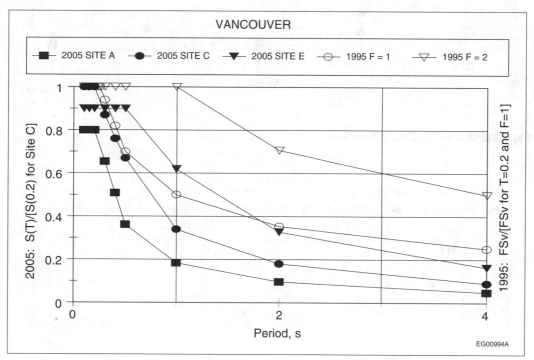

Figure J-15
Normalized spectral shapes for sites in Vancouver

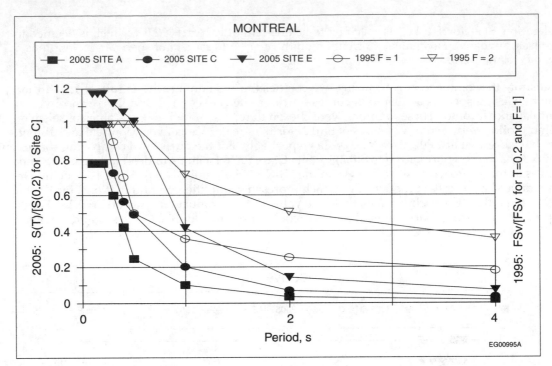

Figure J-16
Normalized spectral shapes for sites in Montreal

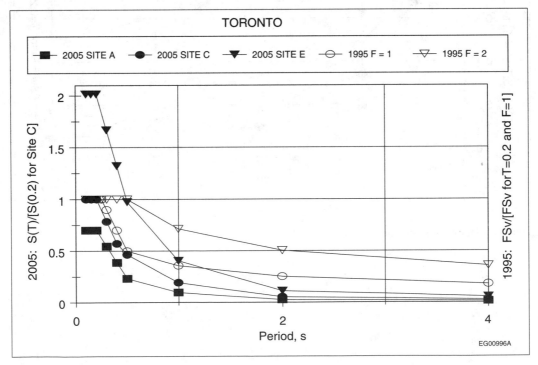

Figure J-17
Normalized spectral shapes for sites in Toronto

111. Comparison of the short period values of S(T) for Site Class E illustrates the importance of including nonlinearity. In Toronto, S(0.2) for Site Class E is over twice the value of that for Site Class C, while in Vancouver there is an actual de-amplification of about 10%. In Montreal, the short period amplification is 20%. The product F·S·v in the NBC 1995 for Site Class C at a period of 0.2 s showed no amplification over the rock site because the NBC 1995 capped this product in the short period range; that cap is clearly non-conservative in low seismic hazard locations such as Toronto.

112. In all three locations, there is a de-amplification between 10% and 30% for Site Class A, reflecting the fact that there are smaller ground motions on hard rock sites, all other conditions being equal.

113. The comparison of long period site amplification effects between the NBC 1995 and the NBC 2005 contained in Figures J-15 to J-17 is complicated by two aspects:
   (1) the spectral shapes on the reference ground condition have changed significantly due to the different approach to calculating seismic hazard (as discussed earlier in this Commentary in the Section titled Seismic Hazard), and
   (2) the long period shape of the site response factor, S, in the NBC 1995 included higher mode effects whereas $S_a(T)$ in the NBC 2005 represents a single-degree-of-freedom response.

114. However, comparing the relative values between Site Classes C and E at T = 1.0 s indicates that the amplification from C to E in the NBC 2005 is approximately the same as the factor F = 2 in the NBC 1995. This can also be noted by examining the values of F_v for Site Class E in Table 4.1.8.4.C., which shows values ranging from 2.1 for small ground motions to 1.7 for large ground motions, i.e. very little nonlinearity.

Importance Factor (4.1.8.5.)

Sentence 4.1.8.5.(1)

115. Table 4.1.2.1. identifies four importance categories for buildings, based on intended use and occupancy: they are Low, Normal, High and Post-disaster. Table 4.1.8.5 provides the values of the importance factor for earthquake loads, I_E, for each of these four categories for use in ULS (Ultimate Limit States) design: 0.8 for Low, 1.0 for Normal, 1.3 for High, and 1.5 for Post-disaster.

116. The primary use of I_E is to act as a multiplier in the calculation of the base shear, V, as specified in Sentence 4.1.8.11.(2). In that calculation, values of $I_E > 1.0$ have the effect of increasing the design spectral acceleration S(T) for High and Post-disaster buildings, i.e. decreasing the probability level for these more important buildings below that specified for Normal buildings. The larger design forces result in these buildings being designed for increased strength. Since, the base shear, V, is reduced to take into account inelastic energy dissipation and overstrength (see the Commentary section on Article 4.1.8.9.), these stronger High and Post-disaster buildings will undergo less inelastic deformation than Normal buildings when subjected to the same levels of earthquake ground motion. As a result, they will sustain less damage and will have more reserve capacity for ground motions, which may exceed the design level. These qualities provide important additional life safety protection in buildings that are used following a disaster to provide shelter or essential services.

117. Structures designed to house essential services should remain operational immediately after an earthquake. However, the mere application of $I_E = 1.5$ will not necessarily ensure the operational readiness of a facility after an earthquake. To determine what would be required for a functional survival would entail a detailed study of what equipment and services need to be operational immediately after an earthquake and of the anticipated behaviour of equipment and structural components. The study should address issues such as what equipment should be on emergency power, how long the emergency generators need to be able to run, how secure the fuel supply is, whether or not a stored supply of potable water is required. Building contents, such as equipment and services, that are required to remain functional immediately after an earthquake should be capable of accommodating the deflections specified in Article 4.1.8.13. (see also the Commentary section on Article 4.1.8.17.).

118. The factor $I_E = 1.5$ is not intended to cover the design considerations associated with special purpose structures, such as facilities for the manufacture or storage of toxic materials, whose failure could endanger the lives of a large number of people or affect the environment well beyond the confines of the building. These types of structures may require more sophisticated analysis.

119. Because earthquake loads are considered rare events (see the definition of earthquake load, E, in Sentence 4.1.2.1.(1)), there is no general requirement for design at the SLS (Serviceability Limit States) level and no SLS importance factors are given in Table 4.1.8.5. However, Post-disaster buildings must retain their capability to function following a major earthquake. So, rather than requiring SLS design for such buildings, their capability to continue to function is enhanced by specifying an operational, performance-level, interstorey lateral deflection limit (as discussed in the Commentary section on Sentence 4.1.8.13.(3)) that is only 40% of that specified for Normal buildings.

Commentary J

Structural Configuration (4.1.8.6.)

120. The primary issue related to structural configuration is whether or not a structure is regular or irregular. Observations of earthquake damage to buildings indicate that, all other considerations being more or less equal, structures having regular Seismic Force Resisting Systems perform considerably better than do those with irregularities. These observations are true even for structures that are well designed and built using good construction practices.

121. There are several reasons why irregular structures behave poorly when subjected to strong earthquake ground motions. In a regular structure, strong ground shaking produces inelastic behaviour, which tends to be well distributed throughout the structure, with energy dissipation and damage widely dispersed rather than being concentrated in just a few locations. However, in irregular structures, inelastic behaviour often tends to be concentrated in the zones of irregularity, resulting in the structural elements in those areas being subjected to excessive deformation and, consequently, rapid failure. This effect is compounded by the fact that designers frequently overlook the potential stress concentrations in the zones of irregularity when detailing the structural system. Another reason for which irregular structures behave poorly is that elastic analysis is normally used to distribute the demands of the earthquake ground motion throughout the structural system; however, elastic analysis—either static or dynamic—cannot adequately predict the distribution of demand in irregular structures, leading to inadequate design in the zones of irregularity. For these reasons, it is preferable that building designers use regular configurations and that gross irregularity be prohibited in locations of high seismicity where the expected very strong ground motions will put high inelastic demands on the structural system and to provide protection against ground motions that are greater than the design requirements.

122. Previous editions of the NBC contained specific requirements for only one irregularity, namely torsion. Detailed equations were provided for the calculation of torsional moments. In addition, the NBC 1995 stated that the design must take full account of the possible effects of setbacks but it was the Commentary that described why this was necessary. For the reasons outlined above, the NBC 2005 includes detailed definitions of a number of types of irregularity and requirements for handling buildings with those types or irregularities. In general, the presence of irregularities triggers restrictions and special requirements based on:
    1. the natural period or height of the building,
    2. the level of seismic hazard, i.e. the values of design spectral acceleration, and
    3. the importance category of the building.

123. The restrictions and special requirements are of the following kinds:
    1. the particular type of irregularity is prohibited,
    2. design forces must be increased,
    3. the design must be based on dynamic analysis, and
    4. special capacity design procedures are required for certain elements.

Sentence 4.1.8.6.(1)

124. The types of structural irregularity are detailed in Table 4.1.8.6., the right-hand column of which references table notes that point to specific provisions, which state the applicable restrictions and special requirements. This approach is intended to assist the designer who can consult the applicable requirements rather than needlessly examining the requirements for all irregularities when dealing with only one specific type.

125. The types of irregularity given in Table 4.1.8.6. can be divided into two broad categories, namely vertical (elevation) and horizontal (plan) irregularities. Types 1 to 6 are vertical irregularities while Types 7 and 8 are horizontal. However, it should be noted that some structural configurations may result in two or more types of irregularity. For example, a building frame in which the upper storeys comprise a tower that is asymmetric in relation to the lower storeys would have both vertical geometric irregularity (Type 3) and torsional sensitivity (Type 7). It is important that sound engineering judgment be applied when assessing irregularity and its influence on structural response.

126. The types of vertical irregularity are described below:

Type 1 – Vertical Stiffness Irregularity: This type of irregularity exists when the lateral stiffness in any storey of an SFRS is less than 70% of the stiffness of any adjacent storey, or less than 80% of the average stiffness of the adjacent 3 storeys, either above or below. A moment-resisting frame in which one storey is much taller than the adjacent storeys is an example of a Type 1 irregularity. Another example is a shear wall with a significant reduction in wall length occurring at one of the floor levels.

Type 2 – Weight (mass) Irregularity: This type of irregularity exists when the weight of any storey is more than 150% of the weight of an adjacent storey, with the exception that a roof with significantly less mass than the floor below is not considered to be irregular. A thicker floor slab supporting an intermediate mechanical floor is an example of a Type 2 irregularity. Another example is the transition from a lighter superstructure with a residential occupancy to a more massive parking garage below.

Type 3 – Vertical Geometric Irregularity: This type exists when the horizontal dimension of the SFRS (not necessarily that of the building envelope) in any storey is more than 130% of that in an adjacent storey. An example of a Type 3 irregularity is a reduction in the overall dimensions of a central elevator/stairwell core assembly (which comprises the SFRS of the building) above a particular floor level. The stepping down of the dimensions of a moment-resisting frame below a certain floor level is another example. In many cases, such as in these examples, both Type 1 and Type 3 irregularities exist in the same SFRS.

Type 4 – In-Plane Discontinuity in Vertical Lateral-Force-Resisting Element: This type of irregularity exists whenever a lateral-load-resisting element in the SFRS has an in-plane offset or has a lower lateral stiffness than the element above it. An example of an in-plane offset is when a system of braces, wall or moment frames comes down between one set of column lines and at some level changes over to another set of column lines that is parallel to and collinear with the first set of columns. An example of a decrease in lateral stiffness below some level would be when a system of braces, wall or moment frames terminates at that level of the building. Another example would be the presence of openings in one storey of a wall with either no openings or smaller ones in the storey.

Type 5 – Out-of-Plane Offsets: This type of irregularity exists when there is a discontinuity in the lateral force path, which is expected to remain in the plane of loading; an out-of-plane offset of the vertical elements of an SFRS produces such a discontinuity. An example of a Type 5 irregularity is a building that has a different spacing of column lines in its superstructure moment frame than in the frame of the parking garage below it. The relocation of the bracing in a steel frame from an exterior bay in lower storeys to an interior bay in upper storeys is another example. This type of irregularity is particularly problematic because of the large shear forces that must be transferred through the floor diaphragm at the level of the discontinuity; these cannot be calculated using a two-dimensional analysis and even a three-dimensional elastic analysis (static or dynamic) cannot accurately estimate the magnitude of such large shear forces.

Type 6 – Discontinuity in Capacity – Weak Storey: This type of irregularity exists when the total strength of all seismic-resisting elements of the SFRS in a storey (i.e. those that share the shear forces in that storey) is less than that in the storey above. Given that there is normally a correlation between strength and stiffness, this type of irregularity is actually a special case of a variation of Type 4. The most common Type 6 irregularity occurs in the bottom storey of buildings where it is architecturally desirable to have large window openings to accommodate commercial occupancies. There have been many incidents of collapse due to the presence of a weak or soft bottom storey, which tends to concentrate demand and resulting deformation in that storey. As stated in Sentence 4.1.8.10.(1), the NBC 2005 prohibits this type of irregularity except in locations of low seismicity; even then, the design forces must be increased significantly to accommodate the expected concentration of demand.

127. The common feature of vertical irregularities is that they result in non-uniform vertical distributions of stiffness and/or mass which, except for Type 5, normally occur in the plane in which the design loads are applied. In these situations, the primary consequence for seismic design is that the distribution of seismic forces throughout the height of the building is likely to be significantly different than that assumed in the Equivalent Static Force Procedure (ESFP), which is based on the assumption that the SFRS is uniform along the height of the building. Dynamic elastic analysis is required to obtain a suitable vertical distribution of seismic forces (see Article 4.1.8.7.). In addition, there are certain other restrictions imposed on structures with vertical irregularities, particularly on post-disaster buildings; these are detailed in Article 4.1.8.10.

128. Two types of horizontal irregularity are listed in Table 4.1.8.6.:

Type 7 – Torsional Sensitivity: This type of irregularity exists when structures with rigid diaphragms are torsionally flexible, leading to large torsionally induced displacements. An SFRS comprising only a central core of elevator/stairwell walls exemplifies a torsionally flexible structural system. The procedure for evaluating whether torsional sensitivity exists is described in Sentence 4.1.8.11.(9). The equivalent static method does not adequately take into account the potential for large displacements in structures with torsional sensitivity; in such cases, dynamic analysis is required as indicated in Clause 4.1.8.11.(10)(b). As for the cases of vertical irregularity, Article 4.1.8.7. describes the exceptions for which the ESFP is permissible.

Type 8 – Non-orthogonal Systems: This type of irregularity exists when the SFRS is not oriented along a set of orthogonal axes, which is the normal assumption with reference to the loads being considered to act independently along the two principal axes of the structure. An example of a Type 8 irregularity is a Y-shaped building plan with parallel sets of walls in each leg of the Y. The requirements for directions of loading that apply to this type of irregularity are given in Sentence 4.1.8.8.(1).

Sentence 4.1.8.6.(2)

129. When none of the various measures of irregularity described in Table 4.1.8.6. occur in a structure then it is classified as regular, which implies that the ESFP may be used for analysis, except in the case of tall buildings with long periods for which higher modes dominate response, as specified in Clause 4.1.8.7.(1)(b).

Sentence 4.1.8.6.(3)

130. Except for structures with a Type 6 irregularity, Post-disaster buildings, and buildings having fundamental lateral periods, T_a, ≥ 1.0 s and $I_E F_v S_a(1.0) > 0.25$, in situations when the product $I_E F_a S_a(0.2) < 0.35$, structures having any of the irregularities described in Table 4.1.8.6. need not satisfy the provisions referenced therein. This product represents the short period design spectral acceleration value, $S(0.2)$, multiplied by the importance factor, I_E; a value < 0.35 indicates that the anticipated earthquake ground motions are relatively small. Consequently, the restrictions specified for irregular structures, like the requirement to use dynamic analysis, are deemed to be unnecessary. The rationale for this particular relaxation of requirements is that the approximations inherent in the ESFP are unlikely to have serious consequences in situations when the ground motions are relatively small.

Signals for Special Requirements

131. Sentence 4.1.8.6.(3) includes the first instance of the use of the product $I_E F_a S_a(0.2)$ to act as a signal for specific design and/or analysis requirements. The most common value for this particular short period signal is 0.35, although values of 0.20 (Sentence 4.1.8.10.(1)) and 0.75 (Sentence 4.1.8.16.(5)) are also used. The NBC 2005 also uses the product $I_E F_v S_a(1.0)$, which has a signal value of 0.25 (Sentence 4.1.8.10.(3)). Table 4.1.8.9. specifies values of these signals to delineate restrictions regarding the use of different types of SFRS.

132. To illustrate situations in which these signals would apply, Table J-3 shows the two products for combinations of locations (Vancouver, Montreal and Toronto), site classes (A, C and E) and earthquake importance factors, I_E (1.0 and 1.5). The Table shows that all combinations of I_E and site class in Montreal and Vancouver have values of $I_E F_a S_a(0.2)$ above the most common short period signal value (0.35). For Toronto, these values are above or below the signal value depending on the particular combination of I_E and site class. With regard to the long period ground motions, the signal value of $I_E F_v S_a(1.0) = 0.25$ is not exceeded in Toronto; in Montreal it is exceeded only for post-disaster buildings on stiff soil sites or worse, or for buildings on soft soil sites.

Table J-3
Products $I_EF_aS_a$ (0.2) and $I_EF_vS_a$(1.0) for Vancouver, Montreal and Toronto

Site Class	I_E	$I_EF_aS_a$(0.2)			$I_EF_vS_a$(1.0)		
		Vancouver	Montreal	Toronto	Vancouver	Montreal	Toronto
A	1.0	0.80	0.54	0.20	0.18	0.07	0.03
	1.5	1.20	0.80	0.29	0.28	0.11	0.04
C	1.0	1.00	0.69	0.28	0.34	0.14	0.05
	1.5	1.50	1.04	0.42	0.51	0.21	0.08
E	1.0	0.90	0.81	0.56	0.62	0.29	0.11
	1.5	1.35	1.21	0.85	0.93	0.43	0.17

Methods of Analysis (4.1.8.7.)

Sentence 4.1.8.7.(1)

133. In contrast with previous editions of the NBC, the Dynamic Analysis Procedure (DAP) is the default method of analysis in the NBC 2005 and the Equivalent Static Force Procedure (ESFP) is permitted only if any of several specified criteria are met. The rationale for favouring the DAP is that structures respond to earthquakes dynamically rather than statically; overall response parameters (e.g. maximum base shear) and their distribution within the structure are affected by the structure's dynamic properties and the input ground motion. By contrast, the ESFP is only an approximate static simulation of that dynamic response and is reasonably accurate only in certain well defined circumstances. For example, when the structure is uniform along its height and has a relatively short fundamental period, T_a, then the static approximations for natural period and for the height-wise distribution of forces within the structure are quite realistic. The ESFP may be used for analysis if any of the criteria given in Clauses (a), (b) or (c) are present:

    Clause (a): Values of $I_EF_aS_a$(0.2) < 0.35 represent relatively small ground motions on which the approximations inherent in the ESFP are unlikely to have serious consequences. See Table J-3, which illustrates values of this product for combinations of locations, site classes and importance factors. Even if the distribution of internal forces in long period structures (e.g. T_a > 2.0 s) determined using ESPF is incorrect, in most instances the resulting design will be satisfactory in regions of low seismic hazard.

    Clause (b): Structures classified as regular (see the Commentary section on Sentence 4.1.8.6.(2)) that are less than 60 m in height and have fundamental periods less than 2 s may be analyzed using the ESFP. As noted previously, regular structures are inherently suited, in most circumstances, to static analysis. The modifying criteria relating to height and fundamental period reflect the fact that tall long period structures respond to earthquake ground motions in the second or higher dynamic modes rather than in the fundamental mode, which is the assumption in the ESFP. Consequently, dynamic analysis is required for such tall long period structures even if their configuration is regular.

    Clause (c): If the structure is less than 20 m in height and has a fundamental period of less than 0.5 s, then the ESFP is permitted for irregular structures, except for those with a Type 7 irregularity (Torsional Sensitivity). Static analysis is permissible in these cases both because, for short period structures, irregularities have minimal effect on the dynamic response and the ESFP specified in Article 4.1.8.11. is inherently somewhat conservative. The exclusion of structures with torsional sensitivity (see the Commentary section on Sentence 4.1.8.6.(1)) reflects the fact that large displacements due to torsionally flexible structural systems can occur regardless of the fundamental period of the structure.

Direction of Loading (4.1.8.8.)

Sentence 4.1.8.8.(1)

134. Earthquake ground motions can originate from a source that may be located in any direction from the site of a building. Consequently, for the purpose of designing structural elements so that they

perform adequately when subjected to such ground motions, the loading on a building can act in any horizontal direction. Such ground motions often exhibit directionality effects (i.e. different amplitudes and frequency content parallel and orthogonal to the direction of fault rupture); in general, the directions of loading of a structure should be such as to produce the most unfavourable effect on any structural element. The NBC 2005 assumes that, for most building configurations, applying the specified loads independently along two orthogonal directions is sufficient for that purpose; Clause 4.1.8.8.(1)(c) states the requirements when this assumption is not applicable.

Clause (a): Where the components of the SFRS are oriented along a set of orthogonal axes, then it is required that independent analyses be performed about the two principal axes of the structure. Although this requirement was included in the NBC 1995, the 1995 Commentary on Effects of Earthquakes only made reference to two horizontal axes, implying that these be principal axes. Designers may think that using their judgment to choose a set of orthogonal axes that reflects the predominant orientation of the elements of the SFRS is sufficient, and that there is no need to make the additional effort to determine the principal axes using methods of mechanics (Beer and Johnston[59]). However, as illustrated by DeVall,[14] the choice of axes can have a significant effect on the forces in members; choosing a more or less arbitrary set of orthogonal axes may well result in member forces that are significantly less than those obtained using principal axes.

Clause (b): Where the components of the SFRS are not oriented along a set of orthogonal axes, independent analysis about any two orthogonal axes is permitted provided $I_E F_a S_a(0.2) < 0.35$. Again, for such relatively low levels of ground motion, the use of an arbitrary set of orthogonal axes is unlikely to have a significant effect on the ability of the resulting structure to perform adequately during an earthquake.

Clause (c): Where the components of the SFRS are not oriented along a set of orthogonal axes, independent analysis about any two orthogonal axes is not permitted when $I_E F_a S_a(0.2) \geq 0.35$. As noted previously, independent analysis about two arbitrary orthogonal axes may not be conservative. The required procedure is outlined below.

Let the two orthogonal axes be called the "x" and "y" axes. Let any effect (e.g. member force or moment) due to the application of the specified loads in the two directions independently be called Effect$_x$ and Effect$_y$ respectively. The design shall be based on the most severe of the following combinations (i.e. that resulting in the greatest element strength):

± 1.00 Effect$_x$ ± 0.30 Effect$_y$ or
± 0.30 Effect$_x$ ± 1.00 Effect$_y$

Of course, these earthquake effects must be combined with other loads in accordance with Sentence 4.1.3.2.(2).

135. Combined directional effects are normally small on beams, girders, slabs and other horizontal elements that resist loads primarily in one direction, but they may be significant in columns and other vertical elements that resist loads applied in several directions (Building Seismic Safety Council[25]).

136. Earthquake ground motions may also contain a substantial vertical component. The amplitude of vertical motion is typically in the range of 60% to 75% of the horizontal amplitude but there have been records in which the vertical amplitude was approximately the same as the horizontal amplitude. Typically, the energy in vertical ground motions is concentrated at higher frequencies (lower periods) than that in horizontal ground motions. Because of the large stiffness in the vertical direction, vertical building periods are very short and normally produce little or no amplification of vertical ground motion. Buildings are also quite strong in the vertical direction and there is little history of damage due to vertical accelerations. For these reasons, the NBC does not require that buildings be designed for vertical ground motions. However, cantilevered building components may be sensitive to vertical accelerations; the loading of horizontally cantilevered floors, balconies and beams is specified in Article 4.1.8.17.

SFRS Force Reduction Factors, System Overstrength Factors, and General Restrictions (4.1.8.9.)

137. The 1995 edition of the NBC included the use of a force modification factor, R, in the denominator of the formula used to calculate the lateral earthquake force, V. This factor represented the capability of the structure to dissipate energy through hysteretic inelastic response during strong earthquake ground motions. R was often referred to as a ductility factor since, in most instances, it corresponded to the displacement ductility and energy-dissipating capacity of the structure during reverse cyclic loading without significant loss of strength or stiffness. Values of R ranged from 1.0 for very brittle

systems (e.g. unreinforced masonry) to 4.0 for the most ductile systems (e.g. steel or reinforced concrete ductile moment-resisting frames).

138. The NBC 2005 includes two force modification factors: the ductility-related factor, R_d, and the overstrength-related factor, R_o. R_d corresponds to the factor R in the NBC 1995 and ranges from 1.0 for the most brittle systems to 5.0 for the most ductile systems. Mitchell et al.[11] provides the rationale for the increased maximum value of this factor as well as discussing similar factors in other codes such as Eurocode 8 (ECS[60]) and NEHRP (Building Seismic Safety Council[25]).

139. As discussed by Mitchell et al.,[11] structures have traditionally been designed so that members have factored resistances that are equal to or greater than the corresponding effects due to factored loads. As a result, many structures, particularly those possessing a capacity for ductile behaviour, can have a considerable reserve of strength, which is not explicitly considered in the design process. Given that in the NBC 2005 ground motions are determined at a probability of exceedance of 2% in 50 years, it is expected that the actual capacity of structures would be more or less fully utilized during such a rare event. Consequently, for this severe level of shaking, it is reasonable to include the reserve strength in design provided it can be shown to exist. The overstrength-related reduction factor, R_o, represents the dependable or minimum overstrength that arises from the application of the design and detailing provisions prescribed in the appropriate CSA standard referenced in Table 4.1.8.9.

140. Mitchell et al.[11] describe the components used to determine R_o and show the detailed calculations for the values assigned to the various SFRS. The components contributing to R_o are: size (restricted choices of sizes of members and elements including rounding of sizes and dimensions), difference between nominal and factored resistances, ratio of actual yield strength to minimum specified yield strength, effect of strain hardening, and effect of mobilizing the full capacity of a structural system by the formation of a collapse mechanism.

Sentence 4.1.8.9.(1)

141. This Sentence specifies that the values of R_d and R_o to be used in design shall conform to those given for various SFRS in Table 4.1.8.9. and that the restrictions presented in that Table and all the requirements of Subsection 4.1.8. must also be observed. For each structural material (i.e. steel, reinforced concrete, timber and masonry), the descriptions of the different types of SFRS are for systems described in the corresponding CSA standards; the design and detailing of the structure must be done in accordance with the applicable standard in order to qualify for the stated values of R_d and R_o.

142. The values of R_d given in Table 4.1.8.9. reflect the degree of continuity and ductility provided by the particular SFRS. A value of R_d equal to 1.0 indicates that the SFRS exhibits little or no ductility (values of 1.0 have been assigned to systems that are not otherwise defined in Table 4.1.8.9. because their ductility capacity has not yet been demonstrated). Values of R_d above 1.0 reflect the increased capability of the SFRS to be designed and detailed to accommodate the required inelastic cyclic deformations.

143. Table 4.1.8.9. includes restrictions, which depend upon the modified short and long period spectral design acceleration "triggers," $I_E F_a S_a(0.2)$ and $I_E F_v S_a(1.0)$ (see the Commentary section on Sentence 4.1.8.6.(3)). As stated in the notes to this Table, the restrictions are designated either NP—not permitted—or a number representing the maximum height, in m, of the particular type of SFRS. The use of conventional construction for steel buildings in regions of moderate and high seismicity is restricted to buildings not exceeding 15 m in height. This restriction is simply intended to retain the traditional three-storey height limit stipulated in previous editions of the NBC; however, this height limit was not intended for and does not apply to single-storey, steel industrial structures. In particular, structures such as steel mills and aircraft hangars may exceed 15 m in height and are permitted to be built using conventional construction. Other tall steel structures such as stadia, exhibition halls, arenas, and convention centres must satisfy the height restrictions. CAN/CSA-S16[61] provides specific connection design requirements for a steel SFRS where $I_E F_a S_a(0.2)$ > 0.45. Other CSA standards specify height limits in terms of number of storeys; given the possible variation in storey height, the lower of the two limits—height or number of storeys—is applicable. For clarity, Table 4.1.8.9. includes the designation NL—not limited—for systems that are permitted without any height restriction, although height may be limited by a requirement elsewhere in the Code. If there is a conflict between restrictions, the most stringent restriction governs.

Commentary J

144. There are no restrictions in low seismicity regions ($I_E F_a S_a (0.2) < 0.2$) with the exception that there is a height limit of 15 m for SFRS not defined in any of the CSA standards listed in Table 4.1.8.9. This conservative approach is taken to limit risk in the case of unusual unproven structural systems. Sentence 4.1.8.9.(5) indicates that an alternate approach may be used for such unusual systems. In general, restrictions increase as the level of modified spectral design acceleration increases for the brittle, limited ductility or moderately ductile SFRS. Mitchell et al.[11] discuss the reasons for the various restrictions on such systems (there are no restrictions for the most ductile systems, i.e. those for which $R_d \geq 3.5$).

145. In choosing the structural system for a building, large dissimilarities in the stiffness and ductility characteristics of the SFRS in the orthogonal directions should be avoided. For example, a flexible ductile moment-resisting frame in one direction and limited ductility masonry shear walls in the other would be unsuitable, whereas ductile reinforced concrete shear walls and moderately ductile shear walls in orthogonal directions would be acceptable. The reason for this recommendation is that seismic displacements induced in ductile flexible framing systems would probably cause failure in the weak directions of relatively brittle elements resisting load in the orthogonal direction.

Sentence 4.1.8.9.(2)

146. For each SFRS, the determinations of R_o and R_d are interdependent in the sense that the resulting product $R_d R_o$ is an integral property of the particular SFRS as opposed to the two parameters being totally independent. Consequently and as specified in Sentence 4.1.8.9.(2), when a particular value of R_d is required, the associated value of R_o in Table 4.1.8.9. must be used. For example, it is not permitted to use a specified value of R_d from Table 4.1.8.9. and then conduct an independent analysis to determine a value of R_o that is different from the one specified in the Table.

Sentence 4.1.8.9.(3)

147. An entire building may be comprised of different types of SFRS combined together to resist lateral load. A common example is a dual structural system comprising a moment-resisting frame and a shear wall or braced frame. In fact, earlier editions of the NBC (e.g. NBC 1985) identified and assigned parameters to dual systems of this kind. Sentence 4.1.8.9.(3) requires that the lowest value of the product $R_d R_o$ be used when combinations of different types of SFRS are acting in the same direction in the same storey. For example, the combination of a ductile steel moment-resisting frame with $R_d R_o = 7.5$ and a moderately ductile concentric braced frame with $R_d R_o = 3.9$ would require the use of $R_d R_o = 3.95$ for the entire SFRS. Similarly, the combination of a moderately ductile, reinforced concrete moment-resisting frame and shear wall would require the use of the lower value of $R_d R_o$ ($2.0 \times 1.4 = 2.8$) for the entire SFRS. The purpose of Sentence (3) is to ensure that the design earthquake force, V, is based on the SFRS with the lower combined reduction factor, which will result in the higher design force. The rationale is that the response of the system will be governed by its most vulnerable part, i.e. the part with the lower combination of ductility capacity and overstrength. The seismic forces between the two types of SFRS in such a dual system are to be proportioned in accordance with their relative stiffnesses using the principles of structural mechanics. For dual systems in which the component SFRS types have different values of the ductility-related factor, R_d, it is important to ensure that the less ductile type can sustain the displacements associated with the more ductile type without loss of strength. Also, if there are structural elements that are common to the two types of SFRS, then detailing of those elements must meet the requirements for the more ductile of the two systems.

148. For dual systems of the kind described above, it is permitted to design the structure so that 100% of the seismic load is carried by the system having the higher value of $R_d R_o$. If this design approach is followed, Sentence 4.1.8.3.(5) specifies that the other system, which is now not part of the SFRS, must be designed so that it can retain its own functionality, e.g. supporting gravity loads while undergoing earthquake-induced deformations.

Sentence 4.1.8.9.(4)

149. The design of a building may also incorporate different types of SFRS throughout its height. An example would be the use of a ductile moment frame SFRS in the upper tower part of a building and a nominally ductile wall or braced frame system in the lower podium part of the building.

150. For such vertical variations of SFRS types, Sentence 4.1.8.9.(4) requires that the design value of R_dR_o in any one storey be less than or equal to the lowest value of R_dR_o used in the same direction of loading in any of the storeys above. In effect, this means that the overall structure must be designed for a base shear determined by the lowest value of R_dR_o used in the building. The intent of this provision is to prohibit the support of one SFRS by another SFRS with a high combined reduction factor, e.g. it is not permitted to use a ductile system in the lower part of a building to support a system with little or no ductility in the upper part of the building. This requirement does not apply to a penthouse having a different structural system than the SFRS of the main building provided that the weight of the penthouse is less than 10% of the weight of the level below it. The implication of this exception is that such a small appendage does not affect the response of the overall structure.

151. As stated in Sentence 4.1.8.15.(3), the NBC also requires that the elements of the SFRS below the level at which the type of system changes be designed for the forces associated with the lateral load capacity of the SFRS at that discontinuity (such capacity is to be determined in accordance with the applicable CSA materials standard).

Sentence 4.1.8.9.(5)

152. Only the most common structural systems are identified and have assigned values of R_d and R_o in Table 4.1.8.9. If an SFRS not specifically identified in that Table is used, then $R_d = R_o = 1.0$ must be used for design; this requirement is based on the assumption that systems that are not described should be designed conservatively. If it can be demonstrated through testing, research and analysis that the performance of a structural system is at least equivalent to that of an SFRS listed in Table 4.1.8.9., then Sentence 4.1.8.9.(5) allows the values for the equivalent listed SFRS to be used.

153. The most common approach for establishing the appropriate value of R_d is by cyclic testing of elements and sub-assemblages of the structural system, which involves subjecting them to a number of cycles of reversing deformations that increase until the capacity is reached. The subsequent evaluation of test results and analysis of typical building configurations incorporating those elements or sub-assemblages is then used to determine expected building performance, primarily the overall displacement ductility capacity. Examples of such approaches are given by Mitchell and Paultre[62] and Rahgozar and Humar[63]. Sentence 4.1.8.9.(5) specifically states that the performance of such a system is to be at least equivalent to that of the systems listed in Table 4.1.8.9. in order to qualify for an R_d that corresponds to that of such an equivalent system.

154. The overstrength-related factor, R_o, can be determined using the methodology described in Mitchell et al.[11] Caution needs to be exercised to ensure that minimum dependable values of the various component factors are used. Some of these factors may be determined from a further evaluation of the results of tests used in the process of determining R_d and, in any case, should be based on assumptions that are compatible with those test results. Again, the R_o determined through this process must be comparable to that for the equivalent system listed in Table 4.1.8.9.

Additional System Restrictions (4.1.8.10.)

Sentence 4.1.8.10.(1)

155. As noted earlier (see the Commentary section on Sentence 4.1.8.6.(1)), structures with a Discontinuity in Capacity – Weak Storey (Type 6 irregularity in Table 4.1.8.6.) are particularly vulnerable to damage and collapse during seismic ground motions. Sentence 4.1.8.10.(1) prohibits structures of this kind except in low seismicity regions where the importance modified short period design spectral acceleration $I_EF_aS_a(0.2) < 0.2$. When used in such low seismicity regions, the forces used for the design of the SFRS must be multiplied by R_dR_o to ensure that the structural system remains elastic when subjected to the design ground motion. Clause 4.1.8.10.(2)(b) prohibits Type 6 irregularities in Post-disaster buildings, even in low seismicity regions.

Sentence 4.1.8.10.(2)

156. As noted in Article 4.1.8.5., special consideration is given to Post-disaster buildings through the specification of an importance factor $I_E = 1.5$. In addition, Sentence 4.1.8.10.(2) imposes other restrictions on the design of the SFRS for such buildings. The intention of these restrictions is to

ensure that such buildings remain operational immediately after an earthquake by avoiding more vulnerable structural forms or types of structures.

Clause (a): This Clause prohibits most types of irregularities in Post-disaster buildings in regions of moderate to high seismicity, i.e. when the importance modified short period design spectral acceleration $I_EF_aS_a(0.2) \geq 0.35$. The irregularities that are prohibited—Types 1, 3, 4, 5 and 7 in Table 4.1.8.6.—are those characterized by geometric or stiffness discontinuities, which can lead to localized concentrations of inelastic deformation.

Clause (b): This Clause prohibits the Type 6 irregularity, Discontinuity in Capacity – Weak Storey, in Post-disaster buildings, regardless of the level of design ground motion.

Clause (c): This Clause requires that Post-disaster buildings have an SFRS with an $R_d \geq 2.0$. Such systems have at least limited ductility in order to provide some minimal capability of dissipating energy through inelastic deformation, which provides some protection against ground motions that exceed the design level.

Sentence 4.1.8.10.(3)

157. This Sentence requires that, for $I_EF_vS_a(1.0) > 0.25$ when the fundamental lateral period, T_a, ≥ 1.0 s, walls forming part of the SFRS be continuous from their top to the foundation and not contain an in-plane or out-of-plane discontinuity (irregularity Types 4 and 5 in Table 4.1.8.6.). The prohibition of these discontinuities is intended to enable such walls, which are normally used as part of the SFRS in medium to tall buildings, to function effectively during strong earthquake shaking.

Equivalent Static Force Procedure for Structures Satisfying the Conditions of Article 4.1.8.6. (4.1.8.11.)

Sentence 4.1.8.11.(1)

158. As described in the Commentary section on Article 4.1.8.7., the Equivalent Static Force Procedure (ESFP) can be used under certain conditions in lieu of dynamic analysis to determine the design earthquake actions, i.e. forces in elements and structural deformations. Sentence 4.1.8.11.(1) specifies that the static earthquake loads must be determined in accordance with the procedures given in Article 4.1.8.11. The lateral loads are to be applied to a linear mathematical model of the SFRS in the directions specified in Article 4.1.8.8. The model must meet the requirements of Sentence 4.1.8.3.(8), including appropriate modelling of the interface between the SFRS and the foundation. A detailed description of the ESFP specified in Article 4.1.8.11. is given by Humar and Mahgoub.[13]

159. The static loading specified in Article 4.1.8.11. is intended to approximate dynamic effects in a rational manner. As noted in other Articles in Subsection 4.1.8., such an approximation may not be valid in certain circumstances, in which case dynamic analysis is required. In particular, the ESFP loading assumes that the response of the structure is predominantly in the fundamental mode; the effects of the participation of higher modes are then incorporated by modifying the fundamental mode behaviour. If the response is not predominantly in the fundamental mode, e.g. in the case of tall flexible long period structures, then the ESFP is not valid; dynamic analysis is required for such structures, as specified in Clause 4.1.8.7.(1)(b).

Sentence 4.1.8.11.(2)

160. For a structure with a fundamental lateral period, T_a, the minimum lateral earthquake force, V—often referred to as the design base shear—is to be calculated in accordance with the following formula:

$$V = S(T_a) M_v I_E W / (R_d R_o)$$

where
$I_ES(T_a)$ is the importance modified design spectral response acceleration, which when multiplied by the weight, W, represents the maximum force in an elastic single-degree-of-freedom system with a period T_a,

M_v is a multiplier that accounts for the participation of higher modes in the actual dynamic response of the structure (the product $S(T_a)M_vI_EW$ represents the maximum force in an elastic system with a fundamental period T_a), and

R_dR_o is the reduction factor, which accounts for both ductility and overstrength, as discussed in the Commentary section on Article 4.1.8.9. (the rationale for reducing the maximum force by placing this product in the denominator of the expression for V is given by Mitchell et al.[11]).

161. Although the design spectral acceleration, S(T), is specified in Sentence 4.1.8.4.(6) for periods greater than 2.0 s, there is considerable uncertainty associated with those values at such long periods. Sentence 4.1.8.11.(2) therefore specifies a minimum value of V, which corresponds to the value when T = 2.0 s:

$$V_{min} = S(2.0)\,M_v I_E W / (R_d R_o)$$

In the above expression for V_{min}, the value of M_v must be that applicable for periods of 2.0 s or greater (see Table 4.1.8.11.).

162. The application of the formula for the calculation of V results in very high values of V at short periods (compared with values computed using the NBC 1995 formulation) for the following reasons:
   (a) hazard is now being computed at a lower probability, i.e. 2% in 50 years rather than 10% in 50 years;
   (b) the use of spectral response accelerations rather than amplified peak ground accelerations results in a response curve with a higher ratio of short to long period values, primarily because the amplification factor applied to peak ground accelerations in the NBC 1995 was too low. This was exacerbated in regions with zonal ratios $Z_a > Z_v$ because the short period values of the seismic response factor, S, assumed only a one zone difference between Z_a and Z_v even though there are many locations for which the difference is two zones (e.g. in Ottawa and Montreal where $Z_a = 4$ and $Z_v = 2$); and
   (c) for site classes that are softer than the reference Site Class C, the short period acceleration-based site coefficient $F_a > 1$ for locations with low to moderate seismicity has a maximum value of 2.1 for Site Class E in locations with $S_a(0.2) \leq 0.25$. The NBC 1995 imposed a short period cap, which limited base shear to the value computed for the foundation factor F = 1, even when the actual specified factor was higher.

163. Experience has demonstrated that damage to well designed short period structures with even a limited ductility is rare during earthquakes. One of the reasons for this is that damage in such structures actually occurs because of deformation and not as a direct result of high force levels; deformations are small because spectral displacements at short periods are very small. Also, the actual excitation of such structures is likely to be less than the specified spectral accelerations due to factors such as finite foundation size and energy dissipation at the foundation-structure interface, e.g. due to sliding.

164. Short period structures tend to have sources of both strength and deformability, which are not readily quantified in a simplified analysis and increase their ability to survive major earthquakes (Standards New Zealand[64]). Such structures are inherently stiff and therefore do not reach deformation levels that cause significant damage, particularly if there is some ductility capacity in the structural system. Very brittle short period structures would, of course, not behave as well because cracking leading to failure can occur without significant deformation.

165. As a consequence of the above, the NBC 2005 includes an experience-based factor of 2/3, which is applied to limit forces in all but the most brittle structural systems. The base shear need not exceed the following value for an SFRS having a value of $R_d \geq 1.5$:

$$V_{max} = (2/3)\,S(0.2)\,I_E W / (R_d R_o)$$

The higher mode factor, M_v, is not included in the above expression because its value is 1.0 for all periods less than 1.0 s (see Table 4.1.8.11.).

166. Other building codes also reduce calculated seismic loads on the basis of experience. NEHRP 2000 (Building Seismic Safety Council[25]), which also uses hazard computed at a 2% in 50 year probability of exceedance, applies a factor of 2/3 to all structures at all periods, on the basis of an experience-based estimated lower bound margin against collapse of approximately 1.5, which is inherent in structures designed according to the NEHRP provisions. The 1992 New Zealand Code of Practice (Standards New Zealand[64]) includes a multiplier of 0.67 in the static base shear expression;

one of the arguments for this factor is that experience in past earthquakes has indicated that, on average, buildings sustain less damage than what can be predicted from simplified calculations.

Sentence 4.1.8.11.(3)

167. The static base shear expression includes the design spectral response acceleration computed at the fundamental lateral period, T_a, in the same direction as the loading being applied. The determination of T_a is particularly significant in the short to medium period range ($0.2 \text{ s} \leq T \leq 1.0 \text{ s}$) in which the gradient of $S_a(T)$ as a function of T declines steeply. In most cases, approximate empirical formulae for calculating T_a based on building geometry (height or number of storeys) are permissible. The empirical formulae are specified in Clauses 4.1.8.11.(3)(a) and (b) (Saatcioglu and Humar[12] discuss the rationale for these approximations) whereas Clause (c) provides an alternative approach to using them.

Clause (a): The formulae for moment-resisting frames are essentially identical to those given in the NBC 1995 with the exception that the height-based formulae must be used for steel and concrete moment frames; the storey-based formula can only be used for other moment frames whereas the NBC 1995 allowed it to be used for any moment frames.

Clause (b): A new formula was developed for braced frames because using the one in Clause (c) was found to be unduly conservative.

Clause (c): The formula for walls and other structures is now in the same height-based format as the one for steel and concrete moment frames rather than including the length of wall or braced frame, D_s, as was the case in the NBC 1995 (the determination of the appropriate value of D_s was problematic for many structural systems).

Clause (d): Established methods of mechanics may be used as an alternative approach to determining T_a. However, it is now required that these methods use an appropriate structural model, the important features of which are given in Sentence 4.1.8.3.(8) (see the Commentary section on that Sentence). Even if these modelling requirements are met, computed periods still tend to be longer than the ones measured in actual structures because modelling usually does not take into account the participation of non-structural elements, which tend to stiffen the structure. The use of computed periods, which are longer than actual periods, results in non-conservative seismic design forces because the design spectral acceleration decreases with an increase in period, thereby resulting in a reduction of design base shear. To guard against the computation of excessively long periods, Clause (d) requires that the computed periods for moment-resisting frames be not greater than 1.5 times the value determined using the empirical formulae in Clause (a), 2.0 times the value determined in Clause (b) for braced frames, and 2.0 times the value established in Clause (c) for shear walls (this larger limit is allowed for shearwall structures because studies have shown that periods calculated for such structures using the methods of mechanics are similar to measured values (Saatcioglu and Humar[12])).

Although shorter periods are conservative with reference to the determination of design forces, they have the opposite effect on the determination of deflections. The use of unrealistically short periods may result in a significant underestimation of lateral deflections and interstorey drifts, which would be problematic for flexible structural systems in which deformations are likely to govern performance, e.g. moment-resisting frames.

The upper limits specified on the calculated periods in Clause (d) are in consideration of the possibility that the actual structure may be stiffer than the model used to compute the period and may therefore attract higher earthquake forces. The deflections calculated by applying these higher forces on the flexible model are quite conservative. For consistency, the model used to calculate the deflections should be the same as the one used to compute the period, and hence the earthquake forces. Therefore, in calculating the deflections it is permitted to use the period determined according to Clause (d) without the upper limit specified therein.

Sentence 4.1.8.11.(4)

168. The weight, W, used in the base shear formula is calculated as the sum of the weights of each of the storeys. Since the weight represents mass in this calculation, it is specified in Article 4.1.8.2. as being dead load (see the definition in Article 4.1.4.1.), plus 25% of snow load, plus 60% of storage loads (parking garages need not be considered as storage areas), plus the full contents of any tanks. If the design of a building includes permanent masses that are normally included in the description of live load, then the weight of these masses should be included in the calculation of W.

Sentence 4.1.8.11.(5)

169. As noted previously (see the Commentary section on Sentence 4.1.8.11.(2)), the calculation of static base shear involves the transformation of the shear in a single-degree-of-freedom system to that in a multi-degree-of-freedom system by the inclusion of the factor M_v to take into account the participation of higher modes in the dynamic response of the structure. The extent of higher mode participation is a function of the type of structural system, the fundamental period of the structure, and the shape of the spectral response acceleration $S_a(T)$ as it varies with period. Table 4.1.8.11. specifies the values for M_v for different combinations of these parameters; the spectral shape is represented by the ratio $S_a(0.2)/S_a(2.0)$. The methodology used to compute M_v and the analysis that resulted in the values specified in this Table are given by Humar and Mahgoub.[13] With regard to the ratio $S_a(0.2)/S_a(2.0)$, values < 8.0 and ≥ 8.0 are predominantly associated with seismic hazard in the active western and eastern Canadian regions respectively.

170. Table 4.1.8.11. shows that the higher mode effects are most significant for long period wall-type structures, with M_v having a maximum value of 2.5 for such structures when $S_a(0.2)/S_a(2.0) > 8.0$. $M_v = 1.0$ for all structures with periods less than or equal to 1.0 s; there are no higher mode effects for such structures. In fact, for short period structures (i.e. periods of 0.5 s or less), Humar and Mahgoub[13] show that the calculated value of M_v is typically 0.8 or less. The benefit of the resulting reduced base shear may be obtained by using dynamic analysis; Sentence 4.1.8.12.(6) permits the dynamically determined base shear to be as low as 80% of the static value for regular structures.

171. Higher mode effects tend to increase base shear (from that calculated for a single-degree-of-freedom structure) in long period structures. The use of the factor M_v to account for these effects in the calculation of base shear has the further effect of overvaluing the overturning moments in the structure. Although the contribution of higher modes to base shear can be significant, the corresponding contribution of higher modes to overturning moment is relatively small. Consequently, it is necessary to compensate by reducing overturning moments. The base overturning moment reduction factor, J, is given in Table 4.1.8.11. Humar and Mahgoub[13] describe the analysis and show the results that lead to these values.

Sentence 4.1.8.11.(6)

172. The ESFP approach involves both the calculation of the value of the equivalent lateral load, V, in accordance with Sentence 4.1.8.11.(2), and the distribution of that load along the height of the building. When the dynamic response is primarily in the first mode, which is the case for short period structures, the shape of this fundamental mode response for regular structures (i.e. those of uniform mass and storey height) is very nearly a straight line, i.e. response is proportional to height above the base of the structure. Since there is normally some variation in storey height and floor weight, Sentence 4.1.8.11.(6) calls for the forces applied at each floor to be proportional to floor weight multiplied by height from the base as follows:

$$V_x \propto w_x h_x / \sum w_i h_i$$

173. However, for medium to long values of the fundamental period, T_a, this inverted triangular loading distribution fails to account for the effect of higher modes, even though the value of V itself has taken those into account. The effect of a higher mode response on the distribution of load, which tends to increase the shear in the upper storeys, is taken into account by specifying that a portion of the base shear, F_t, be applied as a concentrated load at the top of the structure with the remaining shear distributed in the same manner as indicated above. The resulting expression for the force at any floor level "i" is to be calculated as follows:

$$F_x = (V - F_t) W_x h_x / \left(\sum_{i=1}^{n} W_i h_i \right)$$

Commentary J

The value of the concentrated force, F_t, depends on the fundamental period, T_a:

$$F_t = 0 \qquad\qquad ; T_a \leq 0.7\,\text{s}$$
$$F_t = 0.07 T_a V \quad ; 0.7\,\text{s} < T_a < 3.6\,\text{s}$$
$$F_t = 0.25 V \qquad ; 3.6\,\text{s} \leq T_a$$

Humar and Mahgoub[13] discuss the reasons why this distribution is adequate for design purposes.

Sentence 4.1.8.11.(7)

174. As previously mentioned, Table 4.1.8.11. gives the overturning moment reduction factor, J, which is to be applied at the base of the structure in recognition of the overestimation of the higher mode effects on overturning moments. Not only does a reduction factor need to be applied to the base overturning moment but also to the overturning moments at other levels in the structure. Sentence 4.1.8.11.(7) requires that the factor J_x applied at level x be calculated as follows:

$$J_x = 1.0 \qquad\qquad\qquad\qquad \text{for } h_x \geq 0.6 h_n$$
$$J_x = J + (1 - J)\,(h_x/0.6 h_n) \quad \text{for } h_x < 0.6 h_n$$

As indicated in the above expressions, no reduction is applied in the top 40% of the height of the building and a linear variation occurs below that height to the reduction factor, J, at the base. The factor J_x is to be applied as a multiplier to the overturning moment normally computed at level x.

Sentence 4.1.8.11.(8)

175. Although the static loads F_x defined in Article 4.1.8.11. are to be applied horizontally to a two-dimensional mathematical model of the structure, the actual structure is three-dimensional and responds both laterally and torsionally to earthquake ground motions. Observations during earthquakes have indicated that torsional vibrations are often the source of significant damage (Esteva[65] and Mitchell et al.[66]). Sentence 4.1.8.11.(8) requires that the design of the structure include the consideration of torsional effects concurrently with those due to the lateral static loads. As indicated in Article 4.1.8.3., earthquake effects are considered by independent analysis in two orthogonal directions; the two sources of torsion described in Clauses (8)(a) and (b) must be included in both of those independent analyses.

176. Because the ESFP is by definition an elastic method of analysis, the torsional effects described in Sentence 4.1.8.11.(8) assume elastic behaviour. However, as previously noted in this Commentary, building structures subjected to ground motions at a probability of exceedance of 2% in 50 years are expected to behave inelastically. The effect of inelastic response on lateral response is accounted for in a simplified manner by the application of the reduction factor R_d; there is no comparable methodology for simplifying the effects of inelastic behaviour on torsional response. These effects are considered and discussed by Humar, Yavari and Saatcioglu[15] who show that, in most instances, the ductility demand at the edges of asymmetric buildings—the positions at which the deformations are the largest—is no greater than that in comparable symmetric or torsionally balanced buildings.

    Clause (a): Torsional motion occurs in asymmetric structures, i.e. those in which the centres of rigidity at each level of the structural system do not coincide with the centres of mass at those levels. The centres of rigidity are defined as the set of positions for each floor at which the application of the full set of lateral forces results only in lateral deflection at all floor levels. When an asymmetric structure responds to a dynamic excitation, such as an earthquake ground motion, then there may also be a dynamic amplification of the torsional motion.

    Clause (b): Torsional motion may also occur in nominally symmetric structures due to uncertainty in the determination of the centres of mass and stiffness, inaccuracy in the measured dimensions of structural elements, or variations in material properties, e.g. modulus of elasticity. Another source of torsional vibration in nominally symmetric structures is rotational ground motion (Rutenberg and Heidebrecht[67]). All of these sources together are referred to as accidental torsion.

Sentence 4.1.8.11.(9)

177. Torsional effects can be considered using static analysis if the structure does not have torsional sensitivity, which is determined using the approach described in Sentence 4.1.8.11.(9). The determination of torsional sensitivity requires static analysis using a three-dimensional elastic model of the SFRS with the static lateral loads at each floor level applied at distances $\pm 0.10\ D_{nx}$ from the centres of mass, in which D_{nx} is the plan dimension of the building at floor level x perpendicular to the direction of seismic loading being considered. A parameter B_x is calculated at each floor level; this parameter is the ratio of the maximum lateral displacement at either of the two edges to the average of the displacements at the two edges. The torsional sensitivity parameter, B, for the entire building is the maximum of all of the values of B_x for both orthogonal directions of loading. The value of B_x for one-storey penthouses whose weight is less than 10% of that of the level below need not be included because low mass appendages have little effect on the overall torsional characteristics of a structure.

178. The determination of torsional sensitivity is only applicable to structures with rigid diaphragms, as indicated in Table 4.1.8.6. Structures with flexible diaphragms are designed so that their loads, including the effects of accidental torsion, are distributed to the vertical elements using the tributary area concept. Accidental torsion should be taken into account by moving the centre of mass by $\pm 0.05\ D_{nx}$ and using the largest of the seismic loads for the design of each vertical element.

Sentence 4.1.8.11.(10)

179. Torsionally stiff structures have small values of B and torsionally flexible structures have large values of B. As shown by Humar, Yavari and Saatcioglu,[15] the static approach for the determination of torsional effects given in Clause 4.1.8.11.(10)(a) is only valid for buildings that are relatively stiff in torsion, i.e. $B \leq 1.7$. When buildings are torsionally flexible, i.e. $B > 1.7$, dynamic, torsionally induced displacements cannot be reliably predicted using static measures of eccentricity. Since displacements in torsionally flexible structures are large and are therefore likely to be the source of significant distress, it is necessary to determine these displacements using dynamic analysis, including the effects of accidental eccentricity, as specified in Clause 4.1.8.11.(10)(b).

> **Clause (a):** The static formulation for the determination of torsional effects, to be used when $B \leq 1.7$, requires the determination of torsional moments, T_x, which are to be applied about the vertical axis at each level of the building. For each direction of loading, the effects of these torsional moments are to be applied in combination with the effects of the lateral loads.
>
> This Clause specifies that the torsional moments, T_x, are to be calculated separately for two different design eccentricities, and that the elements of the building be designed for the most severe effect; since these are to be applied with lateral loads in two orthogonal directions, this represents four distinct load cases.
>
> The two design eccentricities at each floor level can be written as
>
> $$e_{d1}, e_{d2} = e_x \pm 0.10 D_{nx}$$
>
> where e_x is the natural eccentricity, i.e. that due to the centres of rigidity and mass being at different positions. DeLaLlera and Chopra[68] show that the portion $\pm 0.05\ D_{nx}$ represents that required to cover accidental torsion; the remainder takes into account natural torsion, including dynamic amplification.
>
> Torsional moments calculated using the provisions of the NBC 1995 included multipliers of 0.5 and 1.5 applied to the natural eccentricity, which implied that an actual value of e_x had to be determined, thus necessitating the determination of the centres of resistance at each floor level, which is often a complex process. There are methods by which the provisions of the NBC 1995 could be met without the explicit calculation of the centres of resistance (e.g. Goel and Chopra[69]) but these methods are convoluted and require many steps.
>
> In the NBC 2005 provisions, the positions of the centres of resistance at each floor do not need to be determined. Because there is no multiplier applied to e_x, the combination of lateral and torsional effects in each direction of loading can be obtained directly by two applications of the lateral loads, one set located $+0.10\ D_{nx}$ from the centres of mass and the other located $-0.10\ D_{nx}$ from the centres of mass. Conveniently, this is exactly the same set of load applications required for the determination of the torsional sensitivity parameter, B (see Sentence 4.1.8.11.(9)).

Commentary J

Clause (b): This Clause requires that the Dynamic Analysis Procedure be used for cases where B > 1.7 and $I_E F_a S_a(0.2) \geq 0.35$ as given in Article 4.1.8.12. The reasons why dynamic analysis is required are discussed earlier in the Commentary (see also Humar, Yavari and Saatcioglu[15]). However, as indicated in Clause 4.1.8.7.(1)(a), the ESFP may be used in regions of low seismic hazard regardless of whether torsional sensitivity or any other permissible irregularity exists; the approximations inherent in the ESFP are unlikely to have serious consequences for such relatively small ground motions.

Dynamic Analysis Procedures (4.1.8.12.)

180. As indicated in Article 4.1.8.7., dynamic analysis is mandatory for the determination of earthquake design actions except for situations in which the simplified ESFP is adequate, as detailed in that same Article. Dynamic analysis must be conducted in accordance with the procedures of Article 4.1.8.12.

Sentence 4.1.8.12.(1)

181. This Sentence indicates that it is permissible to do either a Linear or a Nonlinear Dynamic Analysis.
   Clause (a): A Linear Dynamic Analysis, using either the Modal Response Spectrum Method or the Numerical Integration Linear Time History Method, is the normal approach because the analysis procedures are straightforward and can be found in texts on structural dynamics (Chopra,[70] Humar[71]). Also, standard software used for structural analysis often includes Linear Dynamic Analysis as one of the options; the Modal Response Spectrum Method is more commonly included in such software. The structural model used in Linear Dynamic Analysis must comply with the requirements of Sentence 4.1.8.3.(8) to ensure that it represents the actual structure in a realistic manner. The other Sentences in Article 4.1.8.3. prescribe how the dynamic excitation is to be determined and how the results are to be used in design, including how accidental torsion is to be taken into account. Saatcioglu and Humar[12] discuss various of these requirements including considerations such as the number of modes required to accurately represent the dynamic response of the structure.

   The Modal Response Spectrum Method is based on the fact that the response of a linear elastic system is made up of the superposition of the responses of individual natural modes of vibration, each mode responding at its natural frequency with its own pattern of deformation, i.e. its mode shape. The most common form of this method involves the combination of the maximum response parameters in each mode to determine the maximum values of the response parameters for the structure as a whole. Only a small number of modes (e.g. 3 to 5) are required to provide a good approximation of the total response; Chopra[70] discusses the factors involved in selecting the number of modes, which are affected both by the desired accuracy and the response quantity of interest. NEHRP 2000 (Building Seismic Safety Council[25]) provides a simple rule for the determination of the number of modes required: the normal requirement is that the combined participating mass of all the modes included in the analysis should total at least 90% of the total mass. The primary sources of uncertainty in this method are: the validity of the structural model, the validity of the modal combination rule, and the value of damping in each mode.

   The Numerical Integration Linear Time History Method involves the determination of the response of a structural model to a specific earthquake ground motion accelerogram through the numerical integration of the equations of motion. The primary advantage of this method, compared with the Modal Response Spectrum Method, is that the various response parameters are obtained as time-histories, providing information on the time-wise fluctuation of the state of deformation of the structure. There are several disadvantages, most notably: i) such analyses produce voluminous amounts of data to be interpreted, and ii) the results depend greatly on the characteristics of the individual ground shaking accelerograms so that analyses need to be done using a number of different time-histories (see the Commentary section on Sentence 4.1.8.12.(3)). Due to these disadvantages and the resulting increased costs of analysis, this method is rarely used for the design of ordinary building structures.
   Clause (b): A Nonlinear Dynamic Analysis is an acceptable alternative provided that a special study is performed. Since such analyses are still primarily done in a research environment, it is essential that the special study be conducted by individuals who are competent and experienced in making the necessary judgments and decisions. In addition, the resulting design should be reviewed by a qualified independent engineering team. Although nonlinear analysis may be used to determine the response of the structure in achieving such a design,

it should be noted that all of the general and specific requirements of Subsection 4.1.8. are still applicable. Particular attention needs to be given to the requirements for stiff elements (Sentences 4.1.8.3.(6) and (7)), the effects of site classification on ground motion (Article 4.1.8.4.), the use of an appropriate importance factor (Article 4.1.8.5.), and structural configuration restrictions (Article 4.1.8.6. and the Sentences referenced therein). The resulting design will, in most instances, be expected to have features (e.g. member sizes and stiffnesses) that are similar to those of a design using Linear Dynamic Analysis or the Equivalent Static Force Procedure.

The following aspects are of particular importance in the special study:

(i) The ground motion time-histories used as input should be representative of the seismotectonic environment at the location of the building, i.e. correspond to earthquake ground motions that have been recorded for magnitudes and epicentral distances similar to those that dominate seismic hazard at the particular location. In addition to being compatible with a response spectrum constructed from the design spectral acceleration values, S(T) (see the Commentary section on Sentence 4.1.8.12.(3)), these time-histories need to have durations and waveforms that will allow the structural model to respond inelastically with sufficient cycles of load reversal. Also, sufficient time-histories need to be used to enable uncertainties in ground motion parameters (e.g. durations) to be reflected in the dispersion of the resulting response parameters (see the Commentary section on Sentence 4.1.8.12.(3)).

(ii) The inelastic properties of the structural elements in the model (e.g. strength, stiffness, ductility capacity and hysteretic behaviour) need to be representative of the behaviour of actual elements that have been subjected to reverse cyclic loading tests. While the modelling of flexural elements with well-defined yielding and hysteretic behaviour is relatively easy, the modelling of other kinds of elements (e.g. wall panels) and their interaction with flexural elements is more complex, particularly if such elements are brittle or have limited ductility. Saatcioglu and Humar[12] present information on hysteretic models commonly used to represent structural elements.

(iii) The interpretation of the results in the design of members must take into account both global (e.g. lateral displacements and interstorey drifts) and local (e.g. member end curvature or rotation) response parameters and their dispersion. In contrast to linear analysis, it is not feasible to simply adopt maximum values of computed member forces for design; in the inelastic regime, member behaviour is described primarily in terms of deformation patterns, which include both maxima and the number of significant deformation reversals.

Sentence 4.1.8.12.(2)

182. The Modal Response Spectrum Method requires that the dynamic excitation be represented as an acceleration response spectrum, i.e. the maximum acceleration response of a single-degree-of-freedom system with varying period when subjected to a specific ground motion-time history. Sentence 4.1.8.12.(2) specifies that the spectral acceleration values, i.e. the ordinates of the acceleration response spectrum, be the design spectral acceleration values, S(T), defined in Sentence 4.1.8.4.(6), which include site effects through the use of the site coefficients F_a and F_v. As noted earlier in the Commentary section titled Seismic Hazard, S(T) is essentially a Uniform Hazard Spectrum (UHS), i.e. a plot of spectral acceleration ordinates at different periods, each ordinate having the same probability of exceedance. While S(T) is not an acceleration response spectrum, Humar and Mahgoub[13] show that the UHS is a slightly conservative representation of a response spectrum but that the degree of conservatism is insignificant for practical purposes, i.e. resulting in no more than a 10% overestimation of the response of a multi-degree-of-freedom structure.

Sentence 4.1.8.12.(3)

183. The Numerical Integration Linear Time History Method requires dynamic excitations, which are represented as acceleration time histories. Sentence 4.1.8.12.(3) requires that such time histories be compatible with a response spectrum constructed from the design spectral acceleration values, S(T) (see the Commentary section on Sentence 4.1.8.12.(2)). A time history is deemed to be "spectrum-compatible" if its response spectrum equals or exceeds the target spectrum throughout the period range of interest, i.e. the periods of the modes contributing to the response of the particular structure (Naeim and Lew[72]). Spectrum-compatible time histories may be obtained by

scaling and/or modifying actual recorded earthquake accelerograms (obtained from earthquakes of similar magnitudes and located at similar distances to those that contribute most significantly to seismic hazard at the site in question) or by creating artificial or synthetic time histories. The latter are often required due to the limited number of actual records available for such purposes; this is particularly the case for earthquake magnitude-distance pairs that dominate seismic hazard in eastern Canada. A stochastically-based approach for obtaining synthetic time histories is given by Atkinson and Beresnev.[73]

184. If actual earthquake accelerograms are used, then they should be scaled so that the spectral acceleration at the fundamental period of the structure corresponds to the design spectral response acceleration for the particular site. The spectral acceleration ordinates at the periods below the fundamental period should also be equal to or greater than those of the design spectral response acceleration, $S(T)$, for those periods. If that is not the case for the selected accelerograms, they can be modified to meet that requirement (Naumoski[74] describes a simple technique for such a modification).

185. Due to the natural aleatory uncertainty arising from the physical variability of earthquake ground motions (see the Commentary section titled Seismic Hazard), it is not feasible to represent the range of possible responses in a single time history. This fact, combined with the sensitivity of time history response calculations to small differences in the characteristics of individual records, means that multiple records must be used so that the realistic dispersion of response parameters due to this variability can be obtained. NEHRP 2000 (Building Seismic Safety Council[25]) requires that a suite of ground motions used for this kind of analysis be made up of at least three records but the NEHRP Commentary recommends that seven or more be used.

Sentence 4.1.8.12.(4)

186. Three-dimensional dynamic analysis provides a good representation of the behaviour of structures with torsional eccentricity and, in accordance with Clause 4.1.8.11.(10)(b), is required for torsionally sensitive structures, i.e. for which the sensitivity parameter $B > 1.7$. However, structural modelling for such analysis does not ordinarily take into account the effects of accidental eccentricities, which must be considered to act concurrently with the effects of lateral motion including actual eccentricities. Clauses 4.1.8.12.(4)(a) and (b) provide alternative approaches for determining the effects of accidental eccentricity, the second of which is only permitted if the sensitivity parameter $B < 1.7$.

> **Clause (a):** In the first approach, which can be used for any value of B but is intended primarily for torsionally sensitive structures, the effects of static torsional moments, $(\pm 0.10 D_{nx})F_x$, at each level x are calculated and then combined with the effects determined from a dynamic analysis that includes the actual eccentricities. The forces F_x may be either those determined during a static analysis (as specified in Sentence 4.1.8.11.(6)) or from a dynamic analysis, i.e. associated with the dynamic base shear, V_d, as specified in Sentence 4.1.8.12.(8). As previously discussed (see the Commentary section on Sentence 4.1.8.11.(10)), the accidental eccentricity is $0.05 D_{nx}$; the required value of $0.10 D_{nx}$ stated in Clause (a) includes a dynamic amplification of the static effect of accidental eccentricity.

> **Clause (b):** The second approach is only permissible for structures that are not torsionally sensitive, i.e. for $B < 1.7$. This approach allows the effects of accidental eccentricity to be included by shifting the centres of mass by $\pm 0.05 D_{nx}$. Two three-dimensional dynamic analyses are therefore required—one for each of the two locations with a shifted centre of mass. The larger of the two values of V_d must be used for determining the design base shear, in accordance with the provisions of Sentence 4.1.8.12.(6). For any effect, the larger of the values obtained from the two dynamic analyses must be used to determine the design value, in accordance with the provisions of Sentence 4.1.8.12.(8).

Sentence 4.1.8.12.(5)

187. Linear Dynamic Analysis using $S(T)$ as the design spectral acceleration results in the elastic base shear, V_e, which does not take into account either the inelastic response or the importance of the structure. Consequently, in order to determine the design base shear, V_d, the elastic base shear must be divided by the product $R_d R_o$ and multiplied by the importance factor, I_E. By making these adjustments, V_d is determined on a comparable basis to the static base shear, V, in Sentence 4.1.8.11.(2). Note that the upper and lower bounds on V specified in Sentence 4.1.8.11.(2) are not

applicable to V_d because the results of the dynamic analysis are deemed to be more accurate; however the requirements of Sentence 4.1.8.12.(6) must be met.

Sentence 4.1.8.12.(6)

188. If the modelling of the structure is done correctly, the base shear, V_d, determined from a Linear Dynamic Analysis will be a more accurate representation of the behaviour of the structural system than the statically determined base shear, V. However, structural models tend to be more flexible than actual structures, one reason being because they don't take into account stiff non-structural elements. Because the design spectral acceleration decreases with increasing flexibility (i.e. increasing period), there is concern that this tendency will result in V_d being less than it should be. Sentence 4.1.8.12.(6) addresses this concern by requiring that V_d be taken as 0.8V when the computed value of V_d is less than 80% of the static base shear, V (as determined in Article 4.1.8.11.). A reduction of up to 20% of V is deemed reasonable because dynamic analysis results in a better distribution of forces within the structure. Of course, if $V_d >$ V, then the actual computed value of V_d must be used as the design base shear; this is required because dynamic analysis is normally expected to yield results that are more accurate than those obtained from static analysis. For example, $V_d >$ V is expected if the dynamic model is stiffer than the static model (resulting in a smaller value of the fundamental period) or if the higher modes dominate the dynamic response, which would be expected in tall flexible structures with long periods.

189. The value of the elastic base shear, V_e, used to determine the minimum value of V_d can be calculated using a fundamental period determined according to established methods of mechanics rather than from empirical formulae, as permitted in Clause 4.1.8.11.(3)(d), provided that this period is not more than 1.5 times the empirical value for moment-resisting frames and 2.0 times the empirical value for braced frames and shear walls. It is acceptable to determine V_e using the fundamental period calculated from the same structural model as the one used for dynamic analysis, subject to the indicated limitation for moment-resisting and braced frames. In this case, the only significant deviation between the two approaches would be the participation of higher modes and their effects on the distribution of forces and deformations along the height of the structure.

Sentence 4.1.8.12.(7)

190. Reducing the base shear to 0.8V is not permitted for situations in which dynamic analysis is required because of the irregularity of the structure, as specified in Article 4.1.8.7. In such cases, the modelling of the structure for dynamic analysis may not fully capture the influence of irregularities on its behaviour during an earthquake, particularly since the actual structure will behave in an inelastic manner, most likely with concentrations of inelastic demand at points of stiffness or mass discontinuity. Consequently, when the presence of irregularities results in dynamic analysis being required, the minimum value of V_d used for design must be V or the actual computed value of V_d, whichever is greater.

Sentence 4.1.8.12.(8)

191. Sentences 4.1.8.12.(5), (6) and (7) specify how the design value of V_d is to be determined from the dynamic elastic base shear, V_e. Although these Sentences address the determination of the design base shear, it is important that all of the other design actions, e.g. element forces, storey shears and interstorey drifts, be proportioned accordingly. Since the initial determination of these actions is associated with V_e, Sentence 4.1.8.12.(8) requires that the design actions be calculated by multiplying the initial actions by the ratio V_d/V_e. It should be noted that the resulting design deflections and interstorey drifts are elastic and need to be multiplied by the product R_dR_o/I_E in order to obtain realistic values of anticipated deflections and drifts, as specified in Sentence 4.1.8.13.(2).

Deflections and Drift Limits (4.1.8.13.)

192. The damage caused to buildings by earthquake ground motions is a direct consequence of the lateral deflection of the structural system. The ability of a building to withstand such ground motions arises largely from the capability of the structural system to deform without significant loss of load-carrying capacity. Article 4.1.8.13. is concerned with both the determination of lateral deflections and limits on those deflections to ensure satisfactory performance. In this context, lateral deflection is relative to the ground, i.e. the top of the foundation at the base of the structure.

Commentary J

Sentence 4.1.8.13.(1)

193. This Sentence requires that the loads and other requirements of Subsection 4.1.8. be used in the calculation of lateral deflections. Static loads are prescribed in Article 4.1.8.11. and the corresponding dynamic input used in dynamic analysis is given in Article 4.1.8.12. The most important of the other requirements is that the structural modelling be representative of the actual building structure, accounting for the specific features listed in Sentence 4.1.8.3.(8). Although the stiffness of elements that are not part of the SFRS is to be accounted for in determining the natural period, as required in Sentence 4.1.8.3.(7), such elements should not be included in the modelling of the structure for the purpose of calculating lateral deflections. Stiff elements not part of the SFRS are likely to crack and lose their stiffness as the structure responds to strong earthquake ground motions; they are therefore not likely to participate in limiting the deflection of the building. Only the structural elements that are part of the SFRS should be used in the determination of lateral deflections.

Sentence 4.1.8.13.(2)

194. As described in Mitchell et al.,[11] design forces are reduced to take into account inelastic behaviour and overstrength. Deflections computed from those reduced design forces are only elastic deflections and do not represent maximum deflections, which include incursions into the inelastic range. As shown in Figure 2 of Mitchell et al.,[11] the maximum deflection is $R_d R_o$ times the deflection determined using the design force V specified in Sentence 4.1.8.11.(2). Sentence 4.1.8.13.(2) requires that the deflections determined using V be multiplied by the same product $R_d R_o$ to obtain realistic values of anticipated maximum deflections. If the overall building structure is made up of types of SFRS having different values of the product $R_d R_o$, then the same value of this product used for the determination of the design forces is to be used as the multiplier. As discussed by DeVall,[14] the application of the importance factor, I_E, to buildings in the High and Post-disaster importance categories to increase design loads has the effect of reducing the inelastic demand on important structures. Because of this reduction in inelastic demand, the deflections determined using V must be divided by I_E in order to obtain realistic values of anticipated maximum deflections. Also, in all cases, the effects of torsion, including those due to accidental eccentricities, are to be included in the calculation of lateral deflection. When torsional effects are included, the largest deflection is that at one of the two extreme edges of the building and not at the centre of mass.

Sentence 4.1.8.13.(3)

195. The deflection parameter that best represents the potential for structural and non-structural damage is interstorey deflection, also known as interstorey drift. Lateral deflection at the top of the structure is not a good indicator of damage potential because the various types of SFRS have differing height-wise deflection profiles. Sentence 4.1.8.13.(3) specifies limits on the largest interstorey deflection at any level of the structure. Ordinarily the limit is $0.025h_s$ (where h_s = interstorey height) except for post-disaster buildings and schools, for which the limits are $0.01h_s$ and $0.02h_s$ respectively. As noted by DeVall,[14] the limit of $0.025h_s$ represents the state of "near collapse" (equivalent to "extensive damage"), but not collapse. The "extensive damage" state is associated with inelastic deformation at or near the capacity of the structural system, which corresponds to the level at which deflections are calculated, i.e. utilizing the full inelastic ductility capacity of the particular structural system.

196. The more stringent drift limit of $0.01h_s$ for post-disaster buildings reflects the need for facilities such as hospitals, power generation stations, and fire stations to remain operational following an earthquake. SEAOC Vision 2000 (Vision 2000 Committee[75]) specifies an "operational" performance level drift limit of $0.005h_s$ for such buildings, but this limit is associated with ground motions at the 10% in 50 year probability of exceedance level. Consequently, because the NBC 2005 design ground motions are specified at the 2% in 50 year probability of exceedance, the drift limit of $0.01h_s$ is comparable with the SEAOC Vision 2000 operational performance level.

197. Although the interstorey drift limits specified in the NBC 2005 may appear to be the same or more liberal than those in the NBC 1995, they are actually more restrictive because the calculated deflections are based on loads computed for ground motions determined at the 2% in 50 year probability of exceedance rather than 10% in 50 years, and are determined using the multiplier $R_d R_o / I_E$ (applied to elastic deflections) rather than R (which is equivalent to R_d).

Sentence 4.1.8.13.(4)

198. This Sentence requires that the deflections calculated in Sentence 4.1.8.13.(2) be used to account for sway effects (i.e. P-delta effects), as specified in Clause 4.1.8.3.(8)(c), i.e. the deflections associated with extensive inelastic deformation. Accordingly, as discussed in the Commentary section on Clause 4.1.8.3.(8)(c), the methodology used to account for P-delta effects must recognize that the structure is near its inelastic capacity.

Structural Separation (4.1.8.14.)

Sentence 4.1.8.14.(1)

199. The provisions in Subsection 4.1.8. are based on the assumption that the building being designed is a stand-alone building that will not interact with any other building during its response to an earthquake. Observations of building behaviour during actual earthquakes have demonstrated that collision between buildings can lead to extensive damage, particularly if adjacent buildings have different heights and floor spacings. Filiatrault et al.[76] discuss the effects of the pounding of buildings during earthquakes. To avoid pounding, there must be a separation between the building being designed and any other building that is adequate for both to undergo seismically induced displacements without any contact between them. Sentence 4.1.8.14.(1) requires that the minimum separation be equal to the square root of the sum of the squares of the calculated displacements of the two buildings, as recommended by Filiatrault et al.[76] and Filiatrault and Cervantes.[77] This separation requirement is less severe than the one in the NBC 1995, which required separation by the absolute sum of the two displacements. Adjacent buildings are likely to have different periods and vibrate out of phase rather than in phase at the same period.

200. Ordinarily, buildings that are adjacent to the building being designed are existing structures. If that is the case, the deflection calculations for the adjacent building must be on the same basis as that for the building being designed rather than using deflections that may have been determined from the application of a previous edition of the NBC.

201. If it is not feasible to separate the two buildings by sufficient distance, then the buildings must be connected to each other. The connection requirements are given in Sentences 4.1.8.14.(2) to (4); they also apply to expansion joints within buildings, which need to be designed for the appropriate seismic forces or must be detailed to ensure that earthquake damage is confined to the joint rather than affecting the principal structural elements.

Sentence 4.1.8.14.(2)

202. When two buildings are connected, their response to earthquake ground motion will be interactive, i.e. they will respond as a single structural system rather than as two independent systems. Although the NBC does not specify how such an interactive system should be analyzed, it does require that the method of connection take into account the properties of each building (i.e. mass, stiffness, strength and ductility), the properties of the connections, and the anticipated response of the connected buildings. The modelling of the elements of each building as well as the connections must meet the requirements of Sentence 4.1.8.3.(8). If the adjacent building is an existing structure, then the modelling of its elements must be based on its actual "as-built" characteristics. In addition to using the results of the analysis for the design of the connections between the buildings, it is advisable to review the capability of the existing structure to perform adequately once connected to the new building. In conducting such a review, the performance standards for the existing building, e.g. interstorey drift limits, should be based on the requirements of the NBC 2005 rather than on the edition of the Code in effect at the time when the existing building was constructed.

Sentence 4.1.8.14.(3)

203. When buildings are rigidly connected, it is required that the loading and design be based on the lowest value of the product R_dR_o for the individual buildings being connected. This requirement ensures that the loading and design requirements for the component building with the least ductility and overstrength will govern, based on the assumption that the performance capacity of the combined buildings will be limited by the capacity of the building with the lowest R_dR_o. Buildings

Commentary J

can be considered rigidly connected if the connection enables both buildings to undergo the same lateral deflection at each storey.

Sentence 4.1.8.14.(4)

204. As previously noted, buildings interconnected with non-rigid elements or energy dissipating elements such as friction or viscoelastic dampers will behave as an interactive structural system. Due to the complexity of such a system—particularly if one component is an existing building—it is required that a special study be carried out rather than just applying the loading and design requirements of Subsection 4.1.8.

Design Provisions (4.1.8.15.)

205. This Article specifies a number of design requirements that are essential for an SFRS and its elements to perform satisfactorily during strong earthquake ground shaking. One of the objectives of seismic design (see the discussion at the beginning of this Commentary) is to prevent structural collapse by ensuring that inelastic behaviour is confined to those elements that can dissipate energy inelastically during reversing cycles of deformation without loss of capacity. One of the important ways of achieving this goal is to ensure that elements not having good energy dissipation characteristics are designed with sufficient strength so that they will not yield. This approach is one of the key features of what is known as the capacity design philosophy (Paulay and Priestley[50]), which is required of all ductile structures in the New Zealand seismic code (Standards New Zealand[64]). Although the NBC 2005 does not specify that capacity design philosophy be followed for all structures, the use of capacity design principles for ductile structures is specified in the CSA material standards for concrete (CSA A23.3[49]), steel (CAN/CSA-S16[61]), and masonry (CSA S304.1[78]); in addition, Article 4.1.8.15. includes several specific provisions that are based on that philosophy.

Sentence 4.1.8.15.(1)

206. Diaphragms are elements whose primary purpose is to transfer lateral loads from their origin (i.e. inertial forces throughout the building) to the elements that resist those loads (e.g. walls or frames). Typically, diaphragms are comprised of some combination of slabs, steel deck, deep beams and trusses. Although such elements are subject to axial, shear and bending actions, their primary action in resisting earthquake loads as part of the SFRS is in shear. Since most of these types of elements have very poor energy dissipation characteristics in shear, it is essential that diaphragms be designed so as not to yield. An important aspect of avoiding yielding is to ensure that the components of the diaphragm are well tied together so that they act as a unit. Since stress concentrations are likely to occur near openings in a diaphragm, the design of the diaphragm must account for any openings. Also, since the connections between diaphragms and lateral-load-resisting elements (e.g. wall anchorages) are extremely important to maintaining the integrity of the structure, they must also be designed not to yield.

 Clause (a): In order to ensure that the diaphragm does not yield, it must be designed so that the forces applied to it reflect the strength of the SFRS and that of the elements of the SFRS to which the diaphragm is connected rather than just the computed lateral earthquake loads. The forces applied to the diaphragm arising from the earthquake loads (as determined from Article 4.1.8.11. or 4.1.8.12.) must be increased to reflect the actual strength of the SFRS when subjected to lateral loads. For example, if the actual base shear capacity of the SFRS is 20% larger than the required base shear, V, then the shear forces applied to the diaphragm due to the lateral loads must also be increased by 20%. In addition, forces must be applied to the diaphragm to account for the transfer of loads between lateral-load-carrying elements of the SFRS. Examples of such load transfers include offset walls (in or out of plane) and discontinuous walls resting on columns; such discontinuities generate large in-plane diaphragm forces. The diaphragm design forces must be associated with the actual capacities of these elements and also account for discontinuities and changes in stiffness. By designing for these capacity-based loads, yielding in the diaphragm will be prevented because connecting elements will of necessity yield first and the amount of load that they can transfer is limited by their capacities. CSA A23.3[49] contains detailed design requirements for structural diaphragms subject to earthquake-induced forces.

 Clause (b): Regardless of the value of the diaphragm design force computed in accordance with Clause (a), the diaphragm at any level x must be designed for a minimum shear force corresponding to the design base shear, V, divided by the total number of storeys, N. This minimum shear force corresponds to the average throughout the height of the building and ensures that there is adequate protection for diaphragms in the lower part of the building, for which the calculated diaphragm shear (based on the load distribution in Sentence 4.1.8.11.(6)) is quite low.

Sentence 4.1.8.15.(2)

207. An SFRS that includes an in-plane discontinuity in a vertical lateral-force-resisting element is designated as irregular (Type 4 irregularity in Table 4.1.8.6.). When $I_E F_a S_a(0.2) \geq 0.35$, Sentence 4.1.8.6.(3) specifies that the requirements for irregular structures listed in Table 4.1.8.6. must be satisfied. For a Type 4 irregularity, Sentence 4.1.8.15.(2) requires that the elements supporting any discontinuous wall, column or braced frame be designed for the forces transferred from above the discontinuity associated with the lateral load capacity of the structure. This means that the design of these supporting elements must be based on the actual capacity of the discontinuous elements being supported rather than just for the forces generated by the loads specified in Articles 4.1.8.11. or 4.1.8.12. Using the capacity as the basis for the design of these supporting elements ensures that yielding will not occur at the discontinuity.

Sentence 4.1.8.15.(3)

208. Sentence 4.1.8.9.(4) specifies the value of the product $R_d R_o$ to be used when there is a vertical variation of $R_d R_o$, i.e. where the type of SFRS changes at one or more levels in the structure. Sentence 4.1.8.15.(3) specifies that the elements of the SFRS below the level where the change occurs be designed for the forces associated with the lateral load capacity of the SFRS above that level. Typically, the upper system is more ductile and therefore has less strength than the lower system. In such cases—where the upper system is designed for higher values of $R_d R_o$ than the lower system—the forces in the upper system would typically be lower than if the same value of $R_d R_o$ were used throughout the building. Sentence 4.1.8.15.(3) requires that the design forces in the lower system be not less than the capacity of the upper system so as to avoid a weak lower level, which would have the undesirable effect of concentrating all the yielding in the less ductile lower level.

Sentence 4.1.8.15.(4)

209. Article 4.1.8.8. requires that earthquake forces be assumed to act in any horizontal direction; this requirement can be met by independent analysis and design along two orthogonal directions. In many cases, some of the elements of the SFRS (e.g. columns common to two orthogonal moment frames or orthogonal walls that are part of a central core) will be subject to forces from two loading directions. Because the design loads are reduced to take into account inelastic response, it is likely that there will be simultaneous yielding in both directions. In accordance with the capacity design philosophy described earlier, Sentence 4.1.8.15.(4) requires that, in such situations, account must be taken of the potential for concurrent yielding of other elements framing into the column or wall from all directions, both at the level under consideration and as appropriate at other levels.

Sentence 4.1.8.15.(5)

210. The application of the principles of capacity design, either to comply with Sentences 4.1.8.15.(1) to (4) or to ensure overall ductile behaviour of an SFRS, may result in very large element or connection forces due to the large inherent overstrength of some of the connecting elements. For example, the required design forces for connections in a steel braced frame would be very large because the tension capacity of the brace is typically many times the compression capacity for which it has been designed. The application of extremely large element or connection forces in design is not necessary and Sentence 4.1.8.15.(5) is intended to provide upper limits on those design forces. The element and connection forces need not be larger than the ESFP forces (determined in accordance with Article 4.1.8.7.) multiplied by the product $R_d R_o$, i.e. the forces corresponding to elastic response. Elastic response of some elements and connections in structures for design earthquake ground motions is assumed to be satisfactory in that the inherent ductility in the remainder of the system will be able to provide an adequate overall ductility capacity, i.e. corresponding to the R_d specified for that particular SFRS in Table 4.1.8.9.

Commentary J

211. Sentence 4.1.8.16.(1) allows for the foundation of the structure to rock (including uplift) and specifies the maximum foundation design forces when this occurs. A rocking foundation is not in static equilibrium and limits the base shear to the level that occurs when the foundation starts to rock, at which time the response begins to decrease because the period of the overall structure-foundation system lengthens due to the softening associated with the rocking foundation. In effect, the rocking foundation limits the forces going into the superstructure to the forces associated with foundation rocking. Sentence 4.1.8.15.(6) allows the elements of the SFRS to be designed for maximum values corresponding to the force for which the rocking foundation is designed.

Foundation Provisions (4.1.8.16.)

212. Although Subsection 4.1.8. is primarily concerned with earthquake loads and their effects on the building structure—usually defined as being above the foundation—it is necessary that the structure and its supporting foundation work integrally in responding to earthquake ground motions. This is particularly important because these ground motions shake the foundation, which then transmits the resulting effects to the structural system. The purpose of the provisions in Article 4.1.8.16. is to ensure that the design of the foundation is compatible with that of the structural system it supports.

Sentence 4.1.8.16.(1)

213. As noted by DeVall,[14] there are several important reasons why foundations need to be designed so as to prevent damage during the design earthquake ground motion; damage in foundations is hard to identify and difficult to repair. Of particular significance is the fact that the foundation is the mechanism for transmitting earthquake loads to the structure; damage to the foundation would place the building at risk even if the structure itself were not damaged. In order to minimize the likelihood of foundation damage, Sentence 4.1.8.16.(1) requires that foundations be designed to resist the lateral load capacity of the SFRS, regardless of the earthquake loads used to design the SFRS. This is a particularly important application of the capacity design philosophy, allowing the structure to dissipate energy inelastically while the foundation continues to behave elastically.

214. Ordinarily, foundations are expected to remain fully embedded or fixed within the supporting ground during earthquake shaking. However, applying this requirement may result in very large footings or rigid mat foundations are necessary to support shear walls or core wall assemblies without rocking of the foundations, particularly since the overturning moment capacity of shear walls or core wall assemblies is often greater than that required to resist earthquakes, e.g. because of architectural or minimum steel requirements. Consequently, it is acceptable to allow foundations to rock under certain conditions, provided that lateral displacements of the structure due to such rocking can be controlled. Historically, as discussed in the Commentary to the 1992 New Zealand Code (Standards New Zealand[64]), it was thought that rocking should only be permitted if the superstructure were stiff and remained essentially elastic during ground shaking. However, Anderson[79] has shown that allowing rocking by reducing the size of footings supporting shear walls to a size consistent with a ductility-based force reduction factor of 2 does not result in a significant increase in lateral displacement compared with the fixed base elastic case. Based on Anderson's work, Sentence 4.1.8.16.(1) states that, when foundations are allowed to rock, the foundation design forces need not exceed those determined in Sentence 4.1.8.7.(1) using R_dR_o equal to 2.0. A similar provision is being proposed in the Draft Australian/New Zealand Standard DR00902.[80]

Sentence 4.1.8.16.(2)

215. This Sentence specifies that the capacities of the soil and rock on which the foundation rests are not to be exceeded during the design ground motion. The evaluation of those capacities must take into account the potential for degradation due to large reversing strains. Also, it is required that the foundation not undergo large lateral displacements during an earthquake due to the loss of strength of the soil.

Sentence 4.1.8.16.(3)

216. Two necessary requirements, in addition to those specified in Sentences 4.1.8.16.(1) and (2), for the foundation to perform satisfactorily are that it act as an integral unit and that it provide a continuous

load path from the structure into the ground. Achieving this requires special attention when the foundation is made up of independent elements such as piles, drilled piers or caissons. Sentence 4.1.8.16.(3) imposes specific requirements regarding the integral functioning of foundation elements other than in cases of low design ground motions, i.e. $I_E F_a S_a(0.2) < 0.35$.

Clause (a): To prevent columns or walls from moving relative to each other, piles or pile caps, drilled piers and caissons need to be interconnected in at least two directions by continuous ties, which may consist of grade beams or slabs, or a combination of both. Such foundation elements are often used in soft or loose soils, which do not have the capacity to provide lateral restraint near the ground surface. Ties are required to provide lateral restraint both to prevent damage to the structural elements immediately above the foundation and to prevent the spreading of and subsequent damage to piles, drilled piers and caissons. Design force requirements for such ties are specified in Sentence 4.1.8.16.(6).

Clause (b): In addition to the foundation elements needing to be tied together as per the requirements in Clause (a), it is necessary to prevent displacements due to sliding between these elements and the building structure. Clause (b) requires that they be embedded in the structure or the pile cap (which is integral with the structure) by at least 100 mm, which is deemed to be sufficient to provide lateral continuity between the structure and the foundation units.

Clause (c): As the structure displaces laterally, the overturning moment generated at its base by the design seismic load may result in a net tension in the piles, drilled piers or caissons at or near the outer edges of the foundation; in accordance with Sentence 4.1.8.16.(2), the connections from the structure to the foundation elements must be designed for such tension in order to prevent separation between the structure and the foundation elements. When the effects of the design seismic load do not result in any tension (owing to the counteracting effects of gravity loads), Clause (c) requires that the connections between the structure and the foundation elements be designed for a minimum tension force equal to 15% of their factored compression capacity. This relatively small nominal tension capacity in the connection is deemed to be necessary to prevent separation in the event the overturning effects should accidentally result in a small amount of tension and to provide integrity at the joint to assist in transferring shear between the pile and the cap. Connections to wood piles are exempted from this requirement because the low lateral pile capacity should be able to be transferred by the minimum embedment.

Sentence 4.1.8.16.(4)

217. In regions of moderate to high seismicity, i.e. where $I_E F_a S_a(0.2) \geq 0.35$, it is required that basement walls be designed to resist increased lateral pressure due to the movement of backfill or natural ground associated with earthquake ground motions (see Mononobe and Matsuo[81] and Seed and Whitman[82]). Such basement walls are normally considered "non-yielding" in that the restraints at the top and bottom of these walls prevent the small amount of movement required to develop minimum active earth pressures. The NEHRP 2000 Commentary (Building Seismic Safety Council[25]) provides information on the dynamic forces acting on a non-yielding wall on a rigid base.

Sentence 4.1.8.16.(5)

218. Additional design requirements for the foundations of buildings located in regions of high seismicity, i.e. where $I_E F_a S_a(0.2) > 0.75$, are specified in Sentence 4.1.8.16.(5) to address the high levels of expected ground motions and the cyclic nature of those motions.

Clause (a): In regions of high seismicity, it is expected that the earthquake forces acting on the structure will generate relatively large moments in piles, drilled piers or caissons. These elements must therefore be designed and detailed to accommodate cyclic inelastic behaviour; Clause (a) requires such detailing when the element design moment is greater than 75% of the element's moment capacity, calculated for the amount of axial load that is present.

Clause (b): Site Classes E and F, as defined in Table 4.1.8.4.A., comprise soft and very soft soils. When spread footings in regions of high seismicity are founded on such soils, they must be tied together to provide lateral restraint to prevent damage to the structural system immediately above the spread footings. Design force requirements for such ties are specified in Sentence 4.1.8.16.(6).

Commentary J

Sentence 4.1.8.16.(6)

219. Although there is no rational analysis available for the determination of the design forces for the ties specified in Clauses 4.1.8.16.(3)(a) and 4.1.8.16.(5)(b), it is standard practice for such horizontal design forces to be proportional to the vertical load in the elements being connected by the ties. NEHRP 1997 (Building Seismic Safety Council[7]) specifies that the tie force be 0.25 times the short period design spectral acceleration times the maximum vertical load while the more recent NEHRP 2000 (Building Seismic Safety Council[25]) reduces that multiplier from 0.25 to 0.10. Sentence 4.1.8.16.(6) requires that the vertical load multiplier of the largest factored vertical load be 0.10 $I_E F_a S_a(0.2)$, which is very similar to the value specified in the NBC 1995 when one takes into account changes in the specification of seismic hazard. Ties are to be designed to carry the tie force in either compression or tension.

220. Sentence 4.1.8.16.(6) also allows for the tie design force to be reduced or for ties to be omitted if it can be demonstrated that equivalent restraint can be provided by other means, e.g. as indicated in NEHRP 2000 (Building Seismic Safety Council[25]). Reinforced concrete beams within slabs on grade or reinforced concrete slabs on grade are acceptable equivalent means of restraint; confinement by passive soil pressure against buried pile caps is not acceptable.

Sentence 4.1.8.16.(7)

221. Although ground shaking, as described in terms of spectral response accelerations for a range of periods, is the normal earthquake-related hazard that affects the design of buildings and their foundations, earthquakes can cause other site hazards such as fault rupture, liquefaction, ground deformation and slope instability. Of these additional site hazards, liquefaction and its consequences, i.e. ground displacement and loss of soil strength and stiffness, have been major sources of building damage during past earthquakes. Sentence 4.1.8.16.(7) requires that the potential for liquefaction and its consequences be evaluated and taken into account in the design of the structure and its foundations. A methodology for the evaluation of liquefaction potential is described by Youd et al.,[83] which requires the PGA values given in Table C-2 of Appendix C of Division B.

Elements of Structures, Non-structural Components and Equipment (4.1.8.17.)

222. Attachments to buildings, i.e. non-loadbearing structural elements, architectural components, mechanical equipment and electrical equipment, need to be designed so that they neither fail nor become detached from the building during design earthquake ground motion. Table 4.1.8.17. lists the categories of such attachments, which include tanks and their contents when located within a building.

223. Experience during earthquakes has demonstrated that the failure or detachment of such items (henceforth referred to as components) can present a major threat to life safety. The design requirements in Article 4.1.8.17. are intended to ensure that these components and their connections to the building will retain their integrity during strong ground shaking. The design force equations and the values of the parameters in those equations are based on those contained in the NEHRP 2000 provisions (Building Seismic Safety Council[25]), which originated from a study done by Bachman et al.[84] Their adaptation for use in the NBC 2005 and the implications for design are described by McKevitt.[85] In contrast to the NBC 1995 requirements, the current provisions provide a unified, consistent approach for all such items. Guidelines for the seismic risk reduction of such components are given in CAN/CSA-S832.[86]

224. Internal structures such as multi-storey racks that are free-standing on the ground but are surrounded by, but not otherwise connected to, the building structure should be analyzed as separate structures. Separation must be in accordance with the requirements of Sentence 4.1.8.14.(1). Values of R_d and R_o must be appropriate for the chosen structural system; the provisions of Sentence 4.1.8.9.(5) may be used to determine R_d and R_o if it can be demonstrated that the system is equivalent to one of the types of SFRS given in Table 4.1.8.9. Adequate resistance to lateral forces must be provided throughout the height of the structure. Once the racks and enclosures are connected, they must act as a combined system and resist the lateral seismic forces in proportion to the relative stiffness of the components. Further information on rack design may be found in RMI 1990.[87]

225. Racking and shelving systems that are connected to the building should be considered as fixtures (Category 11 or 12) when using Table 4.1.8.17. The components, assemblies, connections and attachments of such systems should be capable of withstanding the specified forces.

226. The design of free-standing tanks is outside the scope of the NBC 2005. Their design should be based on current industry-accepted practice and consensus design standards (API 650,[88] API 620,[89][90] AWWA D100,[91] AWWA D110,[92] AWWA D115,[93] BSSC 2003[94]). In applying these industry standards to Canadian locations, the designer should use ground motion parameters consistent with those used in the NBC 2005.

Sentence 4.1.8.17.(1)

227. Attached components need to be designed and detailed so that they retain their integrity and do not become detached from the structure when subjected to forces arising from the design level earthquake ground motion. In order to retain their integrity, they also need to be able to accommodate the resulting component deflections as well as the earthquake-generated building deflections. An example of the latter requirement is the need for interior wall panels to accommodate the in-plane and out-of-plane interstorey drifts. Of equal importance is the design and detailing of the connections between the components and the building structure (Sentence 4.1.8.17.(8) gives additional requirements regarding connections).

The component design force, V_p, which is to be applied through its centre of mass, is given by:

$$V_p = 0.3 I_E F_a S_a (0.2) S_p W_p$$

where

$0.3 I_E F_a S_a (0.2)$ is equivalent to the expected peak acceleration at the base of the building (this particular value is based on experience and is approximately equal to the corresponding factor used in the NEHRP 2000 provisions (Building Seismic Safety Council[25])),

S_p is the component response factor, described in detail below, which accounts for the nature of the element, its position in the building and its dynamic properties in relation to those of the supporting structure, and

W_p is the weight of the component.

The component response factor, S_p, is determined as follows:

$$S_p = C_p A_r A_x / R_p \quad \text{subject to } 0.7 \leq S_p \leq 4.0$$

The factors in the above expression are defined as follows:

C_p accounts for the risk associated with the failure of the component. Higher values are assigned to components that contain toxic or explosive materials in recognition of the consequences associated with the possible release of these materials. C_p has a value of 1.00 for ordinary components and of 1.50 for those containing toxic or explosive materials. The value of 0.70 assigned to Category 13 (flat bottom tanks attached directly to a floor at or below grade within a building) reflects the low risk of failure associated with such tanks.

A_r represents the dynamic amplification of the component relative to the position of its attachment to the building structure; it is a function of the ratio of the natural period of the component to the fundamental period of the building structure. Highest amplifications (2.50) occur when the two periods are similar; there is no amplification ($A_r = 1.00$) when they are far apart.

A_x represents the amplification of the acceleration at the base of the building structure to the height at which the component is attached. This factor is only dependent upon the height at which the component is attached and is given by:

$$A_x = (1 + 2 h_x / h_n)$$

R_p is the component response modification factor, which recognizes the energy dissipation capability of the component and its connection to the structure; it serves the same function as the ductility-related force modification factor, R_d. Values assigned to the different categories of components range from 1.00 to 5.00 and are based on experience from past earthquakes and on the judgment of engineers familiar with their behaviour.

The values of the factors C_p, A_r, and R_p for 21 different categories of components are given in Table 4.1.8.17. The categories in this Table can be grouped as follows:
Structural components: Categories 1 through 6
Architectural components: Categories 7 through 10
Mechanical and electrical components, including tanks: Categories 11 through 17
Other components: Categories 18 through 21

Sentence 4.1.8.17.(2)

228. Non-structural components attached to non-post-disaster buildings pose little risk to life safety in regions of low to moderate seismicity. Consequently, Sentence 4.1.8.17.(2) exempts such components (i.e. Categories 7 through 21) when the importance modified short period design acceleration $I_E F_a S_a(0.2) < 0.35$. Category 6 components (horizontally cantilevered floors, balconies, beams, etc.) are also exempted in such situations because they are subject to vertical earthquake ground motions, which tend to be lower in amplitude than horizontal motions.

Sentence 4.1.8.17.(4)

229. Categories 11 and 12 in Table 4.1.8.17. (machinery, fixtures, equipment, ducts and tanks containing or not containing toxic or explosive materials) each have subcategories that differentiate components that are rigid and rigidly connected and those that are flexible or flexibly connected. The distinctions are significant in that each subcategory has different values of the dynamic amplification factor, A_r, and the response modification factor, R_p. Components that are rigid and rigidly connected have no dynamic amplification ($A_r = 1.00$) while those that are flexible or flexibly connected have substantial dynamic amplification ($A_r = 2.50$). On the other hand, rigid and rigidly connected components have minimal energy dissipation ($R_p = 1.25$) while those that are flexible or flexibly connected have significant energy dissipation ($R_p = 2.50$). Because of the significant differences in the values of these factors for the two subcategories, it is necessary to provide a clear way of distinguishing between the two. Sentence 4.1.8.17.(4) establishes the fundamental period as being the distinguishing characteristic. If the fundamental period of a component and its connection is less than or equal to 0.06 s, then it can be classified as rigid and rigidly connected; if that period is greater than 0.06 s, then it can be classified as flexible or flexibly connected. The flexibility in the second subcategory may be due to flexibility in the component and/or in its connection to the structure. If it is not feasible to reliably determine the fundamental period, then it would be appropriate for the designer to compute the force V_p on the assumption that the component is flexible or flexibly connected, since that case results in the larger force.

Sentence 4.1.8.17.(5)

230. In determining the force V_p for access floors (Category 9), it is necessary to include both the dead load of the access floor itself and the weight of permanent equipment attached to the access floor; the latter is to be not less than 25% of the floor live load. This minimum value of added weight is necessary to ensure that floors and connections are adequately designed in situations where the equipment that is initially installed is relatively light but where subsequent modifications could result in the installation of heavier equipment. Both the connection of the access floor to the structure and the anchorage of equipment mounted on the access floor need to be designed to take into account shear and overturning moment arising from the motion of the equipment. The possibility of overturning is particularly important when the equipment is relatively tall and slender because of the possible risk to life safety; in such instances the force V_p should be applied at 75% of the height of the equipment (rather than at the centre of mass as specified in Sentence 4.1.8.17.(1)) to ensure an adequate representation of overturning effects. It should also be noted that the full weight, W_p, should be included in the floor weight, W_i, for use in the determination of the base shear, V, in accordance with Article 4.1.8.7.

Sentence 4.1.8.17.(6)

231. When the mass of a tank, including its contents, is more than 10% of the mass of the supporting floor, then the tank interacts dynamically with the floor rather than simply being an appendage attached to the floor. In such situations, the lateral forces must be determined by an analysis that considers the tank and the supporting structure as a dynamically coupled system.

Sentence 4.1.8.17.(7)

232. For all categories of components except Category 6 (horizontally cantilevered floors, balconies, beams, etc.), the design force, V_p, is to be applied horizontally in the direction that is the most critical for design. In some cases, e.g. electrical cable trays or piping, the critical direction may vary for different connections of the same component. For Category 6, V_p is to be applied vertically, either up or down, whichever direction produces the most critical effect; component gravity loads are to be included.

Sentence 4.1.8.17.(8)

233. As previously noted, the connections between the attached components and the supporting structure have an important role. They must be designed to transfer the attachment forces, V_p, and the gravity loads arising from support of the components. Clauses 4.1.8.17.(8)(a) through (f) specify some important additional requirements that must be met.

    Clause (a): Friction due to gravity loads cannot be used to provide resistance to seismic forces; the three-dimensional dynamic motion of a component during seismic response can include rocking and twisting about the vertical axis, which can cause the component to "walk." This type of movement has been observed in past earthquakes for equipment such as tanks and transformers.

    Clause (b): R_p for inherently non-ductile connections, such as the adhesive bonding of components to the surface of the structure, or power-actuated fasteners, such as nails or bolts, should be taken as 1.0 to reflect the lack of ductility.

    Clause (c): Anchorage using post-installed anchors in concrete, such as expansion and undercut anchors, epoxy anchors and cast-in-place anchors where the depth of embedment is less than 8 times the nominal diameter of the anchors, is limited to an R_p of 1.5, which accounts for the limited ductility of such anchors. This type of anchor should be qualified by testing procedures similar to those outlined in ACI 355.2[95] and CSA A23.3.[49]

    Clause (d): Power-actuated connections such as nails and bolts in concrete and shallow "drop-in" anchors shall not be used for tension loading. This restriction is placed on this type of connection because of its inability to withstand the cyclic tensile loading imposed by seismic response.

    Clause (e): Where interior or exterior walls and appendages (i.e. Categories 1 to 3 in Table 4.1.8.17.) are attached to the building structure at heights above the first floor, there is a significant risk to life safety associated with such components becoming dislodged or falling off the side of the building. The loss of life due to external walls and parapets falling off the sides of buildings during earthquakes has been significant. To avoid this possibility, Sentence 4.1.8.17.(8) requires that the fasteners used to attach such components to a building be designed for forces larger than those used to design the components. When the connection is ductile, the factors used for the connection are to be the same as for the component except that $R_p = 1.0$ must be used, which will result in a connection design force that is 2.5 times that for the component. When the connection is not ductile, the same conditions apply except that the factor C_p is increased to 2.0, which further increases the connection design force by a factor of 2.

    Clause (f): A connection must yield at its design load to be considered as a ductile connection. If the connection yield force is greater than the design load, it is not considered ductile because the maximum force in the connection is not limited to the design value.

Sentence 4.1.8.17.(9)

234. Although floors and roofs acting as diaphragms are listed as Category 4 in Table 4.1.8.17., no values of the factors C_p, A_r and R_p are specified. These structural components are not to be designed using the provisions of Article 4.1.8.17. but must meet the requirements of Article 4.1.8.15.

Sentence 4.1.8.17.(10)

235. The load V_p specified in Sentence 4.1.8.17.(1) is to be used in analyzing components and their connections for the purpose of determining lateral deflections. When an elastic analysis is used for determining lateral deflections, the computed deflections must be multiplied by R_p in

order to determine realistic values of the anticipated deflections. This is directly analogous to the requirement (see Sentence 4.1.8.13.(2)) for the determination of building structure deflections because the component forces have been reduced by R_p to take into account the inelastic energy dissipation capacity of the component and its connection. If the connection and component have different values of R_p, such as is required by Clause 4.1.8.17.(8)(e), then the higher of the two values shall be used as the multiplier.

Sentence 4.1.8.17.(11)

236. The approach for designing components and their connections as specified in Article 4.1.8.17. assumes that components do not interact with the structure other than at connection points. It is therefore important that there be sufficient clearance or separation between attached components and the structure, based on the deflections computed in Sentence 4.1.8.17.(10), so that accidental interactions do not occur causing the transfer of unexpected forces to the structure itself. When the components are rigid walls or panels, the requirements of Clause 4.1.8.3.(6)(b) must be satisfied, which requires that such components be made part of the SFRS if there is insufficient separation to preclude interaction.

Sentence 4.1.8.17.(12)

237. Suspended equipment (e.g. pipes, ducts and cable trays), if not isolated, may be damaged due to pounding against the structure or other pieces of equipment. Such damage can be prevented by using seismic restraints, such as sway bracing, to restrict the lateral motion of the suspended equipment. Such restraints must be designed to meet the force and displacement requirements specified in Article 4.1.8.17. and they must be located so that they do not impose bending on the hanger rods used to suspend the equipment because such rods are only designed to carry tension forces.

Sentence 4.1.8.17.(13)

238. If suspended equipment is located so that it is isolated from other pieces of equipment and nearby walls (e.g. pendent lights), then it may be designed as a pendulum system in which case the supporting chains or rods must be designed to support twice the weight of the suspended equipment and the deflection requirements of Sentence 4.1.8.17.(10) must be met unless there is sufficient clearance for the suspended equipment to swing 45° without impacting adjacent equipment or walls, as indicated in CAN/CSA-S832.[86]

References

[1]   Heidebrecht, A.C. 1995. Insights and challenges associated with determining seismic design forces in a loading code. Bulletin of the New Zealand National Society for Earthquake Engineering, 28: 224-246.

[2]   Hall, J.F., ed. 1994. Preliminary Reconnaissance Report Northridge Earthquake January 17, 1994. Earthquake Engineering Research Institute, Oakland, California.

[3]   Park, R., Billings, I.J., Clifton, G.C., Cousins, J., Filiatrault, A., Jennings, D.N., Jones, L.C.P., Perrin, N.D., Rooney, S.L., Sinclair, J., Spurr, D.D., Tanaka, H. and Walker G. 1995. The Hyogo-ken Nanbu earthquake of 17 January 1995. Bulletin of the New Zealand Society for Earthquake Engineering, Vol. 28, No.1, pp. 1-98.

[4]   Borcherdt, R.D. 1994. New developments in estimating site effects on ground motion. Proceedings of the ATC-35 seminar on new developments in earthquake ground motion estimation and implications for engineering design practice, Applied Technology Council, California, pp. 10-1 to 10-44.

[5]   Adams, J. and Halchuk, S. 2003. Fourth generation seismic hazard maps of Canada: Values for over 650 Canadian localities intended for the 2005 National Building Code of Canada. Geological Survey of Canada Open File 4459, 155 pp. (see also http://earthquakescanada.nrcan.gc.ca)

[6]   Adams, J. and Atkinson, G. 2003. Development of seismic hazard maps for the 2005 National Building Code of Canada. Canadian Journal of Civil Engineering.

[7]   Building Seismic Safety Council. 1998. NEHRP recommended provisions for seismic regulations for new buildings and other structures, 1997 Edition, Part 1: Provisions (FEMA 302) and Part 2: Commentary (FEMA 303), Washington, D.C.

[8]   Finn, L. and Wightman, A. 2003. Ground motion amplification factors for NBCC 2005. Canadian Journal of Civil Engineering.

[9]   Heidebrecht, A.C., Basham, P.W., Rainer, J.H. and Berry, M.J. 1983. Engineering applications of new probabilistic ground-motion maps of Canada. Canadian Journal of Civil Engineering, 10: 670-680.

[10]   Tso, W.K. 1992. Overview of seismic provision changes in National Building Code of Canada 1990. Canadian Journal of Civil Engineering, 19: 383-388.

[11]   Mitchell, D., Tremblay, R., Karacabeyli, E., Paultre, P., Saatcioglu, M. and Anderson, D.L. 2003. Seismic force modification factors for the proposed 2005 NBCC. Canadian Journal of Civil Engineering.

[12]   Saatcioglu, M. and Humar, J.M. 2003. Dynamic analysis of buildings for earthquake resistant design. Canadian Journal of Civil Engineering.

[13]   Humar, J. and Mahgoub, M.A. 2003. Determination of seismic design forces by equivalent static load method. Canadian Journal of Civil Engineering.

[14]   DeVall, R. 2003. Background information for some of the proposed earthquake design provisions for the next edition of the National Building Code of Canada. Canadian Journal of Civil Engineering.

[15]   Humar, J.M., Yavari, S. and Saatcioglu, M. 2003. Design for forces induced by seismic torsion. Canadian Journal of Civil Engineering.

[16]   Adams, J. 1990. Paleoseismicity of the Cascadia subduction zone – evidence from turbidites off the Oregon-Washington margin. Tectonics, Vol. 9, pp. 569-583.

[17]   Satake, K., Shimazaki, K., Tsuji, Y., and Ueda, K. 1996. Time and size of a giant earthquake in Cascadia inferred from Japanese tsunami records of January 1700. Nature, Vol. 379, pp. 246-249.

[18]   Basham, P.W. 1995. Recent advances in understanding of earthquake potential and seismic hazards in Canada. Proc. 7th Canadian Conference on Earthquake Engineering, Montreal, pp. 45-64.

[19]   Atkinson, G.M. and Boore, D.M. 1995. New ground motion relations for eastern North America. Bull. Seism. Soc. Am., Vol. 85, pp. 17-30.

[20]   Atkinson, G.M. 1995. Ground motion relations for use in eastern hazard analysis. Proc. 7th Canadian Conference on Earthquake Engineering, Montreal.

[21]   Atkinson, G.M. 1997. Empirical ground motion relations for earthquakes in the Cascadia region. Canadian Journal of Civil Engineering, Vol. 24, pp. 64-77.

[22]   Boore, D.M., Joyner, W.B., and Fumal, T.E. 1997. Equations for estimating horizontal response spectra and peak acceleration from western North American earthquakes: A summary of recent work. Seismological Research Letters, Vol. 68, pp. 128-153.

[23]   Cornell, C.A. 1968. Engineering seismic risk analysis. Bulletin of the Seismological Society of America, Vol. 58, pp. 1583-1606.

[24]   McGuire, R.K. 1993. Computations of seismic hazard. Giardini, D. and Basham, P.W., eds. Global Seismic Hazard Assessment Program, Annali di Geofisica, Vol. 34, pp. 181-200.

[25]   Building Seismic Safety Council. 2001. NEHRP recommended provisions for seismic regulations for new buildings and other structures, 2000 Edition, Part 1: Provisions (FEMA 368) and Part 2: Commentary (FEMA 369), Washington, D.C.

[26]   International Code Council 2001. 2000 International Building Code and 2000 Commentary Volume 1, Falls Church, Virginia.

[27]   Tremblay, R. 1998. Development of design spectra for long duration ground motions from Cascadia subduction earthquakes. Canadian Journal of Civil Engineering, 25: 1078-1090.

[28]   Tremblay, R. and Atkinson, G.M. 2001. Comparative study of the inelastic seismic demand of eastern and western sites. Earthquake Spectra, 17: 333-358.

[29]   Seed, H.B. 1986. Influence of local soil conditions on ground motions and building damage during earthquakes. Eighth Nabor Carillo Lecture, Mexican Society for Soil Mechanics, Mazatlan, Mexico, Nov. 22.

[30]   Housner, George W. "Competing Against Time," Report to Governor Deukmejian of California, Governor's Board of Inquiry on the 1989 Loma Prieta Earthquake, George W. Housner, Chairman.

[31]   Idriss, I.M. 1990. Response of soft soil sites during earthquakes. Proc. H. Bolton Seed Memorial Symposium, Berkeley, California, Vol. II.

[32]   Schnabel, P.B., Lysmer, J. and Seed, H.B. 1972. SHAKE: A Computer Program for Earthquake Response Analysis of Horizontally Layered Sites. Report EERC 71-12, University of California at Berkeley.

[33]   Associate Committee on the National Building Code 1995. National Building Code of Canada 1995. National Research Council of Canada. Ottawa, Ontario.

[34]   Building Seismic Safety Council. 1995. NEHRP recommended provisions for seismic regulations for new buildings and other structures 1994 Edition, Part 1: Provisions (FEMA 222A), Washington, D.C.

[35]   Borcherdt, R.D. 1992. Dependent code provisions, Proc., NCCER, SEAOC, BSSC Workshop on Site Response During Earthquakes and Seismic Code Provisions, University of Southern California, Los Angeles, Simplified Site Classes and Empirical Amplification Factors for Site California, Nov. 18-20.

[36]   Borcherdt, R.D. 1994. Estimates of site-dependent response spectra for design (methodology and justification). Earthquake Spectra, Vol. 10, No. 4, pp. 617-653.

[37]   Dobry, R., Martin, G.M., Parra, E. and Bhattacharyya, A. 1994. Development of site-dependent ratios of elastic response spectra (RRS) and site categories for building seismic codes, Proc., NCCER, SEAOC, BSSC Workshop on Site Response During Earthquakes and Seismic Code Provisions, University of Southern California, Los Angeles, California, Nov. 18-20.

[38]   Dobry, R., Martin, G.M., Parra, E. and Bhattacharyya, A. 1994. Studies of ratios of response spectra soil/rock and of site categories for seismic codes. National Center for Earthquake Engineering Research, Buffalo, N.Y.

[39]   Borcherdt, R.D. 2002. Empirical evidence for site coefficients in building code provisions. Earthquake Spectra, Vol. 18, No. 2, pp. 189-218.

[40]   Kelly, J.M., 1991. Base Isolation: Origins and Development, EERC News, Earthquake Engineering Research Center, Berkeley, California, Vol. 12, No. 1, January.

[41]   Naiem, F. and Kelly, J.M. 1999. Design of seismically isolated structures: from theory to practice. John Wiley & Sons, 304 pp.

[42]   CAN/CSA-S6-00, Canadian Highway Bridge Design Code. Canadian Standards Association, Mississauga, Ontario, 2000.

[43]   Hanson, R.D. and Soong, T.T. 2001. Seismic design with supplementary energy dissipation devices, Monograph MNO-8, Earthquake Engineering Research Institute, Oakland, California, 135 pp.

[44]   Anderson, D.L., DeVall, R.H., Loeffler, R.J. and Ventura, C.E. 2000. Preliminary guidelines for the non-linear analysis and design of hysteretic (displacement dependent) energy dissipation devices in buildings. Private report to RJC Consulting Engineers, Vancouver, B.C.

[45]   Applied Technology Council. 1997. NEHRP guidelines and commentary for the seismic rehabilitation of buildings, FEMA 273 and 274, Federal Emergency Management Agency, Washington, D.C.

[46]   Applied Technology Council. 1996. The seismic evaluation and retrofit of concrete buildings. ATC 40, Redwood City, California.

[47]   CAN/CSA-O86-01, Engineering Design in Wood. Canadian Standards Association, Mississauga, Ontario, 2001.

[48]   Ceccotti, A. and Karacabeyli, E. 2002. Validation of seismic design parameters for wood-frame shearwall systems. Canadian Journal of Civil Engineering, 29: 484-498.

[49]   CSA A23.3-04, Design of Concrete Structures. Canadian Standards Association, Mississauga, Ontario, 2004.

[50]   Paulay, T. and Priestley, M.J.N. 1992. Seismic Design of Reinforced Concrete and Masonry Buildings. John Wiley & Sons, Inc., 744 pp.

[51]   MacRae, G.A., Priestley, M.J.N. and Tao, J. 1993. P-Δ design in seismic regions. Report No. 93/05, Department of Applied Mechanics and Engineering Sciences, University of California, La Jolla, California, 114 pp.

[52]   Tremblay, R., Cote, B. and Leger, P. 1999. An evaluation of P-Δ amplification factors in multistory moment resisting frames. Canadian Journal of Civil Engineering, 26: 535-548.

[53] Bernal, D., 1987. Amplification Factors for Inelastic Dynamic P-Delta Effects in Earthquake Analysis. Journal Earthquake Eng. Struct. Dyn., Vol. 15, pp. 635-651.

[54] Bernal, D., 1992. Instability of Buildings Subjected to Earthquakes. Journal Struct. Eng., ASCE, Vol. 118, No. 8, pp. 2239-2260.

[55] Montgomery, C.J., 1981. Influence of P-Delta Effects on Seismic Design. Can. J. Civ. Eng., Vol. 8, pp. 31-43 with erratum on p. 273.

[56] Gupta, A. and Krawinkler, H. 2000. Dynamic P-Delta effects for flexible inelastic steel structures. ASCE Journal of Structural Engineering, 126: 145-154.

[57] Krawinkler, H., Bertero, V. and Popov, E. 1975. Shear behavior of steel frame joints. Journal of the Structural Division, ASCE, 101: 2317-2336.

[58] Kramer, S.L. 1996. Geotechnical Earthquake Engineering, Prentice Hall, New Jersey, 653 pp.

[59] Beer, F.P. and Johnston, E.R. Jr. 1992. Mechanics of Materials 2nd Edition. McGraw-Hill Book Co., 736 pp.

[60] ECS 1998. Eurocode 8: Design of structures for earthquake resistance, May 2001 draft, European Committee for Standardization, Brussels.

[61] CAN/CSA-S16-01, Limit States Design of Steel Structures. Canadian Standards Association, Mississauga, Ontario, 2001.

[62] Mitchell, D. and Paultre, P. 1994. Ductility and overstrength in seismic design of reinforced concrete structures. Canadian Journal of Civil Engineering, Vol. 21, No. 6, p. 1049, 12 pp.

[63] Rahgozar, M.A. and Humar, J.L. 1998. Accounting for overstrength in seismic design of steel structures. Canadian Journal of Civil Engineering, Vol. 25, No. 1, p. 1, 15 pp.

[64] Standards New Zealand 1992. Code of practice for general structural design and design loadings for buildings: Volume 1 Code of Practice (134 pp.) and Volume 2 Commentary (96 pp.), Wellington.

[65] Esteva, L. 1987. Earthquake engineering research and practice in Mexico after 1985 earthquake. Bulletin of the New Zealand National Society of Earthquake Engineering, 20: 159-200.

[66] Mitchell, D., Tinawai, R. and Redwood, R.G. 1990. Damage to buildings due to the 1989 Loma Prieta earthquake – a Canadian perspective. Canadian Journal of Civil Engineering, 17: 813-834.

[67] Rutenberg, A. and Heidebrecht, A.C. 1985. Rotational ground motion and seismic codes. Canadian Journal of Civil Engineering, Vol. 17, No. 3, pp. 583-592.

[68] DeLaLlera, J.C. and Chopra, A.K. 1994. Accidental and natural torsion in earthquake response and design of buildings. Report No. 94/07, Earthquake Engineering Research Centre, University of California, Berkeley, California.

[69] Goel, R.K. and Chopra, A.K. 1993. Seismic code analysis of buildings without locating centres of rigidity. Journal of Structural Engineering. ASCE, 119: 3039-3055.

[70] Chopra, A. 1995. Dynamics of Structures, Prentice-Hall, Inc., 729 pp.

[71] Humar, J. 1990. Dynamics of Structures, Prentice-Hall, Inc., 780 pp.

[72] Naiem, F. and Lew, M. 1995. On the use of design spectrum compatible time histories, Earthquake Spectra, 11: 111-127.

[73] Atkinson, G.M. and Beresnev, I.A. 1998. Compatible ground-motion time histories for new national seismic hazard maps. Canadian Journal of Civil Engineering, 25: 305-318.

[74] Naumoski, N. 2001. "Program SYNTH - Generation of artificial accelerograms compatible with a target spectrum," Department of Civil Engineering, University of Ottawa, Ottawa, Ontario, 18 pp.

[75] Vision 2000 Committee. 1995. Performance based seismic engineering of buildings. Structural Engineers Association of California (SEAOC), Sacramento, California.

[76] Filiatrault, A., Cervantes, M., Folz, B. and Prion, H. 1994. Pounding of buildings during earthquakes: a Canadian perspective. Canadian Journal of Civil Engineering, 21: 251-265.

[77] Filiatrault, A. and Cervantes, M. 1995. Separation between buildings to avoid pounding during earthquakes. Canadian Journal of Civil Engineering, 22: 164-179.

[78] CSA S304.1-04, Design of Masonry Structures. Canadian Standards Association, Mississauga, Ontario, 2004.

Commentary J

[79]   Anderson, D.L. 2003. Effect of foundation rocking on the seismic response of shear walls. Canadian Journal of Civil Engineering.

[80]   Draft Australian/New Zealand Standard DR00902. 2002.

[81]   Mononobe, N. and Matsuo, H. On the Determination of Earth Pressures During Earthquakes. Proc. World Engineering Congress, 1929, Vol. 9, pp. 177-185.

[82]   Seed, H.B. and Whitman, R.V. Design of Earth Retaining Structures for Dynamic Loads. Am. Soc. Civ. Eng., Specialty Conference – Lateral Stresses in the Ground and Design of Earth Retaining Structures, Cornell University, Ithaca, New York, 1970.

[83]   Youd, T.L., Idriss, I.M., Andruss, R.D., Arango, I., Castro, G., Christian, J.T., Dobry, R., Finn, W.D.L., Harder, L.F. Jr., Hynes, M.E., Ishihara, K., Koester, J.P., Liao, S.S.C., Marcuson, W.F. III, Martin, G.R., Mitchell, J.K., Moriwaki, Y., Power, M.S., Robertson, P.K., Seed, R.B. and Stoke, K.H. III. 2001. Liquefaction resistance of soils: summary report from the 1996 NCEE and 1998 NCEER/NSF workshops on evaluation of liquefaction resistance of soils, ASCE Journal of Geotechnical and Geoenvironmental Engineering, Vol. 127, No. 10.

[84]   Bachman, R.E., Drake, R.M., and Richter, P.J. 1993. 1994 Update to 1991 NEHRP Provisions for Architectural, Mechanical, and Electrical Components and Systems, letter report to National Center for Earthquake Engineering Research, February 22.

[85]   McKevitt, W. 2003. Proposed Canadian code provisions for seismic design of elements of structures, non-structural components and equipment. Canadian Journal of Civil Engineering.

[86]   CAN/CSA-S832-06, Seismic Risk Reduction of Operational and Functional Components of Buildings. Canadian Standards Association, Mississauga, Ontario, 2006.

[87]   RMI 1990. Specification for the design, testing and utilization of industrial steel storage racks, Rack Manufacturers Institute.

[88]   API 650-1998, Welded Steel Tanks for Oil Storage. American Petroleum Institute, Washington, D.C.

[89]   ANSI/API 620-1992, Design and Construction of Large, Welded, Low Pressure Storage Tanks. American Petroleum Institute, Washington, D.C.

[90]   API 620-2002, Design and Construction of Large, Welded, Low-Pressure Storage Tanks. American Petroleum Institute, Washington, D.C.

[91]   ANSI/AWWA D100-1996, Welded Steel Tanks for Water Storage. American Water Works Association, Denver, Colorado.

[92]   ANSI/AWWA D110-1995, Wire and Strand-Wound Circular Prestressed Concrete Water Tanks. American Water Works Association, Denver, Colorado.

[93]   ANSI/AWWA D115-1995, Circular Prestressed Concrete Tanks with Circumferential Tendons. American Water Works Association, Denver, Colorado.

[94]   Building Seismic Safety Council 2003. NEHRP recommended provisions for seismic regulations for new buildings and other structures 2003 Edition, Part 1: Provisions (FEMA 450) and Part 2: Commentary (FEMA 450), Washington, D.C.

[95]   ACI 355.2-01/355.2R-01, Evaluating the Performance of Post Installed Mechanical Anchors in Concrete and Commentary, American Concrete Institute, 2001.

Additional Sources of Information

Arnold, C. and Reitherman, R. 1982. Building configuration and seismic design, John Wiley & Sons, Inc., 296 pp.

Biddah, A.M.S. 1998. Evaluation of the Seismic Level of Protection of Steel Moment Resisting Frame Building Structures. Doctoral Thesis. McMaster University, Hamilton, Ontario.

EERI Ad Hoc Committee on Seismic Performance. 1994. Expected Seismic Performance of Buildings. Earthquake Engineering Research Institute, Oakland, California.

Heidebrecht, A.C. 1996. Major issues affecting the seismic design of building structures in Canada, presentation at CSCE Annual Conference 1st Structural Specialty Conference, Edmonton.

Heidebrecht, A. C. 1997. Seismic level of protection for building structures. Canadian Journal of Civil Engineering, 24: 20-33.

Heidebrecht, A.C. 1999. Implications of new Canadian uniform hazard spectra for seismic design and the seismic level of protection of building structures, Proceedings of the Eighth Canadian Conference on Earthquake Engineering, Vancouver, B.C.

Heidebrecht, A.C. 1999. Concerning the seismic level of protection for the next edition of NBCC, unpublished report to CANCEE.

Heidebrecht, A.C. 2000. What's happening with seismic design in Canada, newsletter of the Canadian Association for Earthquake Engineering.

Naumoski, N. and Heidebrecht, A.C. 1997. Seismic level of protection of medium height reinforced concrete frame structures: design of frames, EERG Report 97-1, Dept. of Civil Engineering, McMaster University, Hamilton, Ontario.

Naumoski, N. and Heidebrecht, A.C. 1998. Seismic level of protection of medium height reinforced concrete frame structures: modelling and analysis, EERG Report 98-2, Dept. of Civil Engineering, McMaster University, Hamilton, Ontario.

Newmark, N.M. and Hall, W.J. 1982. Earthquake spectra and design, Monograph Series, Earthquake Engineering Research Institute, Oakland, California.

Okamoto, S. "Introduction to Earthquake Engineering," University of Tokyo Press, Tokyo, Japan, 1973, p. 126.

Stafford Smith, B. and Coull, A. 1991. Tall Building Structures: Analysis and Design. John Wiley & Sons, Inc.

Uzumeri, S.M. 1993. Development of Canadian seismic-resistant design code for reinforced concrete buildings, Proceedings of the Tom Paulay Symposium "Recent Developments in Lateral Force Transfer in Buildings." La Jolla, California.

Commentary K
Foundations

Introduction

1. This Commentary provides guidance, compatible with sound engineering practice, for the design of foundations and temporary excavations in accordance with the provisions of Section 4.2., Foundations, of the National Building Code of Canada 2005 (NBC). NBC Subsection 4.1.3. requires the use of limit states design for the design of buildings and their structural components. This Commentary deals with this approach for the design of shallow and deep foundations. The material herein is intended as a first approximation dealing with routine problems of foundation design and construction. Neither this material nor the papers or texts to which it refers should substitute for the experience and judgment of a professional engineer competent in dealing with the complexities of foundation design practice.

2. This Commentary is divided into three principal parts: Temporary Excavations, Shallow Foundations, and Deep Foundations. Limit states design of temporary excavations has not yet been introduced and such excavations are to be designed according to the traditional allowable stress or global factor of safety procedures.

3. This Commentary does not deal specifically with the identification and classification of soils and rocks, with subsurface investigations, with swelling and shrinking clay, with frost action as related to foundations, with soil and hydrostatic pressures, or with retaining walls; these topics are included in the "Canadian Foundation Engineering Manual," (CFEM).[1]

Limit States Design

4. Limit states refer to those conditions of a structure in which the structure ceases to fulfil the function for which it was designed. The limit states are classified into two main groups:
   * ultimate limit states (ULS), and
   * serviceability limit states (SLS).

5. Ultimate limit states are primarily concerned with collapse mechanisms for the structure and, hence, safety. For foundation design, ultimate limit states consist of:
   * exceeding the load-carrying capacity of the foundation (i.e., ultimate bearing capacity),
   * sliding,
   * uplift,
   * large deformation of foundation, leading to an ultimate limit state being induced in the superstructure or building,
   * overturning, and
   * loss of overall stability.

6. Serviceability limit states consider mechanisms that restrict or constrain the intended use or occupancy of the structure. They are usually associated with movements that interrupt or hinder the purpose (i.e., serviceability) of the structure. For foundation design, serviceability limit states can be categorized as:
   * excessive movements (e.g., settlement, differential settlement, heave, lateral movement, and tilt or rotation), and
   * unacceptable vibrations.

7. The basic design equation for limit states design is:

$$\phi R_n \geq \Sigma \alpha_i S_{ni}$$

Commentary K

where ϕR_n is referred to as the factored geotechnical resistance. The resistance factor, ϕ, accounts for variability in the soil strengths and as-built dimensions, and variabilities introduced by inaccuracies in the calculation model. It also indirectly allows for ductile and catastrophic failures. The nominal resistance, R_n, is the engineer's best estimate of the ultimate resistance of the foundation. The value of R_n should allow, at least partially, for variabilities resulting from geotechnical uncertainties. It is based on the characteristic (nominal) strengths of the soil, nominal (specified) dimensions, and the normal calculation model.

8. The term S_{ni} is the nominal value of the forces on the foundation resulting from the ith load. These forces are obtained from the specified loads by structural analysis. The term α_i is the load factor for the ith load. It accounts for the variability in the load itself, approximations in the loading model given in the Code and variability introduced by the structural analysis.

9. The load factors and load combinations are as given in NBC Subsection 4.1.3.

10. The recommended resistance factors are given in Table K-1. The resistance factors in this Table have mainly been derived by direct calibration to traditional working (allowable) stress design. This means that the dimensions of foundations governed by bearing capacity should not be significantly different using limit states design procedure as compared to the working stress design procedure. The derivation of the resistance factor in Table K-1 is described in detail in Reference [24], where it is shown that the estimated reliability index (β) for shallow foundations using the resistance factors in Table K-1 ranges from 2.8 to 3.5, a range that is consistent with values commonly used for the design of the building structure. Figure K-1, which is taken from Reference [24], shows the relationship between global safety factor, resistance factor and reliability index, β, using statistical assumptions for variability in bearing resistance (coefficient of variation 0.3 and ratio of mean to nominal of 1.1) that is typical for shallow and deep foundations. The advantage of Figure K-1 is that β can be readily interpreted by geotechnical engineers who have considerable experience in using the traditional values of global safety factor. This can assist in bridging the gap, during the transitional stage, between the use of working stress and limit states concepts for geotechnical aspects of foundation design. Additional discussion on these aspects is provided in the CFEM.[1]

Table K-1
Resistance Factors for Shallow and Deep Foundations

Description	Resistance Factors
1. Shallow foundation	
(a) Vertical resistance by semi-empirical analysis using laboratory and in situ test data	0.5
(b) Sliding	
(i) based on friction (c = 0)	0.8
(ii) based on cohesion/adhesion (tan f = 0)	0.6
2. Deep foundation	
(a) Bearing resistance to axial load	
(i) semi-empirical analysis using laboratory and in situ test data	0.4
(ii) analysis using static loading test results	0.6
(iii) analysis using dynamic monitoring results	0.5
(iv) uplift resistance by semi-empirical analysis	0.3
(v) uplift resistance using loading test results	0.4
(b) Horizontal load resistance	0.5

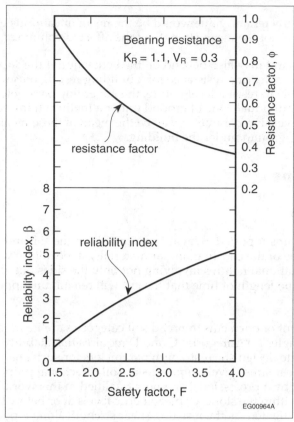

Figure K-1
Relation between safety factor, resistance factor and reliability index for bearing resistance, $K_R = 1.1$, $V_R = 0.3$

11. The selection of characteristic values of soil and rock properties, appropriate for the limit states investigated, shall be based on the results of laboratory and field tests and shall take account of the following:
    (a) geological and other background information, such as data from previous projects,
    (b) the variabilities of the property values,
    (c) the extent of the zone of ground governing the behaviour of the geotechnical structure for the limit state considered,
    (d) the influence of workmanship on artificially placed or improved soils,
    (e) the effect of construction activities on the properties of in situ ground.

    The selection of the characteristic value shall take into account the possible difference between the properties measured in the tests and the soil and rock properties governing the behaviour of the ground due to factors such as:
    (a) the presence of fissures, which may play a different role in the test and in the geotechnical structure,
    (b) the time effects, and
    (c) the brittleness or ductility of the soil and rock tested.

12. In essence, the characteristic value corresponds to the geotechnical engineer's best estimate of the most appropriate likely value for geotechnical properties relevant for the limit states investigated. A cautious estimate of the mean value for the affected ground (zone of influence) is generally considered as a logical value to use as the characteristic value. Additional information and guidance on the selection of appropriate characteristic values are provided in the CFEM.[1]

13. In many cases, the variability of a mean value of a soil or rock property should be investigated, as well as the variability of an individual value resulting from a test. The extent of the zone of influence governing the behaviour of the ground for a limit state is usually much larger than the extent of the zone involved in a soil or rock test; consequently, the governing parameter is often a mean value over a certain surface or volume of the ground. An exception to this would be the presence of a weak layer, within the zone of affected ground, that would control the most likely failure mechanism (limit

state). The appropriate characteristic value would be the mean or cautious estimate of the mean strength of the weak layer – not the mean strength of the affected volume of ground.

14. The governing zone of ground may also depend on the behaviour of the supported structure. For instance, when considering a bearing resistance for a building resting on several spread footings, where the building is unable to resist a local failure, the governing parameter would likely be the mean strength over each individual zone of ground under a footing. If instead the building is stiff and strong enough, the governing parameter may be the mean of these mean values over the entire zone or part of the zone of ground under the building.

Temporary Excavations

Unsupported Excavations

15. The safety and stability of unsupported excavations depends on the soil and groundwater conditions and on the depth and slope of the cut. In granular materials, slope failure will generally be fairly shallow; in clays, deep rotational failures involving not only the sides but also the base of the excavation are possible. The length of time that the cut will remain unsupported must also be considered.

16. Guidelines for the treatment of open cuts in broad soil categories are included in Table K-2. The selection of stable slope angles for Categories C and D requires that stability analyses be carried out. The selection of appropriate design shear strength parameters for such analyses requires a careful assessment of imposed shear stress levels, time effects, soil directional properties and uniformity, and should be carried out by a professional engineer qualified in this work. The influence of groundwater conditions within the slope, or piezometric levels at or below the toe of the proposed slope, should also be investigated, as the resisting shear strength along a potential failure surface may be greatly reduced by hydrostatic pressures. Additional information and guidance on the design of unsupported excavations are provided in the CFEM.[1]

Table K-2
Open Cut Excavation Guidelines[1][2]

Category	Soil Type	Groundwater	Typical Failure Mode	Time to Failure	Remarks	References
A	Free-draining, granular, non-plastic silts	Below cut or controlled by advance dewatering	Shallow surface or slope wedge	Generally rapid	Rarely a problem if groundwater under control and slope angle does not exceed friction angle of soil. Unsaturated temporary steeper cuts rely on apparent cohesion and may slough with time; cuts steeper than 45° are not recommended; vertical cuts more than 1.2 m in depth should never be used.	[2]
B	As for Category A	Cut below groundwater	Sloughing to flow	Rapid	Uniform fine soils may flow for considerable distances if pumping from within excavation is attempted. Slopes are controlled by hydraulic effects and may range from 1/3 or less to full value of friction angle.	As for Category A

Table K-2 (Continued)

Category	Soil Type	Groundwater	Typical Failure Mode	Time to Failure	Remarks	References
C	Non-sensitive clays. Plastic and cohesive silts	Saturated[3]	Rotational. Plane of weakness or composite surface	Rapid or delayed depending on per cent of operational soil shear strength mobilized	Analytical methods generally reliable for prediction of stability in soft to firm clays	As for Category A
D	Sensitive clays	Saturated[3]	Rotational. Retrogressive slides and as per Category C	As per Category C: little advance warning	Extreme caution required; once initial failure is provoked, retrogressive action may affect wide area; reliability of analytical prediction methods generally poor.	—

[1] Mixed soils such as glacial tills should be classified into Category A, B, or C, depending on grain size, plasticity and permeability, and treated accordingly.

[2] The stability of an open cut slope, which is only marginally stable at the end of excavation, may be adversely affected by such factors as the nature and magnitude of crest loading, vibrations, rainfall, the length of time the cut remains open or disturbance of the soil in the vicinity of the toe of the slope.

[3] Excavations through alternate layers of cohesive and granular soils or excavations terminated within a cohesive soil underlain by granular strata require an investigation of groundwater conditions in each layer, and the factor of safety against excavation base heave or slope failure as a result of upward water pressure should be assessed.

Supported Excavations

17. Temporary shoring support of vertical excavation faces requires the assessment of a number of factors, including the length of time the excavation is to be supported, earth pressures, pressures from frost action and corrosion from aggressive soil or groundwater. The shoring wall elements may either be open, permitting full drainage, or closed, providing a barrier to groundwater flow, depending mainly on the soil permeability (hydraulic conductivity) and groundwater conditions. Closed systems are designed for soil and full groundwater pressures, whereas hydrostatic pressures are not included in open systems where seepage through the wall can take place. Additional information and guidance on the analysis and design of supported excavations are provided in the CFEM[1] and CAN/CSA-S6[47] and its Commentary.

Earth pressures

18. For flexible and semi-flexible shoring walls, which are commonly used to support the vertical faces of excavations and may have a variety of support conditions, no satisfactory general theoretical solutions for the prediction of earth pressures are available. The design earth pressure must take into account the method and sequence of construction and the tolerable deformation limits of the sides or faces of the excavation.

19. The yield of one part of a flexible wall throws pressure onto the more rigid parts. Hence, pressures in the vicinity of supports are higher than in unsupported areas, and the loads on individual supports vary, depending largely on the stiffness characteristics of the supports themselves and the construction technique.

20. The pressure envelopes, which represent the pressures that would normally be anticipated, can be represented in triangular, trapezoidal or rectangular form, and the applicable earth pressure

Commentary K

coefficients will range between the active K_A[*] case and the earth pressure at rest K_O,[**] depending on permissible wall and soil movements.

21. **Non-cohesive (granular) soils.** As a first approximation, the guidelines in Table K-3 are suggested for essentially granular soils such as fills, sands, silts, sandy silts, gravelly sands, and gravels, or alternating layered conditions composed of such strata.

Table K-3
Envelope of Earth Pressure for the Design of Temporary Supports for Granular Soils

Restraint	Design Total Pressure[(1)]	Envelope of Pressure Distribution[(2)]	Ability to Restrict Adjacent Soil Movements[(3)]
Cantilever	$1.0\ P_A$	Triangular	Generally very poor unless wall extremely stiff and embedded in dense soil
Braced	1.2 to $1.3\ P_A$	Rectangular or trapezoidal	Generally poor where control of groundwater inadequate or where workmanship poor; can be moderate to good where these factors are properly controlled and bracing properly designed and tightly wedged or preloaded
Tied back	1.1 to $1.4\ P_A$	Rectangular or trapezoidal	Generally good where high total pressures are used; movements usually less than for braced walls and dependent on degree of prestressing, workmanship and wall stiffness

[(1)] P_A = theoretical total active pressure = $0.5\rho gH^2 \times K_A$ where

ρ = total (bulk) density of soil (submerged if below groundwater), kg/m³,

H = depth of cut, and

g = acceleration due to gravity, m/s².

The value of 0.2 is suggested as a lower bound for K_A even in dense soils. Surcharge pressures, compaction-induced pressures, and hydrostatic water pressures should be added where appropriate.

[(2)] After increasing P_A by the appropriate multiplier, distribute total pressure over depth of cut as indicated in this column: triangular limits of trapezoid generally taken as 0.2H to 0.25H at top and bottom.

[(3)] Where greater control of adjacent ground movements is required, earth pressure should be computed using the at-rest K_o earth pressure coefficient with prestress in struts or tie-backs to the full design load. Additional measures would include choice of a stiff wall and close vertical spacing of struts or tie-backs.

22. **Cohesive soils.** For cohesive soils, a distinction must be made between soft to firm clays and stiff to very stiff clays. The effects of clay sensitivity and the factor of safety against base heave must also be taken into account.

23. For stiff clay soils ($C_u > 50$ kPa)[***] including silty clays, sandy clays and clayey silts, the guidelines in Table K-4 are suggested. Similarly, for soft (12 kPa < C_u < 25 kPa) to firm (25 kPa < C_u < 50 kPa) clays, reference should be made to Table K-5.

Earth pressure distributions calculated using nominal (unfactored) values of K_A or K_O and distributions based on Tables K-3, K-4 and K-5 represent nominal (specified) earth pressure distributions. In the calculation of lateral earth load for ULS conditions, these distributions are multiplied by appropriate load factors.

---

[*] $K_A = (1 - \sin\phi')/(1 + \sin\phi')$, where ϕ' = effective friction angle of soil and the ground surface is horizontal.

[**] K_O is frequently assumed to be equal to $1 - \sin\phi'$

[***] $C_u = 1/2$ unconfined compressive strength = undrained shear strength

Table K-4
Envelope of Earth Pressure for the Design of Temporary Supports for Stiff Cohesive Soils

Restraint	Design Total Pressure	Envelope of Pressure Distribution[1]	Ability to Restrict Adjacent Soil Movements
Cantilever	1.0 P_A but not less than 0.15$\rho g H^2$ [2]	Triangular	May be poor depending on length of cantilever, wall stiffness, embedment conditions and clay sensitivity[3][4]
Braced or tied back	0.15$\rho g H^2$ to 0.4$\rho g H^2$ [5]	Rectangular or trapezoidal	Depends on soil strength, sensitivity, effective preloading or prestressing, and wall stiffness

[1] Surcharge pressures and compaction-induced pressures should be added where appropriate; hydrostatic pressures need not be included; total density of soil, ρ, is to be used in calculations.

[2] P_A may be computed using short-term strength, i.e. $P_A = \rho g H - 2C_u$, if the excavation is open for a limited period. Regardless of whether pressures are negative or zero, minimum positive pressures indicated should be used.

[3] Computed passive pressures below the base of the excavation should be reduced by 50% to account for unavoidable disturbance due to strain effects and stress release.

[4] The factor of safety against base heave in stiff over-consolidated clays, as a result of high locked-in lateral stresses, should also be investigated.

[5] Use higher range where clay is of high sensitivity. If the construction sequence or workmanship allow significant inward movement during any stage of excavation, pressures may build up to essentially fluid soil values in very sensitive clays. With good workmanship, clay pressures are similar to those given in Table K-2. Strength tests taken on intact samples of stiff clays that are jointed or fissured may overestimate the strength characteristics and thus lead to an underestimation of earth pressures. The effects of joints and fissures should be taken into account as appropriate to determine the operational strength of the soil mass.

Table K-5
Envelope of Earth Pressure for the Design of Temporary Supports for Soft to Firm Clays

Restraint	Design Total Pressure	Envelope of Pressure Distribution[1]	Ability to Restrict Adjacent Soil Movements[2][3]
Cantilever	1.0 P_A but not less than 0.15$\rho g H^2$ [4]	Triangular	Very poor; this type of support generally to be avoided in soft, sensitive clays
Braced or tied back	0.4$\rho g H^2$ to 0.8$\rho g H^2$ [5]	Rectangular	Depends on clay shear strength and stability[6]

[1] Essentially fluid soil pressures in very sensitive clays may be realized as a result of unavoidable wall movements prior to insertion of restraint supports.

[2] Computed passive pressures below the base of the excavation should be reduced by at least 50% to account for unavoidable disturbance due to strain effects.

[3] Additional precautions in soft to firm sensitive clays would include (a) insertion of the top strut or anchor prior to excavation beyond 1.5 to 3 m depth, and (b) where the excavation area is of limited size, placing of a 150- to 300-mm-thick concrete mat at the base of the excavation, where practical, immediately on completion of excavation.

[4] P_A may be computed using short-term strength, i.e. $P_A = \rho g H - 2C_u$, if the excavation is open for a limited period. Regardless of whether pressures are negative or zero, minimum positive pressures indicated should be used.

[5] Higher range should be used where clay is of soft consistency, and lower range where clay is of firm consistency. This value may be conservative for non-homogeneous, non-sensitive sandy-silty cohesive soils of firm consistency. If stability number $N = (\rho g H + \text{surcharge})/C_u$ approaches 5 to 6, use the higher range. At this depth, base heave may also take place and suitable precautions should be taken.

[6] Design of a suitable shoring and bracing system in soft to firm clay conditions is not a routine matter, and the advice of a specialist should be obtained to establish earth pressures, to check overall stability and base heave, and to predict adjacent soil movements.

Movements Associated with Excavations

24. Movements associated with excavations are primarily related to construction technique and commonly consist of lateral yield of the soil and support system towards the excavation, with corresponding vertical movement adjacent to the excavation walls. Both lateral and vertical movements due to yield are generally of the same order of magnitude; however, if very flexible vertical wall elements are used, lateral movements can be grossly increased. Where construction technique is poor, erratic movements can also occur due to loss of ground or erosion behind the wall.

25. Movements due to yield of cantilever walls are related to the wall and soil stiffness. For most flexible or relatively flexible wall types, the lateral deformations will exceed the values required for

the mobilization of active soil pressures. For most soils and particularly cohesive soils, there is a danger that a further buildup of lateral pressures beyond active values will take place as a result of loosening due to strain effects. An exception would be where lateral soil pressures of an at-rest magnitude or greater are used in design, and an appropriately stiff wall, such as large diameter cylinder piling, is provided and embedded in competent soil. Lateral earth pressure induced by compaction equipment should also be taken into account (CFEM,[1] CAN/CSA-S6[47]).

26. Movements due to yield in strutted excavations are, to a large extent, unavoidable, since they are controlled not by design assumptions but by construction details and procedures. Such movements develop in each excavation phase before the next level of struts is installed.

27. The yield movements of anchored walls are controlled to a larger extent by design methods more than is the case with strutted walls. The number of anchors and the vertical spacing of such anchors play a significant part in controlling the degree of lateral deformation. In normal practice, movements due to the yield of anchored diaphragms, sheeted or soldier pile walls are usually less than for strutted walls for the same depth of excavation.

28. For general guidance Table K-6 summarizes the approximate range of vertical and lateral movements to be expected. In certain cases, more favourable results may be achieved with proper design, good construction workmanship and careful field supervision, including monitoring the behaviour of the excavation. Additional information and guidance are provided in the CFEM.[1]

Table K-6
Vertical and Lateral Movements Associated with Excavation[1][2]

Restraint[3]	Wall Details	Granular Soils, % depth	Stiff Clay, % depth	Soft to Firm Clay,[4] % depth	Remarks
Cantilever	Conventional stiffness	Moderate to large	Moderate	May collapse	Movements related to wall, soil stiffness and embedment condition
Braced	Soldier piles or sheet piles	0.2 to 0.5	0.1 to 0.6[5]	1 to 2[5]	Struts installed as soon as support level reached and prestressed to 100% design load
	Rakers or struts loosely wedged	0.5 to 1.0	0.3 to 0.8	> 2	Poor workmanship would result in greater values
Tied back	Soldier piles or sheet piles	0.2 to 0.4	0.1 to 0.5	1 to 2	Prestressed to pressure between active and at-rest
	Concrete diaphragm walls	< 0.2	< 0.1 to 0.5	< 1 to 2	Prestressed as above, since wall stiffness and design earth pressures are normally greater, movements are generally less than for soldier piles or sheet piling; little data available

(1) Movements indicated apply directly behind wall; for granular soils and stiff clays, movements would feather out in approximately linear fashion over a horizontal distance of 1.0 to 1.5 depth of excavation (H). For soft to firm clays, and assuming average workmanship, this distance increases to 2.0 to 2.5H, and with poor workmanship to greater than 3H.

(2) If groundwater is not properly controlled in granular strata, movements may be much larger than indicated, and loss of ground could also result.

(3) Experience indicates that movements are reduced by using close vertical spacing between strut or tie-back levels and by careful attention to prestress details.

(4) If the factor of safety against base heave for soft to firm clays is low, large deformations will result.

(5) Upper range of movements usually applies for highly sensitive clays in either stiff or soft to firm category.

Underpinning

29. Structures adjacent to excavations frequently need to be supported. The need for underpinning depends on the location of the structure, the details of its foundation support, its sensitivity to settlement and lateral deformations, the cost of underpinning or provision of extra excavation face support and other precautions, and the cost of repairs or the consequences if the structure is not underpinned.

30. The geometry of zones within which support for adjacent structures is usually considered necessary, as a result of adjacent excavation through soil, is shown in Figure K-2. Where adjacent structures are founded on bedrock and excavation is through rock, less underpinning and more face support should be considered.

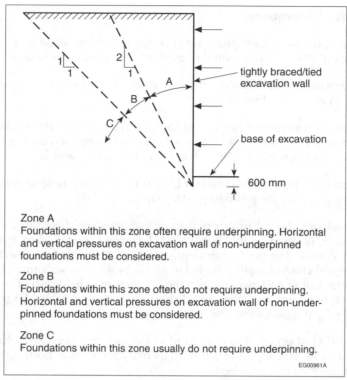

Zone A
Foundations within this zone often require underpinning. Horizontal and vertical pressures on excavation wall of non-underpinned foundations must be considered.

Zone B
Foundations within this zone often do not require underpinning. Horizontal and vertical pressures on excavation wall of non-underpinned foundations must be considered.

Zone C
Foundations within this zone usually do not require underpinning.

EG00961A

Figure K-2
Requirements for underpinning

31. The general order of magnitude of movements as a result of excavation with various support methods in different soil conditions has been summarized in Table K-6. This Table may also be used to assist in judging the necessity for underpinning. Additional information and guidance can be obtained from the CFEM.[1]

Factors to be Considered with Soil and Rock (Ground) Tie-Back Anchors

32. Anchors are usually inclined downwards, transmitting the vertical component of the anchor force into the anchored vertical member. This force should be considered in design, together with the weight of the vertical member itself.

33. Forces that resist downward movement due to the inclined anchor load are skin friction and the reaction at the base of the vertical member. When soldier piles are used, vertical forces are concentrated in the piles. Only minimal friction, if any, can be mobilized. Such vertical forces are supported at the base of the pile. The vertical and horizontal base capacity of the pile should be checked; otherwise, unacceptable vertical and horizontal deformation may take place.

34. Settlement of vertical members produces some reduction in anchor loads, with a consequent tendency for outward displacement of the supported face. Vertical and horizontal movements at the top and bottom of the excavation should be monitored at regular intervals throughout the course of the work.

35. The performance of soil and rock anchors depends not only on minor variations in soil and groundwater conditions but also on construction techniques and details. Consequently, the prediction of anchor capacity by theoretical calculations may not be reliable. Anchorage capacities should be established by load test, taking into account the load deformation and "creep" properties of the ground, and each anchor should be proofloaded during construction.

36. The overall stability of a ground anchorage system should be checked by analyzing the stability of the block of ground lying between the wall and the anchorages. In general, the anchors should be extended beyond a 1:1 line drawn from the base of the excavation, and no allowance for any load-carrying support should be assumed within this line.

Design and Installation of Members

37. Members such as walers, struts, soldier piles and sheeting should be sized in accordance with the structural requirements of Part 4 of Division B of the National Building Code of Canada 2005.

38. The depth of penetration of the vertical wall member should be at least 1.5 times the depth required for moment equilibrium about the lowest strut.

39. For driven soldier piles, the maximum horizontal force on the flange of the soldier pile below the bottom of the excavation may be taken as 1.5 times the values computed for the width of the flange, providing that the pile spacing is not less than five times the flange width.

40. For piles placed in a concrete base, the diameter of the concrete filled hole may be used in place of the flange width as discussed in the preceding paragraph.

41. The selection of material and sizes of timber planks or lagging should conform with good practice, and the lagging should be of good quality hardwood. Lagging is installed by hand after a depth of about a metre is excavated. The maximum depth made each time before a section of lagging is placed depends on the soil characteristics. Soft clay and cohesionless soils must be planked in short depths to reduce the amount of soil moving into the excavation. The depth of excavation below any lagging boards that have not yet been placed should not exceed 1.2 m. Lagging should be tightly backfilled or wedged against the soil.

42. To minimize the possibility of erratic loss of ground in local areas when excavating sands and silts below original groundwater, straw packing, burlap or in extreme conditions, grouting should be used behind the lagging as it is installed.

43. The design of all members including struts, walers, sheet piling, walls and soldier piles should be checked for several stages of partial excavation when the wall is assumed to be continuous over the strut immediately above the excavation level and supported some distance below the excavation level by the available passive resistance. This condition could produce the maximum loading in struts and walers.

44. Where excessive stresses or loads would result from interim construction conditions using regular construction procedures, trenching techniques can be employed to advantage.

45. The design of members should also be checked for the scenario when portions of the building within the excavated area are completed and lower struts are removed. Consideration must be given to the possible increase in loading on the upper struts remaining in place; also the span between that portion of the building that has been completed and the lowest strut then in place should be considered in relation to flexural stresses.

Control of Groundwater in Excavations

46. Good practice requires that the following conditions be fulfilled when dewatering excavations:
    (a) A dewatering method should be chosen that will not only assure the stability of the sides and bottom of the excavation but will also mitigate damage to adjacent structures, such as by settlement.
    (b) The lowered water table should be kept constantly under full control, and fluctuations liable to cause instability of the excavation must be avoided.
    (c) Effective filters must be provided where necessary to prevent loss of ground.
    (d) Adequate pumping and standby pumping capacity must be provided.
    (e) Pumped water must be discharged in a manner that will not interfere with the excavation or cause pollution.
    (f) For most soils, the groundwater table during construction must be maintained at least 600 to 1 500 mm below the bottom of the excavation so as to achieve dry working conditions. The groundwater table should be maintained at a somewhat lower level for silts than for sands

in order to prevent traffic from pumping water to the surface and making the bottom of the excavation wet or "spongy."

(g) Adequate monitoring of groundwater levels by piezometers or by observation standpipes should be maintained.

(h) Where low permeability strata are underlain by pervious water-bearing layers, depending on the depth of excavation and the hydrostatic head in the pervious strata, it may be necessary to lower the head in the pervious stratum in advance of excavation, to prevent a "blow" or excessive disturbance of the base as a result of upward hydrostatic pressure.

(i) Pumping from sumps or ditches inside the excavation is normally carried out where dense, low permeability soils, such as certain glacial tills or cohesive soils, are present or where the excavation is in bedrock. This method is not recommended for excavation in semi-pervious or pervious soils, such as silts or fine sands, because it often leads to extensive sloughing of the excavation sides and disturbance of the bottom.

Shallow Foundations

General

47. A shallow foundation means a foundation unit that derives its support from the soil or rock close to the lowest part of the building that it supports. The depth of the bearing area below the adjacent ground is usually governed by the requirement to provide adequate protection against climatic or frost effects; vertical loads on the sides of the foundation due to adhesion or friction are normally neglected.

Limit States Design Procedure for Shallow Foundations

48. The limit states to be considered are as discussed in Paragraphs 4, 5 and 6 of this Commentary.

49. When designing a spread (shallow) foundation, one of the following design methods shall be used:
    (a) Direct Method, in which separate analyses are carried out for each limit state using calculation models recommended in the CFEM[1] and appropriate load factors and resistance factors described in this Commentary (refer to Table K-1). In the case of serviceability limit states related to settlement, the settlement under the service loads is determined in accordance with the methods given in the CFEM,[1] using characteristic (nominal) soil properties. In the case of ultimate limit states related to bearing capacity, the foundation forces due to factored loads (including wind or earthquake) are compared with the factored geotechnical resistance (i.e. nominal ultimate resistance multiplied by the resistance factors given in Table K-1).
    (b) Empirical Method, in which geotechnical resistances/pressures estimated empirically in the CFEM[1] are compared to the pressures due to the specified loads. The serviceability limit pressures in the CFEM[1] are generally based on a maximum settlement of approximately 25 mm. The Empirical Method is convenient for the initial design of foundations of buildings as well as for the final design of most ordinary buildings. The foundations of tall buildings or towers, special buildings sensitive to movements or buildings on sensitive ground, however, should be evaluated using the appropriate direct procedures described in (a).

50. The following limit states terms should be used for expressing recommended geotechnical criteria for the design of the building structure, including its foundations:
    Bearing pressure for settlement means the bearing pressure beyond which the specified serviceability criteria are no longer satisfied. This is also referred to as serviceability limit pressure.
    Factored bearing resistance means the calculated ultimate bearing resistance, obtained using characteristic soil parameters, multiplied by the appropriate recommended resistance factor (refer to Table K-1).
    Factored sliding resistance means the calculated ultimate sliding resistance, obtained using characteristic soil parameters, multiplied by the appropriate recommended resistance factor (refer to Table K-1).
    Factored pull out resistance (i.e., against uplift) means the calculated ultimate pull out (uplift) resistance, obtained using characteristic soil parameters, multiplied by the recommended resistance factor.

Commentary K

Ultimate Bearing Capacity and Settlement (Serviceability)

51. The design of a foundation unit requires that both ultimate bearing capacity (ULS condition) and settlement (SLS condition) be checked. In many circumstances, settlement (serviceability considerations) governs the design. Distress from differential settlement is usually evidenced by cracking and distortion of doors and window frames. Bearing capacity (ultimate limit states) failures are rare, except perhaps during construction, where shallow temporary footings are frequently used with falsework.

52. The ultimate bearing capacity of cohesive and non-cohesive soils can be determined with reasonable reliability by assuming that the strength parameters for the bearing soil are accurately known within the depth of influence of the footing. The ultimate bearing capacity of shallow foundations can be calculated using classical bearing capacity formulae or semi-empirical correlations with the results of in situ testing such as the Standard Penetration Test (SPT) – N values or Cone Penetration Test (CPT). Correlations with laboratory tests such as uniaxial compression tests are frequently used to estimate bearing capacity and ultimate anchor bond resistance for bedrock. Characteristic (nominal ultimate) soil and rock strength properties are used in the classical bearing capacity formulae. The prediction of ultimate bearing capacity is multiplied by an appropriate resistance factor to provide factored bearing resistance. Additional information and guidance are provided in the CFEM[1] and CAN/CSA-S6.[47]

53. **Cohesive soil.** The settlement of a structure on cohesive soil is affected by a number of complicating factors usually requiring experience and judgment to assess. The most important of these is an estimate of the preconsolidation pressure, that is, the maximum past consolidation pressure on the in situ soil. Because of the various uncertainties, errors of a factor of 2 are not uncommon in the calculation of settlement. Cohesive soils also display significant time-dependent (post-construction) settlement. Elastic theory, with appropriate modifications, can predict settlement with reasonable accuracy. Many other theoretical and empirical methods are available to predict settlement of shallow foundations (CFEM[1] and CAN/CSA-S6[47] and its Commentary).

54. **Non-cohesive soil.** The settlement of a structure on non-cohesive soil is normally estimated by empirical and theoretical methods. Settlement in granular (non-cohesive) soils generally occurs quite rapidly, often during the construction period. Post-construction settlement is usually negligible.

55. Post-construction settlement can occur for a considerable period after construction, even after a period of successful performance of the structure, as a result of vibrations or changes in the groundwater conditions, whether natural or man-made, due to earthquake or blasting, flooding or groundwater lowering.

Bases for the Design of Shallow Foundations

56. In limit states design, the relevant limit states are identified and through the design process shown in Figure K-3, it is verified that no limit state is exceeded. The design process may be simplified in many cases as experience will often show which type of limit state will govern the design and the other limit states are checked to ensure that they are not exceeded. Guidance is provided only for footings supporting vertical loads.

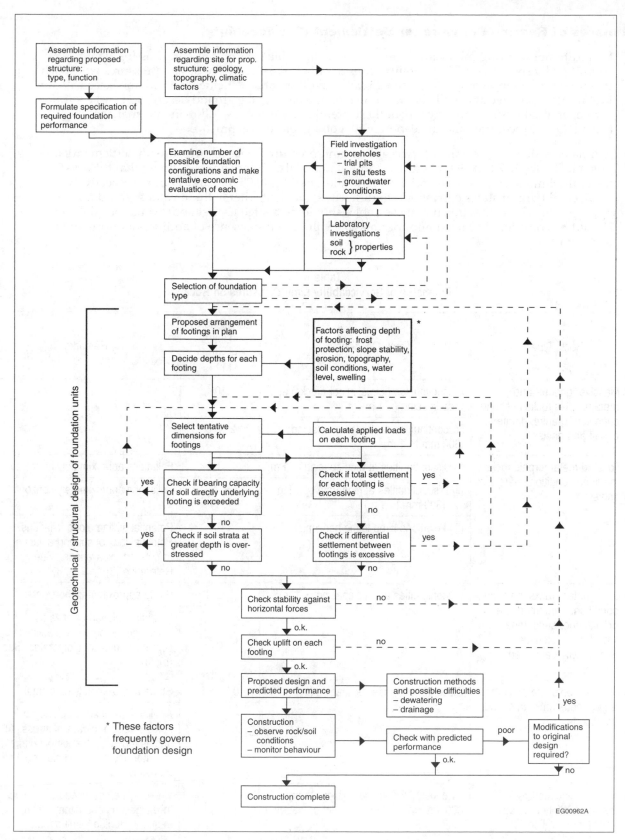

Figure K-3
Flow diagram for the design of shallow foundations

Commentary K

Estimates of Bearing Pressure for Settlement (Serviceability)

57. In traditional working (allowable) stress design, allowable bearing pressure was frequently controlled by settlement (serviceability) considerations. Normally the design pressures were such that total settlement would not exceed 25 mm and differential settlement would not exceed 19 mm. Preliminary design can usually be performed on the basis of the ground description and condition. However, final design should confirm these preliminary estimates following normal analytical (calculation) procedures and in keeping with good geotechnical practice.

58. Estimated values of presumed serviceability limit pressures (bearing pressure for settlement) are given in Tables K-7 to K-9 for bedrock and soil materials. Experience has shown that these values generally limit total and differential settlement of footings to 25 mm and 19 mm, respectively. If serviceability limit states correspond to different settlement criteria, these values would not be appropriate. The values given in these Tables should be treated as first approximations only and should be considered as maximum permissible values in the absence of additional information and data.

Table K-7
Estimates of Serviceability Limit Pressures on Rock

Rock Type	Rock Conditions[1]	Serviceability Limit Pressure,[2] MPa	Remarks
(a) Massive igneous and metamorphic rocks in sound condition; granite, diorite, basalt and gneiss	Discontinuities (joints, minor cracks) at wide spacing (> 1 m)	10	—
	Discontinuities at moderate spacing (300 mm to 1 m)	2 to 5	
(b) Foliated metamorphic rocks in sound condition: slate and schist	(i) Discontinuities at wide spacing (> 1 m)	3	Foliations approximately horizontal
	(ii) Discontinuities at moderate spacing (300 mm to 1 m)	< 1	Foliations approximately horizontal
	(iii) Foliations tilted to the horizontal	—	Potential sliding along foliations. Potential lack of support adjacent to cuts on excavations. See Reference [3].
(c) Sedimentary rocks in sound condition: cemented shale or siltstone, sandstone, limestone, dolomite and heavily cemented conglomerate	Discontinuities at wide spacing (> 1 m)	1 to 4	Strata approximately horizontal
		—	Potential solution cavities in limestone, dolomite. Variability in cementation of conglomerates. See (b)(iii).
(d) Compaction shale and other argillaceous rocks in sound condition	Discontinuities at wide spacing (> 1 m)	0.5 to 1	Strata approximately horizontal
		—	Argillaceous shales are subject to some swell on release of stress. All shales tend to soften on exposure to water and certain shales swell markedly.
(e) All closely jointed rocks including thinly bedded limestones and shales	Discontinuities at spacing less than 300 mm apart. Random joint or crack patterns.	—	Can only be assessed by detailed investigations and examination in situ, including loading tests if necessary.
(f) Heavily shattered or weathered rocks	—	—	See (e).

(1) Spacing of discontinuities is critical to the bearing pressure allowable on a rock mass. Discontinuities, such as joints or cracks, are considered widely spaced if greater than 1 m apart and moderately spaced when greater than 300 mm. The thickness or width of such discontinuities is

Table K-7 (Continued)

presumed to be less than 5 mm (or less than 25 mm if completely filled with soil or rock debris). Where such conditions do not exist, Types (e) or (f) must be assumed.

(2) Values of bearing pressures given above, except for (f), are based on the assumptions that the foundations are close to the rock surface but carried down to unweathered rock with adequate frost protection and that the foundation is greater than 300 mm wide.

Table K-8
Estimates of Serviceability Limit Pressure on Non-Cohesive Granular Soils

Soil Type and Conditions[1]	Serviceability Limit Pressure, [2] kPa	Potential Problems[3]	Remarks
(a) Dense well-graded sands, dense sand and gravel	400 to 600	Density of sands containing large sizes or gravels is frequently overestimated when inferred from standard or cone penetration tests only. See Reference [4].	For general reference, see References [1] and [5].
(b) Compact well-graded sands, compact sand and gravel	200 to 400		
(c) Loose well-graded sand, loose sand and gravel	100 to 200	Potential settlement when subject to shock or vibrations. See (f).	
(d) Dense uniform sands	300 to 400	Density usually better defined by standard or cone penetration tests, as compared to (a) to (c). Considerable caution required in interpretation of test data.	See References [6] to [8].
(e) Compact uniform sands	100 to 300		
(f) Loose uniform sands	< 100	Even where very low bearing pressures are used, settlement can occur due to submergence, vibrations from blasting machine operation or earthquake.	See Reference [9].
(g) Very loose uniform sands, silts	—	Subject to possible liquefaction. Should never be used for support of foundations.	—

(1) Density condition of the soil is assumed to be established in conformance with good geotechnical practice.

(2) Values are based on the assumptions that the foundation (B) is not less than 1 m wide and that the groundwater level will never be higher than a depth B below the base of the foundation. When the groundwater level is, or could be, higher than such depth, the values listed should be divided by a factor of 2. Total and differential footing settlements are expected not to exceed 25 mm and 19 mm respectively.

(3) Long-term settlement of foundations on compact to dense non-cohesive deposits is normally modest, provided such deposits are not underlain by compressible cohesive deposits at depth.

Table K-9
Estimates of Serviceability Limit Pressure on Cohesive Soils (for sensitive clays, see Table K-10)

Soil Type and Conditions[1]	Serviceability Limit Pressure,[2] kPa	Applicability for Support of Shallow Foundations[2]	Settlement[2][3]
(a) Very stiff to hard clay, heterogeneous clayey deposits or mixed deposits such as till	300 to 600	Good	Normally estimated on the basis of investigations, sampling and laboratory test data. For general reference, see References [1] and [10] to [12].
(b) Stiff clays	100 to 200	Fair to good	
(c) Firm clays	50 to 100	Poor — except for minor structures little affected by distortion	
(d) Soft clays	0 to 50	Very poor — not recommended	
(e) Very soft clays	—	Not permitted	

[1] Strength of cohesive soils is assumed to be established in conformance with good geotechnical practice.

[2] Cohesive soils are susceptible to long-term consolidation settlement. For Types (b) to (d) inclusive, such long-term (post-construction) settlement often governs the design. In the case of Type (a) soils, heave can take place with excavation and consequent relief of stress.

[3] Total and differential footing settlements are expected not to exceed 25 mm and 19 mm, respectively.

59. Table K-10 identifies problematic ground conditions where presumed values cannot be estimated without detailed investigations and analysis.

Table K-10
Problem Soils, Rocks or Conditions[1]

Type or Condition	Examples	References
Organic soils	Muskeg terrain: estuarine organic silts and clays	[13]
Normally consolidated clays	Lacustrine deposits and varved glacio-lacustrine deposits in Manitoba, Northern Ontario, Northern Quebec	[14]
Sensitive clays	Marine clay deposits in St. Lawrence River Valley, Eastern Ontario, Quebec	[15][16][17]
Swelling/shrinking clays	Clay-rich deposits in Alberta, Saskatchewan, Manitoba	[18]
Metastable soils	British Columbia loess	[19]
Expansive shales	Western Canada – Bearpaw and Cretaceous deposits Eastern Canada – weathering of sulphide minerals accelerated by oxidizing bacteria	[20][21]
Permafrost	Northern Canada, Arctic	[22][23]

[1] No ultimate bearing pressure or serviceability limit pressure can be presumed without detailed investigations.

Total and Differential Settlements

60. The total and differential settlements and relative rotations for foundations shall be estimated to ensure that these do not lead to the occurrence of an ultimate limit state or a serviceability limit state, such as unacceptable cracking or jamming of doors, in the supported structure. This requires attention and interaction between the geotechnical and the structural engineers.

61. The maximum acceptable relative rotations for open frames, infilled frames and loadbearing or continuous brick walls are likely to range from about 1/2000 to about 1/300 to prevent the occurrence of a serviceability limit state in the structure, and about 1.5 to 2 times these values for long-term movements over many years because of creep of building materials. A maximum relative

rotation of 1/500 for short-term movements and 1/300 for long-term movements is acceptable for many structures. The relative rotation likely to cause an ultimate limit state is about 1/150.

62. For normal structures with isolated foundations, the maximum acceptable differential settlement is about 20 mm between adjacent columns. On sand, the differential settlement of foundations is unlikely to exceed 75% of the maximum settlement and the maximum total settlement should not exceed about 25 mm. For a raft foundation, the maximum total settlement may be increased to 50 mm. The maximum allowable total and differential settlement may be increased in the case of foundations on clay soils provided the relative rotations remain within acceptable limits and provided the total settlements do not cause problems with the services entering the building, with tilt, etc. The above guides concerning limiting settlements apply to simple routine buildings. They should not be applied to buildings that are out of the ordinary or for which the loading intensity is markedly non-uniform.

63. Differential settlements calculated without taking account of the stiffness of the structure tend to be overpredictions. An analysis of ground-structure interaction may be used to justify reduced values of differential settlements.

64. Differential settlement caused by variability of the ground should be taken into consideration unless it is prevented by the stiffness of the structure. For spread foundations on natural ground, the magnitude of the differential settlement may typically be up to 10 mm, but it does not usually exceed 50% of the calculated total settlement.

65. Calculation models for settlement analyses are given in the CFEM.[1] It is important to keep in mind that differential settlement of isolated footings will always occur because of the natural variability of soils.

66. In situations where calculation models are not available or are considered to be unnecessary, limit states may be avoided by the use of prescriptive measures. Prescriptive measures may be used, for example, to ensure durability against frost action and chemical or biological attack. These measures involve conventional and generally conservative details in the design, and attention to specification and control of materials, workmanship, protection and maintenance procedures.

Frost Penetration

67. The best assessment of frost penetration in a particular locality is local experience. In the absence of local experience, however, daily air temperature measurements can be used to estimate the combined effects of both depth and duration of freezing. The cumulative total of the difference between daily mean air temperatures and the freezing point is known as the "Freezing Index," and is expressed in degree-days. Freezing indices for a large number of weather stations in Canada have been published by Environment Canada.[26] As a general guideline the variation in freezing indices across Canada is illustrated in Figure K-4. Information on how the "Freezing Index" may be used to estimate depth of frost penetration is given in References [27] to [30].

Commentary K

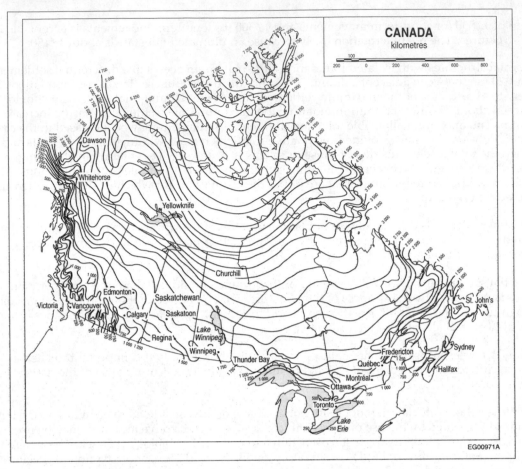

Figure K-4
Normal freezing index in degree-days Celsius, based on the period 1931 to 1960

Insulated Shallow Foundations

68. Lightweight plastic insulation has been used to reduce the loss of ground heat and thereby reduce the depth of frost penetration. Insulation should be used for this purpose only after careful examination of the pertinent conditions and with a thorough understanding of its effect on the temperature at the soil-foundation interface.[30] Insulation is of particular benefit in the design of unheated buildings such as warehouses, garages and refrigerated buildings. It is also used to restrict the depth of frost penetration beneath artificial ice surfaces.

69. Insulation with relatively high compressive strengths can be obtained, so that slabs of these materials can be placed directly below the bearing surfaces of foundations. Substantial economic advantages may accrue where such designs are used, because foundations can be located closer to the ground surface, thereby reducing the costs of providing granular fill to replace frost-susceptible soil.[30] Design guidance is also given in the CFEM.[1]

Deep Foundations

General

70. A deep foundation is a foundation unit that provides support for a building by transferring loads either by end-bearing to a soil or rock at considerable depth below the building, or by adhesion or friction, or both, in the soil or rock in which it is placed. Piles are the most common type of deep foundation.

71. Piles can be pre-manufactured or cast-in-place; they can be driven, jacked, jetted, screwed, bored, drilled or excavated. They can be of wood, concrete or steel or a combination thereof. (Drilled shafts of diameter greater than about 750 mm are frequently referred to as caissons in Canada.)

Limit States Design Procedure For Piles

72. The limit states to be considered are as discussed in Paragraphs 4, 5 and 6 of this Commentary.

73. The ultimate limit states for pile foundations should also consider structural failure of the pile in compression, tension, bending, buckling, or shear.

74. The design of pile foundations shall be based on one of the following methods:
    (a) empirical or analytical calculation models as recommended in the CFEM[1] in which separate analyses are carried out for each limit state with appropriate values for the loads and characteristic soil parameters and appropriate resistance factors as described in this Commentary (Table K-1), or
    (b) the results of load tests which have been demonstrated, by means of calculations or otherwise, to be consistent with other relevant experience.

75. The load factors and load combinations are as outlined in NBC Section 4.1.

76. The characteristic values for the geotechnical parameters are selected as discussed in Paragraphs 11 to 14.

Geotechnical Requirements of Deep Foundations

77. Loads that may be applied to a deep foundation depend not only on the properties of the foundation as a structural unit (e.g., the shaft strength of a drilled shaft determined on the basis of CSA A23.3[48]), but also on the properties of the foundation soil (or rock) and of the soil/foundation system (e.g., pile capacity as a function of soil strength, settlement of a drilled shaft as a function of contact pressure). Thus, the designer must distinguish the structural from the geotechnical capacity of a deep foundation unit or system, analyze each very carefully and define the application of loads that may be safely carried, both from a structural and a geotechnical point of view. In many applications, geotechnical considerations limit the permissible loads to levels well below those that might be arrived at on the basis of structural considerations alone. An exception to this possibly occurs when the pile is founded on strong bedrock (CAN/CSA-S6[47]) or other ground considered to be unyielding.

78. Geotechnical criteria for assessing the permissible loads on a deep foundation are determined on the basis of site investigations and geotechnical analyses. However, in most cases, the quality of a deep foundation is highly dependent on construction technique, equipment and workmanship. Such parameters cannot be quantified or reliably taken into account in normal design procedures. Consequently, as implied in NBC Subsection 4.2.7., the design capacity/performance of deep foundations should be confirmed on the basis of in situ load tests on actual foundation units.

79. Criteria relating to structurally permissible loads are defined in the design sections of the NBC applicable to the structural materials used in the deep foundation unit. However, the standards referenced in the NBC were written mainly for the purpose of designing elements and assemblies in the superstructure. A structural designer involved in the design of deep foundations must recognize that installation and quality control conditions below grade differ from those above grade; the permissible loads determined by the usual structural design methods may have to be reduced, sometimes to a marked degree, to account for these differences. Permissible loads can only be selected on the basis of close cooperation and interaction between the geotechnical and structural engineers for the project.

80. In this section of the Commentary, suggested values of permissible service loads are given for several kinds of foundation units. These values are listed solely to provide a first approximation of the probable loads which, under routine conditions, might be safely applied to a given kind of unit. In each case, both geotechnical and structural evaluations and analyses are mandatory. However, as discussed above, because construction procedures often have a dominant influence on the load/deformation behaviour of the deep foundation, the choice of a permissible service load is always subject to judgment and experience and to the provision that appropriate review be carried out as specified in Article 4.2.2.3. of the NBC. Review must be considered an integral part of the design process.

81. Deep foundations that are placed on rock or on a dense basal deposit, such as till or hard clay, are bored, drilled or excavated and cast-in-place, and are commonly referred to as drilled shafts. In this case, the area of end-bearing contact is known and, provided this area and the character of

Commentary K

the foundation stratum can be defined by inspection, the serviceability performance of the deep foundation can be evaluated on the basis of the serviceability limit pressure of the foundation stratum. (Refer to Tables K-7, K-8 and and K-9 on shallow foundations.) Additional information and guidance for design is provided in the CFEM[1] and CAN/CSA-S6[47] and its Commentary.

82. **Rock sockets.** Frequently, cast-in-place foundations are socketed into rock, either to obtain higher end-bearing capacity at depth or to transfer load to the rock by adhesion or bond along the walls of the socket. Adhesion is highly dependent on the rock type and on the socket wall condition after drilling. Characteristic (nominal) values used for adhesion in sound rock lying below weathered or shattered rock range from 0.7 MPa to 2.0 MPa; however, much lower values have been observed in practice, where the construction methods used have produced a poor contact area. Careful inspection of all rock sockets prior to concreting is essential. Socketing may also be employed to provide base fixity and resistance to horizontal movement.[31][32]

83. Deep foundations may also be driven to rock or into dense basal deposits. In this case, which includes H-piles, pipe piles driven closed-end or precast concrete piles, the exact area of contact with the foundation stratum, the depth of penetration into it or the quality of the foundation stratum are largely unknown. Consequently, the load capacity of such driven deep foundations should be determined on the basis of observations during driving, load tests and local experience. (Refer to Table K-11.)

Table K-11
Load Capacities of Driven Piles

Pile Type	Load Capacity	Recommendations	References
(a) End-bearing on rock, dense till or other similar materials	High to very high, but dictated by driving conditions, conditions of basal deposits, pile types and stiffness	Ultimate pile capacity usually high but load/deformation can only be assessed by load test (ASTM D 1143,[52] Method A).	—
(b) Piles driven into dense sand, sand and gravel	See (a).	See (a).	[33][34]
(c) Piles driven into loose to compact sand, sand and gravel	Medium to high, part point resistance, part skin friction	First approximation to load capacity, use skin friction[(1)] (kPa) = 50 ± 25. Define by load test (ASTM D 1143,[52] Method A).	[33][34][35][36]
(d) Piles driven into compact to dense silts	Medium, but "relaxation" effects must be checked	See (c). Essential to define by load test.	[37]
(e) Piles driven into cohesive soils	Low to medium, susceptible to long-term settlement	First approximation, use skin friction.[(1)] Soft cohesive soil, 0 – 30 kPa. Firm to stiff cohesive soil, 30 – 60 kPa. Define by load test (ASTM D 1143,[52] Method B).	[38][39]

[(1)] The skin friction values refer to characteristic (nominal) values.

Piles in granular soils

84. Piles that are driven into granular soils derive their load-carrying capacity from both point resistance and shaft friction. The relative contributions of point resistance and shaft friction to the load-carrying resistance (capacity) of the pile depend essentially on the density of the soil and on the characteristics of the pile.

85. It is commonly assumed that pile driving in granular soils increases the density of the deposit. Because of this, piles in granular soils should be driven to the maximum depth possible, without causing pile damage, in order to obtain the maximum working (service) load on the pile. However, in some granular soils, such as fine sands or cohesionless silts, the pile resistance (capacity) may decrease after driving. This effect is known as "relaxation." In contrast, in some coarse sands or

other coarse grained deposits, the load-carrying capacity of piles may increase after driving. Neither of these effects can be assessed quantitatively, except on the basis of redriving and load testing.

86. **Compacted concrete piles.** Compacted or rammed concrete piles in granular soils derive their load-carrying capacity mainly from the densification of the soil around the base. The capacity/resistance of such piles is, therefore, entirely dependent on the construction technique and can only be assessed on the basis of load tests and detailed local experience.

Piles in cohesive soils

87. The load-carrying capacity of piles driven into cohesive materials is governed by the adhesion between the pile and the soil and, to a much lesser extent than in granular soils, by the point resistance. This is particularly true for soft to firm clays.

88. The adhesion is not always equal to the undrained shear strength of the soil because, in some circumstances, the effect of pile driving markedly changes the character of the soil. In soft sensitive clays, complete remoulding of the soil may occur on driving. This effect diminishes with time following driving, as the soil adjacent to the pile consolidates. In some cases, soil strength has not returned to the original undisturbed value even after a considerable period of time.[40]

89. Because of the slow rate of regain of strength in certain cohesive soils, load testing should sometimes be delayed until several weeks have elapsed after driving.

90. In stiff to very stiff cohesive soils, evidence indicates that, in driving, a gap is formed between the pile and soil; this gap is not always fully closed with time, thus minimizing the adhesion to the pile relative to the high shear strength of the soil. For this reason, an approximate limit of 60 kPa has been suggested for the adhesion value, even for stiff clays (Table K-11).

91. **Drilled shafts in cohesive soils.** Except for shafts drilled through stiff or very stiff cohesive deposits, the major portion of drilled shaft capacity/resistance is derived from the hard or dense stratum at the base. For a first approximation of service loads, Tables K-7 and K-8 may be used. For a more detailed assessment of bored piles, see Reference [41].

Spacing and arrangement of piles and drilled shafts

92. The following should be considered during the spacing and arrangement of piles and drilled shafts:
    (a) the overlap of stresses between units, which influences total load-carrying capacity and settlement,
    (b) overstressing of weaker zones at depth, and
    (c) installation difficulties, particularly the effects on adjacent piles or drilled shafts.

93. In most cases the spacing, D, between the centres of driven piles of average diameter, d, should not be less than 2.5d.

Settlement and group effects in piles

94. In practice, piles are frequently used in groups; however, most of the published literature deals with the behaviour of single piles. Leonards [42] states that, "there is no consistent relationship between the settlement of a single pile and the settlement of the pile group at the same load per pile. Therefore, selecting a design load on the basis of the load at a given gross or net deflection, or at a given fraction of the ultimate pile capacity, is equivalent to accepting an unknown factor of safety with respect to satisfactory performance of the foundation." This statement is certainly valid for all piled foundations where the piles derive their support from skin friction, or from combined skin friction and end-bearing; however, group effects may be less critical where piles derive all of their support or the major portion of it from end-bearing on a relatively incompressible stratum. An example of such support is where piles are driven through weak deposits to end-bearing on rock. For this case, the engineer normally relies on some means of assessing the dynamic resistance during pile driving complemented by load tests to define the deformation characteristics of the piles under load.

95. In contrast to true end-bearing pile foundations, where the load/deformation characteristics of individual piles are significant, the use of friction pile foundations is generally governed by considerations of group action and, for cohesive soils, long-term consolidation settlement. The actual capacity and load/deformation characteristics of individual piles are not significant in this

case. The purpose of friction piles in the upper part of a deep deposit of cohesive soils or of granular soils (or silts) is to reduce the intensity of pressure acting at ground level and to shift the zone of maximum stress to the lower levels, where less settlement will result.

96. In the case of an individual pile or where the building is narrow in relation to the depth of piles, the zone of pressure increase is spread over a large area in comparison with the width of the foundation. In contrast, where the building is wide, friction piles spread the load out very little, and the effect of the pile foundation on the soil is practically the same as that of a raft foundation without piles. In this case, the resistance of the group of piles in the foundation bears no relation to the resistance of an individual pile by itself; the settlement of the foundation is, therefore, governed by the character of the subsoil, not by the load capacity of the piled foundation.

Load tests on deep foundations

97. **Use of load tests.** As previously indicated, load testing of piles is the most precise method of determining load-carrying capacity for ULS and SLS conditions. Depending upon the type and size of the foundation, load tests may be performed at different stages during design and construction.

98. **Load tests during design.** The best method of designing a pile foundation is to perform pile driving and loading tests. The number of tests, the type of pile tested, the methods of driving or of installation and of test loading should be selected by the professional engineer responsible for the design. The following points should be considered:
    (a) The test program should be carried out by a person competent in this field of work.
    (b) Adequate geotechnical information should be obtained at the test location.
    (c) The piles, the equipment used for driving or other method of installation, and the procedure should be those intended to be used in the construction of the foundation.
    (d) As a minimum, the head of a pile should be instrumented to record the total pile and soil deformation. Where possible, deformation measurements should also be made at the tip of the pile and at intermediate points to allow for a separate evaluation of point resistance and skin friction.
    (e) The driving process should be observed in detail and, wherever possible, stress levels in the pile assessed (e.g., by means of the wave equation method of analysis).
    (f) The piles should be loaded to at least twice the proposed service load and preferably to failure.

99. **Load tests during construction.** Load tests should be performed on representative deep foundation units at early stages of construction. The purpose of such tests is to ascertain that the loads obtained by design are appropriate and that the installation procedure is satisfactory.

100. The selection of the test piles should be made by the professional engineer responsible for the design on the basis of observed driving behaviour or installation features.

101. **Load tests for control.** Where full advantage is to be taken of Clause 4.2.4.1.(1)(c) and Sentence 4.2.7.2.(2) of the NBC, a sufficient number of load tests must be carried out on representative units to ascertain the range of the pile performance under load. Load tests for control should be performed on one out of each group of 250 units, or portion thereof, of the same type and performance criteria. Load tests should also be performed on one out of each group of units where driving records or other observations indicate that the soil conditions differ significantly from those prevailing at the site. Selection of the deep foundation units to be load tested is the responsibility of the design engineer.

Installation and Structural Requirements of Deep Foundations

102. In most cases, the load-carrying capacity/resistance of a deep foundation unit is governed by geotechnical considerations. The capacity of a deep foundation unit determined from structural considerations represents the maximum axial load that could theoretically be carried; however, this load is generally less than could be applied to a comparable unit used in the superstructure of a building because
    (a) the actual placing of deep foundations frequently deviates from the position and alignment assumed in design,
    (b) once in place, deep foundation units often can neither be inspected nor repaired, and
    (c) the placement of concrete in cast-in-place deep foundations frequently cannot be done with the same degree of control as in structural columns.

103. In Tables K-12 to K-14 guidelines are given to assist in determining a reasonable axial service load for deep foundation units under common conditions. These Tables are not a substitute for structural analysis and design, but only provide a conservative guide for routine situations that a designer may encounter, where a unit may be considered as a short column and where axial load governs the design.

Table K-12
Guidelines for Driven Piles

Type of Pile	Normal Size Range	Typical Pile Load, kN	Structural Considerations	Installation Considerations	Notes
(a) Timber	180 to 250 mm tip	180 to 450	Must be checked in accordance with NBC Subsection 4.3.1.	Cannot be inspected. Susceptible to damage during hard driving. Tip reinforcement recommended where driven to end-bearing stratum.	Preservative treatment normally required. (CSA O80 Series[49])
(b) Steel sections (H, WF)	200 to 350 mm	350 to 1 800	• Must be checked in accordance with NBC Subsections 4.3.3. and 4.3.4. • In pipe piles, concrete strength does not normally contribute to pile capacity unless the pile is driven to end-bearing stratum.	May be damaged during driving but load-carrying capacity not necessarily reduced.	Tip points often required for hard driving. Average thickness of flange or web, $t \geq 10$ mm. Projection of flange $\leq 14t$.
(c) Pipe sections	200 to 600 mm diam	350 to 1 800		Suitable for inspection after driving. Concrete quality highly dependent on placement method.	Normally driven closed-end. Tip reinforcement required or drive to be visible when driven open-end. Pipe thickness > 5 mm, but 10 mm recommended.
(d) Precast concrete sections	200 to 300 mm	350 to 1 000	• End bearing: capacity must be checked in accordance with NBC Subsection 4.3.3. Normally $f'_c > 27.5$ MPa. • The capacity of friction piles is normally governed by both installation method and geotechnical considerations; average compressive stress under load rarely exceeds 10 MPa.	Cannot be inspected. Careful selection and driving method required to prevent damage.	Refer to ACI 543R.[44] Possible tensile stresses in concrete during "soft" driving. High compressive stresses in concrete during "hard" driving. Tip reinforcement usually essential.
	300 to 900 mm	900 to 2 500			

Table K-13
Guidelines for Compacted, Expanded Base Piles

Type of Pile	Normal Size Range, mm	Typical Load, kN	Structural Considerations	Installation Considerations	Notes
(a) Rammed shaft	350 to 600	450 to 1 350	Concrete quality highly dependent on technique	Cannot be inspected. Contamination of concrete. 'Necking' of shafts. Possible damage by adjacent piles.	Load frequently determined on the basis of energy required to expel measured volumes of concrete at base. Highly dependent on judgment and experience. Possible heave of all piles must be continuously monitored.
(b) Steel pipe shaft, concrete filled	300 to 500	450 to 1 550	Where the pipe wall thickness < 5 mm, the structural contribution of the pipe should be disregarded.	Less subject to damage than (a) above. Shaft can be inspected prior to filling.	See (a) above.

Table K-14
Guidelines for Drilled Shafts

Type of Shaft	Normal Size Range	Typical Load, kN	Structural Considerations	Installation Considerations	Notes
(a) Uncased plain concrete	300 to 700 mm diam shaft	250 to 450	Good concrete quality not always possible	Where shaft diameter < 700 mm, cannot normally be inspected.	Not recommended for normal application where caving can occur.
(b) Uncased. Reinforced or plain concrete. Under-reamed or straight	750 to 1 500 mm diam shaft	450 to 45 000	Generally good concrete quality possible with 35 MPa > f'_c > 20 MPa. Can normally be designed in accordance with NBC Subsection 4.3.3. (CSA A23.3[48])	Can be inspected. Where temporary casing is used to retain wet, caving soil, high slump concrete may be required. Precautions should be taken to prevent contamination of concrete.	Usually under-reamed to provide belled base. Bell sides typically at 2(V) to 1(H). Often not under-reamed where bearing on sound rock.
(c) Cased. Permanent steel pipe lining	450 to 1 500 mm diam shaft	450 to 45 000	See (b) above. Must be checked as composite unit in accordance with NBC Subsections 4.3.3. (CSA A23.3[48]) and 4.3.4.	Can be inspected.	Usually not under-reamed. Generally socketed where taken to rock. Design for complete load transfer through socket. Essential to seat liner on rock bearing surface. Drive shoe usually fitted to pipe liner.

104. The flexural capacity and ductility of piles should be considered when, under certain soil conditions, the soil either does not provide lateral support or could cause lateral loads to be applied to the piles.

105. Frequently, savings can be had by using piles with a higher capacity/resistance or different techniques. Higher performance requirements should only be used in conditions where they can be justified as suitable and when quality can be ensured through an adequate program of inspection and load tests.

Driven piles

106. This type of deep foundation unit may suffer structural damage while being driven. Determination of capacity/resistance is generally made by comparing driving resistance (blows per 30 cm) with the energy or size of hammer blow and relating these values to previous experience or to the behaviour of similar piles subjected to static load tests. For this purpose, observations of pile driving must include:
    (a) pile length and weight,
    (b) hammer type (e.g., drop, diesel, ram weight),
    (c) hammer energy applied,
    (d) type and thickness of packing,
    (e) blows per 30 cm and elastic rebound of pile, or
    (f) acceleration and stress at head of pile.

107. The assessment of pile stresses during driving by the theory of wave propagation or by the "wave equation" method of pile analysis is useful. By assigning appropriate elastic properties to such parameters as the pile/cushion system and the pile/soil system, the penetration per blow and pile stresses for a given hammer energy can be computed; however, these results and the extrapolation of the penetration per blow to a definition of ultimate pile capacity are, at best, only approximations. The "wave equation" method, in common with all empirical dynamic pile formulae, calls for the exercise of judgment and experience. No method, in itself, can provide definitive values either for driving criteria or load/deformation characteristics of a driven pile. Pile load tests are essential to confirm the driving criteria used and to assess load/deformation performance.

108. **Damage to driven piles.** Piles may be damaged by attempting to drive to an excessively small "set" per blow or to an excessively large number of blows at high resistance. This is known as "overdriving." The driving set should be established so as to achieve a reasonable performance under load without incurring the risk of serious damage. Driving stresses depend upon the hammer, blows, size and type of pile, length of pile, cushion material and soil conditions. These factors must be examined for each situation and acceptable "set" criteria determined on the basis of previous experience and load testing.

109. Piles may also be damaged by driving through obstructions, such as boulders or fill material, or by sloping rock surfaces, which may deflect the pile or create high local stresses leading to serious deformation or breakage.

110. Excessive bend or sweep may be experienced when driving long piles (30 m or more). A discussion of permissible bending of piles is given in Reference [43].

111. The use of steel reinforcing tips is strongly recommended whenever ends may be damaged. Tip reinforcement may also reduce damage incurred through overdriving.

112. **Movement of adjacent piles during driving.** Where a group of piles is to be placed through silt or clay, measures shall be taken to indicate any movement of each pile during the installation of adjacent piles. Horizontal and vertical movement should be recorded.

113. Piles that have sustained vertical movement should generally be redriven. Piles that have sustained horizontal displacement must be investigated for structural damage.

114. **Jetting or pre-excavation.** When jetting, predrilling or other pre-excavation methods are used during pile installation, the pile tip should be driven below the depth of pre-excavation to the required bearing stratum. Care must be taken to avoid jetting, pre-driving or pre-excavating to a depth or in a manner that will affect the design capacity/resistance of previously placed piles. This is discussed in detail in ACI 543R.[44]

Cast-in-place deep foundations

115. Cast-in-place deep units can be divided into two main categories: compacted expanded base piles (Table K-13) and drilled shafts (Table K-14).

116. The placement of the materials forming such units is crucial. It is difficult, if not impossible, to ensure the same level of quality in placing concrete in such units as in a building superstructure. Careful attention must be given to the methods of installation, concrete mix proportions and placement methods, and to the degree of inspection possible. The performance requirements of such units should be adjusted accordingly, in keeping with sound design, engineering experience and judgment.

117. Concrete cast in place. The placing of concrete in pipe piles, expanded base pile shafts and in drilled shafts can be classified in two categories:

(1) Concrete placed in dry conditions should be placed by guided free fall, bucket or chute. Segregation may occur if concrete is allowed to fall through a reinforcing cage or similar obstruction. Concrete of more than 100 mm slump placed by free fall of 5 m or more in unreinforced or lightly reinforced shafts generally receives adequate compaction and does not usually require vibration. Placement by tremie methods is preferable in most cases and is necessary when a considerable inflow of groundwater is present or when there is standing water in the hole.

(2) Concrete placed under water should be placed through a tremie pipe or by pump in such a way as to eliminate any contamination, washing or dilution of the concrete by the water. It should have a 150 to 200 mm slump and vibration should not be applied. (Refer to CAN/CSA-A23.1[50])

118. Reinforcing steel for cast-in-place units. Reinforcing steel is generally placed pre-assembled as in a cage. During placement, the steel may be subjected to severe handling and placement stresses and to impact. Placement cannot be made with as high a degree of accuracy as in a superstructure, nor can it be easily checked.

119. For the design of cast-in-place foundations, the provisions of CSA A23.3[48] should therefore be amended in the following respects:

(a) Reinforcing steel assemblies should be designed and constructed so as to withstand all handling and placing stresses without deformation, which would impair the structural performance of the unit.

(b) Weldable steel should be employed, in most cases, to permit construction of rigid and strong assemblies.

(c) The clear distance between longitudinal bars should not be less than 75 mm.

(d) Ties or spirals may be welded to the longitudinal bars. Welding should be in accordance with CSA W59.[51] Welded spirals or ties should be of wire not less than 7.0 mm in diam, with a pitch not more than 300 mm and with not less than 75 mm clear space between ties or spirals.

(e) The possibility of misplacing the reinforcing bars should be allowed for in the design, and reasonable tolerances established for field performance: e.g., ±75 mm of correct bar location in plan, ±150 mm of correct bar location in elevation.

(f) Generally, longitudinal steel should be uniformly distributed around the cross-section, as an assembly may become twisted during placement.

Location and alignment

120. The exact location of each deep foundation unit should be staked in advance and checked immediately prior to the installation of each unit. After completion of the installation, the location of each unit should be checked against design location and permissible deviation as indicated on the design documents.

121. As required in NBC Article 4.2.7.3., permissible deviations from the design location shall be determined by design analysis. In practice, piles and shafts can usually be positioned within a tolerance of 80 mm; for practical reasons smaller tolerances should not be specified.

122. As required in NBC Article 4.2.7.4., where a deep foundation unit is wrongly located, the condition of the foundation shall be assessed by the person responsible for the design and the necessary changes made.

123. During and after installation of any deep foundation unit, its alignment should be checked against the design alignment and the permissible deviation as indicated on the design documents.

124. Current practice is to limit the total deviation from design alignment to a percentage of the final length of the deep foundation unit; 2% is a common value. However, such practice does not ensure proper structural behaviour of the unit since it does not take into account the length over which this deviation is distributed.

(a) The total deviation from alignment of a deep foundation unit has little influence on its geotechnical capacity unless it reaches values greater than 10% of the length of the unit.

(b) Practically all piles, particularly when driven, are more or less out of design alignment. A straight pile is a theoretical concept seldom achieved in practice.

(c) Only the radius of curvature of a deep foundation unit is important for its structural and geotechnical behaviour. The maximum permissible radius of curvature should be determined by design whenever such radius is required to be measured during inspection. A discussion of permissible bending of piles is given in Reference [43].

Permafrost

125. The lines on Figure K-5 indicate the approximate southern limit of permafrost and the boundary between the discontinuous and continuous permafrost zones in Canada. The distribution of permafrost varies from continuous in the north to discontinuous in the south. In the continuous zone, permafrost occurs everywhere under the ground surface and is generally several decametres thick. Southward, the continuous zone gives way gradually to the discontinuous zone, where permafrost exists in combination with some areas of unfrozen material. The discontinuous zone is one of broad transition between continuous permafrost and ground having no permafrost. In this zone, permafrost may vary from a widespread distribution with isolated patches of unfrozen ground to predominantly thawed material containing islands of ground that remain frozen. In the southern area of this discontinuous zone, permafrost occurs as scattered patches and is only a few metres thick.

126. The lines on this map must be considered as the approximate location of broad transition bands many kilometres wide. Permafrost also exists at high altitudes in the mountains of western Canada a great distance south of the southern limit shown on the map. Information on the occurrence and distribution of permafrost in Canada has been compiled by the Institute for Research in Construction, National Research Council Canada.[45][46] Special analysis and assessment procedures are necessary for foundation design in permafrost. Such design should only be carried out by professional engineers who are suitably qualified and have the requisite knowledge and experience.

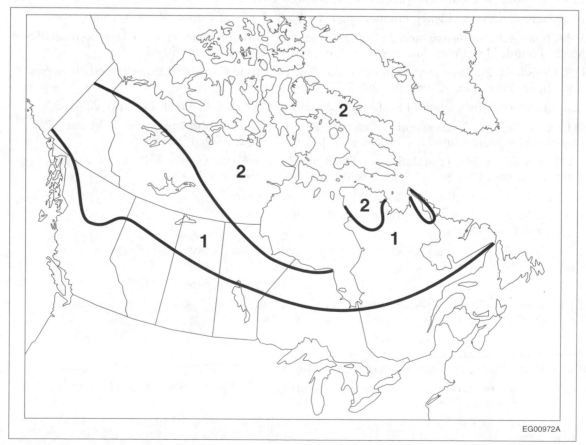

EG00972A

Figure K-5

Permafrost region. 1 – Discontinuous zone, 2 – Continuous zone.

Commentary K

References

[1]   Canadian Foundation Engineering Manual 4th Edition, Canadian Geotechnical Society, 2006. (Available from BiTech Publishers, Suite 173, 11860 Hammersmith Way, Richmond, B.C. V7A 5G1.)

[2]   K. Terzaghi and R.B. Peck, Soil Mechanics in Engineering Practice. J. Wiley & Sons, New York, 1967.

[3]   E. Hoek and J.W. Bray, Rock Slope Engineering. Inst. of Mining and Metallurgy, 1972.

[4]   G.F.A. Fletcher, Standard Penetration Test: Its Uses and Abuses. Journal of Soil. Mech. Found. Div., Proc., Am. Soc. Civ. Eng., Vol. 91, SM4, 1965, pp. 67-75.

[5]   R.B. Peck, W.E. Hanson and T.H. Thornburn, Foundation Engineering. J. Wiley & Sons, New York, 1974.

[6]   J.W. Gadsby, Discussion of the "The Correlation of Cone Size in the Dynamic Cone Penetration Test with the Standard Penetration Test." Geotechnique, Vol. 20, 1971, pp. 315-319.

[7]   F.A. Tavenas, Difficulties in the Use of Relative Density as a Soil Parameter. ASTM, STP 523, 1973.

[8]   F.A. Tavenas, R.S. Ladd and P. LaRochelle, The Accuracy of Relative Density Measurements: Results of a Comparative Test Programme. ASTM, STP 523, 1973.

[9]   K. Terzaghi, Influence of Geological Factors on the Engineering Properties of Sediments. Economic Geology, 5th Anniv. Volume, 1955, pp. 557-618.

[10]   L. Bjerrum, Engineering Geology of Norwegian Normally-consolidated Marine Clays as Related to Settlements of Buildings, Seventh Rankine Lecture. Geotechnique, Vol. 17, 1967, pp. 83-117.

[11]   C.B. Crawford, Interpretation of the Consolidation Test. Journal of Soil Mech. Found. Div., Proc., Am. Soc. Civ. Eng., Vol. 90, SM5, 1964, pp. 87-102.

[12]   J.H. Schmertmann, Estimating the True Consolidation Behavior of Clay from Laboratory Test Results. Proc., Am. Soc. Civ. Eng., Vol. 79, Separate 311, 1963.

[13]   I.C. MacFarlane, ed., Muskeg Engineering Handbook. Univ. of Toronto Press, Toronto, 1969.

[14]   V. Milligan, L.G. Soderman and A. Rutka, Experience with Canadian Varved Clays. Journal of Soil Mech. Found. Div., Proc., Am. Soc. Civ. Eng., Vol. 88, SM4, 1962, pp. 31-67.

[15]   C.B. Crawford, Engineering Studies of Leda Clay. In Soils in Canada. R.F. Legget, ed., Roy. Soc. Can., Spec. Publ. No. 3, 1961, pp. 200-217.

[16]   C.B. Crawford, Quick Clays of Eastern Canada. Eng. Geol., Vol. 2, No. 4, 1968, pp. 239-265.

[17]   P. LaRochelle, J.Y. Chagnon and G. Lefebvre, Regional Geology and Landslides in Marine Clay Deposits of Eastern Canada. Can. Geotech. J., Vol. 7, No. 2, 1970, pp. 145-156.

[18]   J.J. Hamilton, Shallow Foundations on Swelling Clays in Western Canada. Proc. Intern. Res. Eng. Conf. Expansive Clay Soils, Texas A & M Univ., Vol. 2, 1965, pp. 183-207.

[19]   R.M. Hardy, Construction Problems in Silty Soils. Eng. Journal, Vol. 33, No. 9, 1950, pp. 775-782.

[20]   R.M. Quigley and R.W. Vogan, Black Shale Heaving at Ottawa, Canada. Can. Geotech. J., Vol. 7, No. 2, 1970, pp. 106-112.

[21]   R.M. Hardy, Engineering Problems Involving Preconsolidated Clay Shales. Trans. Eng. Inst. Can., Vol. 1, 1957, pp. 5-14.

[22]   R.J.E. Brown, Permafrost in Canada. Univ. of Toronto Press, Toronto, 1970.

[23]   F.J. Sanger, Foundation of Structures in Cold Regions. Cold Reg. Res. Eng. Lab., Cold Reg. Sci. Eng. Monogr., Vol. 111-C4, 1969.

[24]   D.E. Becker, The Eighteenth Canadian Geotechnical Colloquium: Limit States Design for Foundations: Part I. An Overview of the Foundation Design Process and Part II. Development for the National Building Code of Canada. Canadian Geotechnical Journal, Vol. 33, No. 6, pp. 956-1007.

[25]   Danish Code of Practice for Foundation Engineering, 3rd Edition. DS 415(1984), Danish Technical Press, Copenhagen, 1984.

[26]   Normal Freezing and Thawing Days for Canada 1931-1960. Environment Canada, 4905 Dufferin Street, Downsview, Ontario M3H 5T4.

[27]   U.S. Army Corps of Engineers. Report on Frost Investigations, 1944-1945. Corps Engrs., New England Division, Boston, 1947.

[28] G.H. Argue, Frost and Thaw Penetration of Soils at Canadian Airports. Can. Dept. Trans., Air Services, Constr. Eng., Arch. Branch, Rep. CED-6-163, 1968.

[29] W.G. Brown, Difficulties Associated with Predicting Depth of Freeze or Thaw. Can. Geotech. J., Vol. 1, pp. 215-226, 1964. (Also NRC 8276, Division of Building Research, National Research Council Canada, Ottawa.)

[30] L. Robinsky and K.E. Bespflug, Design of Insulated Foundations. Journal of Soil Mech. Found. Div., Proc., Am. Soc. Civ. Eng., Vol. 99, SM9, 1973, pp. 649-667.

[31] D.F. Coates, Rock Mechanics Principles. Mines Branch Monograph 874, Queen's Printer, Ottawa, 1967, p. 358.

[32] F.A. Tavenas, Contrôle du roc de fondations de pieux forés à haute capacité. Can. Geotech. J., Vol. 8, 1971, pp. 400-416.

[33] G.G. Meyerhof, Penetration Tests on Bearing Capacity of Cohesionless Soils. Journal of Soil Mech. Found. Div., Proc., Am. Soc. Civ. Eng., Vol. 82, SM1, Paper No. 866, 1956.

[34] V.G. Berezantsev, V.S. Kristoforov and V.N. Golubkov, Load Bearing Capacity and Deformation of Pile Foundations. Proc. Intern. Conf. Soil Mech. Found. Eng., Paris, Vol. 2, 1961, pp. 11-15.

[35] A.S. Vesic, Tests on Instrumented Piles, Ogeechee River Site. Journal of Soil Mech. Found. Div., Proc., Am. Soc. Civ. Eng., Vol. 96, SM2, 1970, pp. 561-584.

[36] E.E. De Beer, The Scale Effect in the Transposition of the Results of Deep Sounding Tests on the Ultimate Bearing Capacity of Piles and Caisson Foundations. Geotechnique, Vol. 13, 1963, pp. 39-75.

[37] N.C. Yang, Relaxation of Piles in Sand and Inorganic Silt. Journal of Soil Mech. Found. Div., Proc., Am. Soc. Civ. Eng., Vol. 96, SM2, 1970, pp. 395-410.

[38] M.J. Tomlinson, The Adhesion of Piles Driven in Clay Soils. Proc. Intern. Soc. Soil Mech. Found. Eng., London, Vol. 2, 1957, pp. 66-71.

[39] P. Eide, J.N. Hutchinson and A. Landva, Short and Long Term Loading of a Friction Pile in Clay. Proc. Intern. Conf. Soil Mech. Found. Eng., Paris, Vol. 2, 1961, pp. 45-53.

[40] M.J. Tomlinson, Foundation Design and Construction. John Wiley & Sons, New York, 1963.

[41] J.D. Burland, F.G. Butler and P. Dunican, The Behavior and Design of Large Diameter Bored Piles in Stiff Clay. Proc. Symp. Large Bored Piles, Inst. Civil Eng., London, 1966, pp. 51-71.

[42] G.A. Leonards, Summary and Review of Part II of the Symposium on Pile Foundations. Hwy. Res. Record No. 333, Highway Research Board, Washington, 1970, pp.55-59.

[43] B.H. Fellenius, Bending of Piles Determined by Inclinometer Measurements. Can. Geotech. J., Vol. 9, 1972, pp. 25-32.

[44] ACI Committee 543R. Recommendations for Design, Manufacture and Installation of Concrete Piles. ACI 70-50, ACI Manual of Concrete Practice, Part 3, Detroit, 1980.

[45] Permafrost Map of Canada (a joint production of the Geological Survey of Canada and DBR/NRC), August 1967, NRC 9769.

[46] R.J.E. Brown, Permafrost Map of Canada. Canadian Geographical Journal, February 1968, pp. 56-63. NRC 10326.

[47] CAN/CSA-S6-00, Canadian Highway Bridge Design Code. Canadian Standards Association, Mississauga, Ontario, 2000.

[48] CSA A23.3-04, Design of Concrete Structures. Canadian Standards Association, Mississauga, Ontario, 2004.

[49] CSA O80 Series-97 (R2002), Wood Preservation. Canadian Standards Association, Mississauga, Ontario, 1997.

[50] CAN/CSA-A23.1-04, Concrete Materials and Methods of Concrete Construction. Canadian Standards Association, Mississauga, Ontario, 2004.

[51] CSA W59-03, Welded Steel Construction (Metal Arc Welding). Canadian Standards Association, Mississauga, Ontario, 2003.

[52] ASTM D 1143-81 (1994), Test Methods for Piles Under Static Axial Compressive Load. American Society for Testing and Materials International, West Conshohocken, Pennsylvania, 1981.

Commentary L

Application of NBC Part 4 of Division B for the Structural Evaluation and Upgrading of Existing Buildings

Introduction

1. This Commentary concerns the structural evaluation and upgrading of existing buildings to achieve a level of performance that is appropriate, based on the intent of the current National Building Code requirements. Buildings that satisfy the guidelines provided here should generally be considered acceptable. More stringent criteria may be appropriate for buildings used for post-disaster services.

2. This Commentary does not apply to new additions to an existing building structure or to a review of newly constructed work that was required to be in conformance with the current codes and standards. In both of these applications, NBC Part 4 applies without any of the relaxations described in this Commentary. New additions, however, may increase loads on the existing building structure.

3. Part 4 of the National Building Code and the structural standards referenced in Part 4 are written primarily for the design of new buildings (or new additions), not for the evaluation and upgrading of existing buildings. As a consequence, difficulties have arisen:
    - Many current requirements specify quantities and arrangements of materials (such as reinforcing details in masonry and concrete structures), which are economical and practical to implement during initial construction but impractical after a structure is completed. In such cases, alternative solutions are needed.
    - Many older buildings consist of structural systems, components or materials that are not addressed by the structural design standards referenced in Part 4. When properly interconnected, however, these old systems can be made to work effectively. Information on the structural properties of such systems is lacking, making evaluation and upgrading difficult. This is especially important for heritage buildings.
    - Despite their lack of compliance with some aspects of current codes, many old buildings have performed satisfactorily over the years without distress or failure. In addition, some structural parameters, such as dead load and material properties, can be ascertained by measurement or test. Such information is not taken into account in the structural criteria of Part 4 and referenced structural design standards.

4. To help overcome these difficulties, this Commentary provides guidance on the application of the requirements of Part 4 to existing buildings, including relaxations where appropriate, and alternatives where available (usually by reference to other documents). NBC Sentence 4.1.1.5.(2) allows structural alternatives that are equivalent to Part 4 but, except for load testing, they are directed primarily to new construction. Except as recommended in this Commentary, structural equivalence should comply with the requirements of NBC Sentence 4.1.1.5.(2) and its Appendix Note.

5. Earthquake requirements provide the greatest difficulty in the application of Part 4 and referenced structural design standards to existing buildings. More specific guidelines to address the seismic evaluation and upgrading of existing buildings have been developed separately from this Commentary, as discussed in Paragraphs 38 to 42.

6. This Commentary does not specify the circumstances that would require a structural evaluation of an existing building. Typical situations where structural evaluation becomes necessary include change of use of the building, damage or deterioration, and where the safety of the building is a concern because of known or potential defects.

7. After the evaluation and before any upgrading, any life-safety implications of the conclusions of the evaluation should be discussed with the owner and authority having jurisdiction to establish the timetable for the work to be done. Each case must be dealt with taking into account its specific circumstances and the degree of urgency in the requirements for upgrading. Actions to be taken

Commentary L

may range from immediate evacuation of the building, to a phased repair program, to monitoring or further evaluation, or to acceptance of the building "as is."

Basic Considerations

8. The structural requirements in Part 4 and referenced structural design standards include general performance requirements and design criteria. These requirements are based on the following fundamental considerations:
   - life safety
   - comfort of occupants
   - function of the building for its intended use
   - durability
   - economics.

9. The structural requirements in Part 4 and referenced CSA standards address life safety first and foremost, but they also address comfort, function and economics. Life safety is addressed by criteria for the ultimate limit states (strength, stability, integrity). Comfort, function and economics are addressed by criteria for the serviceability limit states and performance under repeated loads is addressed by criteria for the fatigue limit state. Economics are also taken into account by basing the criteria on appropriate levels of structural reliability, thereby helping to avoid any unnecessary consumption of materials.

10. The basic considerations of safety and serviceability apply equally to existing or renovated buildings and to new construction. However, other basic considerations related to construction costs, user disruption and conservation (heritage value, reduction of waste and recycling) may be more critical for existing buildings than for new construction. These other basic considerations usually result in a requirement for minimized structural intervention for the continued use or renovation of an existing building. Therefore, where it can be shown that the resultant life safety (defined as an appropriately low probability of death or injury due to structural failure) is generally equivalent to that required by the National Building Code, and the building is known to be functional, some departure from current code design criteria may be appropriate.

11. Structural criteria in Part 4 and referenced CSA structural design standards are based primarily on the limit states methodology (NBC Subsection 4.1.3.). Criteria recommended in this Commentary are based on the limit states method.

12. This Commentary principally addresses criteria for the ultimate limit states, because these limit states directly affect life safety. Criteria for the ultimate limit states include loads, load factors and load combinations specified in NBC Section 4.1., and resistances and resistance factors specified in the CSA structural design standards. Serviceability and durability problems may also occur as a consequence of renovation or change of use or environment, and these are discussed. Criteria for the fatigue limit state, applied principally to crane-supporting structures, are addressed in CAN/CSA-S16.[14]

Quality Assurance

13. The structural criteria contained in Part 4 and referenced CSA structural design standards are based on a level of quality assurance corresponding to the requirements contained in Part 1 of Division A and Part 4 of Division B the Code and in the referenced structural design standards. The most important of these are NBC Sentence 2.2.1.2.(1) of Division C, which requires that the designer be a professional engineer or architect skilled in the work concerned, and NBC Subsection 2.2.7. of Division C, which requires that construction be reviewed for conformance to the design.

14. These quality control requirements also apply to the structural evaluation and upgrading of existing buildings. The quality assurance may have to be greater for the evaluation and upgrading of an existing building because the uncertainties concerning the structural properties of an existing building can be considerably greater than for new construction. More engineering judgment is generally required for the structural evaluation and upgrading of existing buildings than for the design of new buildings. For these reasons, the following recommendations are based on the prerequisite that:
   - an appropriate structural evaluation of the building has been carried out, and the engineering evaluator has examined construction details that are considered critical by the evaluator, and

- the designer will carry out a field review during any upgrading work.

Recommended Code or Standard

15. Recommendations on the codes or standards that may be applied to the evaluation and upgrading of existing buildings are summarized in Table L-1. Sometimes the standard used for the design of the building may be preferred to a current standard; for example, some old buildings were made with products no longer used, such as undeformed reinforcement. Restrictions on the use of earlier versions of standards are given in Notes 1 and 2 of Table L-1.

16. Buildings designed and built in accordance with previous codes may be considered acceptable provided:
    - the previous code or standard essentially satisfies the life-safety requirements of the current code or standard, and
    - the building or its use is not altered in such a way as to affect its structural behaviour or to increase the loadings on the structure.

Table L-1
Recommended Codes/Standards

	2005 Code/Standard			Commentary L	Code/Standard when Built	
	Loads	Load Factors	Material Standards	Load Factors	Loads	Material Standards
Evaluation						
- no change in use or occupancy loads	✓	✓	✓	✓	✓ [1]	✓ [1][2]
- change in use or occupancy loads	✓	✓	✓	✓	X	✓ [2]
Design of upgrade	✓	✓ [3]	✓	✓ [3]	X	X
✓ acceptable				X unacceptable		

[1] Acceptable provided the following conditions are met:
  - no significant damage, distress or deterioration
  - designed and built in accordance with recognized codes
  - no changes that could impair the performance of the structure
  - excludes seismic considerations

[2] Acceptable provided experience does not show serious deficiencies in the standard.

[3] NBC 2005 load factors are preferred (see Paragraph 24).

17. A benchmark version of a code or standard is the earliest version that satisfies the life-safety intent of the current requirement. Use and occupancy loads, with one or two exceptions, have essentially not changed over the years. On the other hand, earthquake requirements have changed considerably over the years and consequently buildings designed to earlier codes often do not provide a level of life safety that meets the intent of current requirements. Table L-2 identifies benchmark versions of NBC Section 4.1. for structural loads. If a structural component was designed prior to the benchmark version in Table L-2, then the current (2005) version should be applied using the load factors recommended in the 2005 NBC or in this Commentary, or the evaluation may be based on satisfactory past performance under the conditions given in Paragraph 18.

Table L-2
Benchmark Versions of NBC Section 4.1., Structural Loads and Procedures

Load	Benchmark Year	As Modified (with year of modification)
Use and occupancy	1941	guards (1975 and 1995[1])
		interior walls over drops (1985)
Snow, ice, rain	1960	snow drifts (1965)
		ground snow loads (1990)
		large flat roofs (1995)
		rain loads – blocked drains (1970)
Wind	1960	flexible structures and canopies (1970)
Earthquake	1970	seismic zones (1985)

[1] The 1995 NBC guard loads, which are less stringent than those in the 1975 to 1990 editions of the NBC, should be used for the evaluation of all guards and their supports.

Evaluation Based on Satisfactory Past Performance

18. Buildings or components designed and built to earlier codes than the benchmark codes or standards, or designed and built in accordance with good construction practice when no codes applied, may be considered to have demonstrated satisfactory capacity to resist loads other than earthquake, provided:
    - careful examination by a professional engineer does not expose any evidence of significant damage, distress or deterioration;
    - the structural system is reviewed, including examination of critical details and checking them for load transfer;
    - the building has demonstrated satisfactory performance for 30 years or more;
    - there have been no changes within the past 30 years that could significantly increase the loads on the building or affect its durability, and no such changes are contemplated.

19. If these conditions are not satisfied, the evaluation should be based on the recommendations in Paragraphs 20 to 36.

Load Factors and Load Combinations Recommended for Use in Evaluations [NBC 4.1.3.]

20. Criteria for the ultimate limit states should be applied in accordance with the basic requirement for life safety. The requirement for life safety, as distinct from structural safety, is based on an acceptable maximum annual probability of death or serious injury resulting from structural failure in a building. This probability is equal to the probability of structural failure (corresponding to a reliability index of approximately 3 for buildings conforming to Part 4) times the likelihood of death or serious injury if failure occurs. If the likelihood is high, there should be no relaxation in the load factors specified in Sentence 4.1.3.2.(2). Where the likelihood is low, as in the case of storage buildings of low human occupancy, the load factors may be reduced. This is recognized in Sentence 4.1.2.1.(3) and Clause 4.1.3.1.(1)(h) by means of an importance factor applied to determine specified loads. For post-disaster buildings, the loads and load factors of NBC Section 4.1. should be applied.

21. Reduced load factors for structural evaluation, incorporating the principle of an importance factor, are recommended in Table L-3. These factors are based on maintaining the level of life safety implied by Part 4 by using the principle described in Paragraph 20.[1] The load factors in Table L-3 are determined by the evaluator based on consideration of three factors that affect life safety—the behaviour of the structure (system behaviour), the likelihood of people being at risk and their number (risk category), and the evidence of safety indicated by past performance. The risk category is addressed in Table L-5.

Table L-3
Principal Load Factors for Structural Evaluation[1]

Reliability Level[2]	Dead Load		Live[3] or Snow Load	Wind Load	Earthquake[4]
	Active	Counteractive[5]			
5	1.25	0.90	1.50	1.40	0.6
4	1.20	0.92	1.40	1.30	0.6
3	1.15	0.95	1.30	1.20	0.6
2	1.11	0.97	1.20	1.10	0.6
1 or 0	1.08	1.00	1.00	1.00	0.6

[1] This Table does not apply to post-disaster buildings.
[2] Reliability Level = sum of the 3 indices for system behaviour, risk category and past performance in Table L-4.
[3] A reduction in load factor may also be justified if the load in question is controlled (e.g. liquid in storage tanks). This may be taken into account in the application of Table L-3, provided that the load factor is not less than the minimum given in Table L-3.
[4] See Paragraph 39 and Reference [2] for more specific guidance on the load factor for earthquakes.
[5] This value applies when dead load resists failure.

Table L-4
Indices for the Calculation of Reliability Level

Factors to be Considered for Reliability Level	Index
System Behaviour	
failure leads to collapse, likely to impact people	2
failure unlikely to lead to collapse, or unlikely to impact people	1
failure local only, very unlikely to impact people	0
Risk Category (see Table L-5)	
high	2
medium	1[1]
low	0[1]
Past Performance	
no record of satisfactory past performance	1
satisfactory past performance[2] or dead load measured[3]	0

[1] Increase by 1 for loads in assembly areas or for wood structures.
[2] At least 20 years with no significant deterioration.
[3] Apply to dead load factor only.

Table L-5
Risk Category[1]

Category	Description
High	Schools and other occupancies where many people are likely to be exposed to risk associated with the failure (N[2] = 100 or more), buildings of major heritage importance, or industrial or other facilities with hazardous occupancies
Medium	Other occupancies where fewer people are likely to be exposed to risk associated with the failure (N[2] = 5 to 100)
Low	Other occupancies where the floor area or adjacent outside area exposed to the failure is not likely to be occupied by people and, when occupied, by a small number of people only (N[2] < 5)

[1] This Table does not apply to post-disaster buildings.

[2] The estimated maximum number of people exposed to risk associated with the failure, N, may be estimated as follows:

N = Occupied area exposed to risk, in m^2 · occupancy density · duration factor

where
- for building occupants the occupancy density and duration factor may be estimated using Table L-6,
- duration factor = average weekly hours of human occupancy/100 ≤ 1.0, and
- for people outside adjacent to the building, these parameters should be approximated, using the same concepts as for building occupants.

Table L-6
Parameters for Estimation of N

Primary Use	Occupancy Density, Persons per m^2	Average Weekly Hours of Human Occupancy
Assembly	1.0	5 – 50
Mercantile and personal services	0.2	50 – 80
Offices, care or detention, manufacturing	0.1	50 – 60
Residential	0.05	100
Storage	0.01 to 0.02	100

22. The choice of the reduced load factor in Table L-3 is made by the evaluator for the specific component addressed by the calculation. The evaluator must consider what will happen if the component fails. Are there protective features of the structural system (including non-structural components) that, given structural failure, reduce the likelihood of people (both outside and inside the building) being injured or killed? Are many people likely to be within the region affected by the failure? For example, the failure of exterior building components (such as masonry parapets) overlooking exits or busy streets presents a greater risk than the failure of components overlooking rarely used areas. Those that fail during earthquake are generally a greater risk than those that fail in very high winds, when fewer people are outside. Finally, if the building is old and its past performance is satisfactory, this evidence of its safety can be taken into account, except for seismic hazards.

23. Table L-5 provides guidance for determining the risk category used in Table L-3, including a procedure for estimating the number of people exposed to risk associated with the failure. In applying this procedure, the engineer should estimate the area of the building that is likely to be affected by the failure mode of the component being evaluated. For example, a punching shear failure of a flat slab building may be likely to cause a major total collapse, whereas a floor joist failure usually affects only a small area.

24. While the minimum load factors in Table L-3 maintain a low risk to life safety, they infer an increased risk of building damage due to structural failure. They should be considered as a minimum to require upgrading. They may not be appropriate for use in the design of the upgrading. Where the difference in upgrading cost due to increasing the minimum load factor is small and the loss due to failure is large, higher load factors, such as those specified in Sentence 4.1.3.2.(2),

are recommended for the structural design of the upgrade. The level of upgrading should be determined in consultation with the owner.

25. The combinations of loads to be used in the evaluation should be in accordance with NBC Table 4.1.3.2. with only the principal load factors reduced in accordance with Table L-3.

Effects Recommended for Use in Evaluations

26. Effects specified in Part 4 concern primarily the ultimate limit states and life safety, and relaxations are therefore generally not recommended. Sometimes, however, as discussed in the following text, it may be possible to determine loads for evaluation more accurately than for design. Earthquake loads are discussed in Paragraphs 37 to 42.

Effects Due to Movements, T [NBC 4.1.2.1.(1) and 4.1.3.2.(3)]

27. Effects due to movements caused by temperature change, moisture change and sustained stress (e.g., shrinkage, creep, differential settlement) may usually be neglected for structural evaluation of an existing building provided an inspection of components and connections indicates no damage affecting the safety of the building. This is because past experience with the existing building will show whether such movements cause local damage or displacements that may affect the strength or integrity of the building. Ten years of experience is usually sufficient except for differential settlements of footings on materials such as clay, which can take approximately 30 years.

28. For upgrading, consideration should be given to differential movements between new and old materials.

Dead Loads, D [NBC 4.1.4.]

29. Where dead loads are determined from field measurements, the uncertainty of dead load is reduced compared to design. Tables L-3 and L-4 take this into account by means of a reduction in the dead load factor. Similarly, Note 3 to Table L-3 allows a reduction in dead load factor where the load is highly controlled.

30. Due to the difficulty of controlling future installations of partitions in office buildings, it is recommended that 1 kPa, as called for in Sentence 4.1.4.1.(3), be maintained in those occupancies.

Live Loads Due to Use and Occupancy, L [NBC 4.1.5.]

31. Loads due to people, such as those for assembly, access and exit areas, have a direct effect on life safety. Note 1 of Table L-4 therefore allows less of a reduction in load factor for loads in such areas than for all other loads.

32. It may be possible in an existing building to control some floor loads to a value less than that specified in Subsection 4.1.5. If the analysis of the projected use of the floor clearly indicates that the NBC load, including dynamic effects, will not be approached, then a reduction may be warranted, provided that any future change from the use contemplated is controlled. For example, Article 4.1.5.6. allows a reduction in specified loads for dining areas from 4.8 to 2.4 kPa, provided the floor area is 100 m² or less and the floor will not be used for other assembly uses, such as dancing. Generally, however, future use is difficult to control and this provision should be used with caution and only with the approval of the authority having jurisdiction.

33. The requirements of Sentence 4.1.3.6.(2) concerning the dynamic analysis of floors supporting rhythmic activities need not be applied if past experience indicates that vibration has not been distinctly noticeable and that a change of use of the floor area is not contemplated.

34. For all other use and occupancy loads, it is recommended that Part 4 be followed.

Loads Due to Snow and Rain, S [NBC 4.1.6.]

35. It is generally difficult to justify a reduction in snow and rain loads from those specified in Subsection 4.1.6. and recommended in Commentary G. Despite apparent structural deficiencies according to current Code requirements, however, many years of satisfactory roof performance may

indicate a need to better assess actual snow loads on the building. Special studies, including a comparison of local records of ground snow accumulation at the building site with those determined at the Environment Canada weather station, as well as special model or analytical studies of snow accumulation on the building in its location, may be used to more closely estimate the site-specific snow load. The assumptions of such studies may not apply, however, if there will be a change in roof geometry or in wind exposure (e.g., due to new buildings). Also a change in snow loads on an existing building can occur due to changes in insulation or indoor heating, or it can occur due to snow sliding off a sloping roof as a result of a change in roofing material. See Commentary G for further guidance.

Wind Loads, W [NBC 4.1.7.]

36. It is equally difficult to justify a reduction in wind load from that specified in Subsection 4.1.7. and recommended in Commentary I. Despite calculated structural deficiencies in a building (according to current Code requirements), many years of satisfactory performance may indicate the need to better assess actual wind loads on the building. Special studies, including measurements of wind speeds at the building site (as compared to those measured at the Environment Canada weather station), as well as model or analytical studies of wind loads on the building in its location, may be used to more closely estimate the site-specific wind load. The assumptions of such studies may not apply, however, if there is a future change in building shape or local topography. See Commentary I for further guidance.

Earthquakes [NBC 4.1.8.]

37. Current earthquake requirements in Part 4 and referenced structural design standards can present major difficulties for rehabilitation, particularly for heritage or other buildings of unreinforced masonry.

38. Specification-type Clauses that cause difficulties include restrictions on structural systems for buildings [NBC Sentence 4.1.8.9.(1) and Article 4.1.8.10.], restrictions related to lateral deflections and pounding [NBC Articles 4.1.8.13. and 4.1.8.14.], as well as restrictions on detailing for earthquakes contained in the referenced structural design standards.

39. To help overcome these difficulties, it is recommended that the NRC Guidelines for the Seismic Evaluation of Existing Buildings[2] be followed. Information on techniques for seismic upgrading is contained in Reference [3]. Reference [4] contains a method of screening buildings prior to detailed seismic evaluations and is essentially a management tool for an owner or authority responsible for a large building inventory.

40. The reduced load factor for earthquakes of 0.6 in Table L-3 should be considered suitable as a triggering criterion for seismic upgrading. For design of the upgrading, the load factor should be increased, preferably to the NBC value, based on considerations of future building use, control of seismic damage (to the building and contents), and the differential in upgrading costs with earthquake force level. An exception is the upgrading of unreinforced masonry buildings covered by the special procedure contained in Appendix A of Reference [2], for which the criteria of that Appendix apply.

41. For many buildings in low to medium seismic zones ($S_a(0.2) \leq 0.75$), life safety can often be greatly improved at relatively low cost by providing lateral support to masonry and other heavy non-structural components.

42. Recent earthquake experience shows that in most seismic areas of Canada, particularly in the east, non-structural building components pose a greater risk than building structures themselves. Also the seismic upgrading for non-structural components can often be carried out much more easily than for the structure—as a part of maintenance. For non-structural components, it is recommended that CAN/CSA-S832, "Seismic Risk Reduction of Operational and Functional Components of Buildings,"[12] be followed.

Serviceability

43. Serviceability requirements in Part 4 (NBC Articles 4.1.3.4., 4.1.3.5., 4.1.3.6. and much of Section 4.2.) and referenced structural standards concern human comfort and the function of the building

structure for its intended use (operation of equipment, drainage, protection function of the building envelope, etc.).

44. The serviceability criteria contained in Part 4 and referenced standards are intended for the design of new buildings. For existing buildings, in many cases demonstration of satisfactory performance eliminates the need to apply the serviceability criteria given in Part 4 and referenced structural standards for structural evaluation. Unacceptable deformation, settlement, vibration or local damage will usually be evident to the occupants within a period of 10 to 30 years from construction. Examples where serviceability evaluations may be required include change of use, or alteration of building components affecting the properties of the structure.

45. A change of use, for example, might include the introduction of activities such as aerobics or jogging into an existing building. In such cases, the existing floor structure should be evaluated for such a use either by means of a performance test or by calculation procedures (see Commentary D for further guidance). An evaluation is also recommended for intended uses such as the installation of reciprocating machinery or the use of equipment that is sensitive to vibration, floor smoothness or slope.

46. An alteration of building components affecting the properties of the structure, and therefore its response to loading, might include the removal of partitions, which reduces the damping and stiffness of the floor system and increases its sensitivity to vibration induced by footfalls. In this case, it is recommended that the floor construction be reviewed for the intended use before removing the partitions. Similar alterations that may affect structural serviceability include alterations to cladding and partitions in tall buildings, which affects wind sway motions, and the addition of heavy components, which results in increased deflection.

47. In the case of earthquakes, the deflection criteria of NBC Sentence 4.1.8.13.(3) are intended to control damage to non-structural components. This will usually not have been tested by experience. For guidance, see Reference [2].

Durability

48. Durability is a major factor affecting serviceability and safety requirements which, although not addressed in the general requirements of Part 4, is addressed in NBC Section 4.2. and in the structural design standards referenced in NBC Sections 4.3. and 4.4. (often by reference to other standards, such as CAN/CSA-A23.1[15]). The CSA standard on parking garages referenced in NBC Subsection 4.4.2. is concerned essentially with durability, as are CSA S448.1[16] on the repair of reinforced concrete in buildings, and CSA S478[17] on durability in buildings.

49. Corrosion failures of unbonded post-tensioned beams and slabs, reinforced concrete parking structures, supports and connections for precast or other wall panels, masonry wall ties and deep foundations may result in unsafe structures without visible deterioration. References [5] and [6] provide guidance for the assessment of such conditions.

50. Change of use (e.g., internal environmental conditions) or alteration of the building components (e.g., insulation) may result in future deterioration where none had occurred in the past, particularly to exterior wall components. Such potential deterioration should be considered in the evaluation.

Structural Integrity

51. In the structural evaluation of an existing building, the ability of the structure to absorb local failure without widespread collapse is an important property, which should be considered by the engineering evaluator. This property can be assessed by considering the likelihood of specific failures due to overloading, accidental damage, defects and deterioration and, if there is such a likelihood, the ability of the building (both structural and non-structural components) to provide alternative paths of support. This consideration, however, is not easily quantifiable and therefore involves considerable engineering judgment. Tables L-3 and L-4 take alternative paths into account by means of a reduction in load factors based on a consideration of system behaviour. See also Commentary B.

Commentary L

Foundations

52. The adequacy of spread footings can generally be demonstrated by satisfactory performance in the past. Consideration should, however, be given to spread footings that will be subjected to a significant increase in loading. Consideration should be given to deep foundations in situations where they may have been weakened by deterioration.

53. Guidance concerning earthquake effects on foundations is given in Reference [2].

Referenced Structural Design Standards

54. For the application of structural design standards to existing buildings, the evaluator is advised to follow the ultimate limit state requirements for resistance (including resistance factors) contained in each standard referenced in NBC Section 4.3. Information contained in Reference [7] may be helpful.

55. Alternatively, the building may be considered adequate on the basis of satisfactory past performance, provided the conditions described in Paragraph 18 are met.

56. Paragraphs 57 to 63 also provide guidance for determining resistance by means of load tests as an alternative to that determined by structural analysis.

Load Testing

57. Load testing can be used for structural evaluation where safety is in doubt (due to lack of drawings or design information, deterioration, fire, or possible inherent deficiencies). In some cases, load testing may be used to monitor the effects of deterioration [see Reference [9] for guidance]. Load testing is generally used in the structural evaluation process as a last resort, because it is usually disruptive and costly.

58. Most load tests of existing building structures consist of proof tests to establish safety. Occasionally it may be useful to carry out destructive ultimate tests of isolated structural components to determine their capacity and mode of failure. Load tests can also be used to determine component forces in a structure where it is difficult to apply a conventional structural analysis.

59. In some situations a load test may not provide sufficient evidence concerning the future safety of the structure. An example is a post-tensioned structure with very little normal reinforcement, where there is hidden corrosion of prestressing. Although such a structure may pass a load test, further deterioration may result in a sudden brittle failure.

60. It is important that in a load test, the structure be exposed and accessible for visual inspection before, during and after the test.

61. For proof tests, the loads should be applied to the structure in a pattern representative of the expected loading and to produce the maximum effects for the critical modes of potential failure as ascertained by the evaluator. The proof test loads should be representative of the effect of factored loads specified in NBC Section 4.1., or some multiple thereof, depending on the type of failure (gradual versus sudden) and whether the whole structure is tested or only a representative portion. For concrete or composite concrete and steel structures, the requirements of Chapter 20 of CSA A23.3[18] should be followed. In the case of non-composite steel frame structures, an evaluation can normally be done by measurement and calculations. For other materials, a test load (including the weight of the structure tested) representing 1.3 times the total dead load of the renovated building plus 1.6 times the live load should be applied for a minimum of 24 hours. The test should include the measurement of deflections and recovery after the load is removed.

62. In general, the structure is considered to pass the load test if there is no evidence of impending failure during the test. In addition, there may be an indication of serviceability problems under specified loads if there is excessive cracking or deflection (short-term or long-term). This should be evaluated considering past experience with the structure and the contemplated future change of use.

63. For more guidance on load testing, see Reference [9].

Further Guidance on Methods of Structural Evaluation

64. Further guidance on methods of structural evaluation is contained in References [10] to [11].

References

[1]   D.E. Allen, Criteria for Structural Evaluation and Upgrading of Existing Buildings. Can. J. Civ. Eng., Vol. 17, No. 6, December 1991.

[2]   D.E. Allen, J.H. Rainer and A.M. Jablonski, Guidelines for the Seismic Evaluation of Existing Buildings. Institute for Research in Construction, National Research Council Canada, Ottawa, 1992. NRCC 36941.

[3]   D.E. Allen, Guideline for Seismic Upgrading of Building Structures. Institute for Research in Construction, National Research Council Canada, 1995. NRCC 38857.

[4]   J.H. Rainer, D.E. Allen and A.M. Jablonski, Manual for Screening of Buildings for Seismic Investigation. Institute for Research in Construction, National Research Council Canada, Ottawa, 1992. NRCC 36943.

[5]   ASCE Standard ASCE11-90, Guideline for Structural Condition Assessment of Existing Buildings. Am. Soc. Civ. Eng., New York, New York, 1991.

[6]   N.R. Webster, Evaluation of Unbonded Post-Tensioned Structures. Proc. of Second Canadian Symposium on Cement and Concrete. Sidney Mindess, ed. University of British Columbia, Vancouver, 1991, pp. 230-241.

[7]   CSA Standard CAN/CSA-S6-00, Canadian Highway Bridge Design Code. Canadian Standards Association, Mississauga, Ontario, 2000.

[8]   CEB Bulletin 192. Diagnosis and Assessment of Concrete Structures. Comité Euro-International du Béton, Lausanne, Switzerland, 1989.

[9]   Load Testing of Structures and Structural Components. Institution of Structural Engineers, London, England, 1989.

[10]   Evaluation, Maintenance and Upgrading of Wood Structures: A Guide and Commentary. Am. Soc. Civ. Eng., New York, New York, 1982.

[11]   Structural Renovation of Traditional Buildings. Construction Industry Research and Information Association, CIRIA Report III, London, England, 1986.

[12]   CAN/CSA-S832-06, Seismic Risk Reduction of Operational and Functional Components of Buildings. Canadian Standards Association, Mississauga, Ontario, 2006.

[13]   International Standard ISO/DIS 13822. Bases for Design of Structures – Assessment of Existing Structures. Geneva, 2001.

[14]   CSA Standard CAN/CSA-S16-01, Limit States Design of Steel Structures. Canadian Standards Association, Mississauga, Ontario, 2001.

[15]   CSA Standard CAN/CSA-A23.1-04, Concrete Materials and Methods of Concrete Construction. Canadian Standards Association, Mississauga, Ontario, 2004.

[16]   CSA Standard S448.1-93, Repair of Reinforced Concrete in Buildings. Canadian Standards Association, Mississauga, Ontario, 1993.

[17]   CSA Standard S478-95, Guideline on Durability in Buildings. Canadian Standards Association, Mississauga, Ontario, 1995.

[18]   CSA Standard A23.3-04, Design of Concrete Structures. Canadian Standards Association, Mississauga, Ontario, 2004.